THE DIRECTION OF HUMAN DEVELOPMENT

BOOKS BY M. F. ASHLEY MONTAGU

Coming Into Being Among the Australian Aborigines, 1937 (George Routledge & Sons)

Man's Most Dangerous Myth: The Fallacy of Race, 1942
(Harper & Row, Publishers, Incorporated)

Edward Tyson, M.D., F.R.S., (1650-1708): And the Rise of Human and Comparative
Anatomy in England, 1943 (American Philosophical Society)

Introduction to Physical Anthropology, 1945 (Charles C. Thomas)

Adolescent Sterility, 1946 (Charles C. Thomas)

On Being Human, 1950 (Henry Schuman, Inc.)

On Being Intelligent, 1951 (Henry Schuman, Inc.)

Statement on Race, 1952 (Henry Schuman, Inc.)

Darwin, Competition, and Cooperation, 1953 (Henry Schuman, Inc.)

The Natural Superiority of Women, 1953 (The Macmillan Company)

Immortality, 1955 (Grove Press)

The Direction of Human Development

Biological and Social Bases

M. F. ASHLEY MONTAGU

Harper & Row, Publishers · NEW YORK & EVANSTON

Dedicated to J. C. FLUGEL

THE DIRECTION OF HUMAN DEVELOPMENT

CONTENTS

93280

Look round our world; behold the chain of love
Combining all below and all above.
See plastic Nature working to this end,
The single atoms each to other tend,
Attract, attracted to, the next in place
Form'd and impell'd its neighbour to embrace.
See Matter next, with various life endued,
Press to one centre still, the general good.
See dying vegetables life sustain,
See life dissolving vegetate again:
All forms that perish other forms supply;
(By turns we catch the vital breath, and die)
Like bubbles on the sea of Matter borne,
They rise, they break, and to that sea return.
Nothing is foreign: parts relate to whole;
One all-extending, all-preserving soul
Connects each being, greatest with the least;
Made beast in aid of man, and man of beast;
All served, all serving: nothing stands alone:
The chain holds on, and where it ends, unknown.

ALEXANDER POPE
Essay On Man (1733)
Epistle III

PREFACE

I will learn
How to set free the soul alike in all,
By searching out the laws by which the flesh
Accloys the spirit.
—ROBERT BROWNING, *Paracelsus*

The content of this book is to me perhaps the most dramatic and important experience of my life. In November, 1944, I was invited by the Department of Sociology (now the Department of Social Relations) at Harvard University to deliver a course of lectures on the socialization process. The examination of the nature and meaning of this process I had thought of as a task for my later years, when I might feel more confidently prepared to undertake it. The challenge to prepare and deliver the course of lectures in the spring term of 1945 was, however, one which I could not resist.

The experience of putting the evidence together concerning the nature and meaning of the socialization process proved extraordinarily exciting. Everything seemed to fall into place in a most enlightening way. Human nature as I was able to see it, largely by putting together the work of a vast number of investigators working in many different but not unrelated fields, became understandable to me for the first time.

Then felt I like some watcher of the skies
When a new planet swims into his ken.

What I had thus discovered for myself I felt was important. All but the last chapter of the book was virtually written between November, 1944, and March, 1945. Most of my students at Harvard found the lectures based on this book not uninteresting, as did my students at Rutgers and The New School for Social Research. I am indebted to them all for their interest and stimulation. There was a continuous demand on the part of my students and of others for publication of the lectures, but I could not find time to write the last chapter. I therefore produced a small interim volume, *On Being Human* (New York, Henry Schuman, 1950), which was largely a precipitate of the pages of lectures which remained in manuscript. *On Being Human* was kindly received. Meanwhile, it became increasingly clear that the present book ought to be brought to completion and published as soon as possible. In the ten years during which the book has been before me it has continuously been kept simmering. Much fundamental research has been published, and I have endeavored to incorporate the most significant of this into the present volume.

Nevertheless, now that the book is in the reader's hands I almost feel like saying to him: Don't read it. There is so much omitted, so much left undiscussed. . . . At the same time I hope the potential reader will not take the advice, for it arises out of my own feeling of frustration, a feeling, no doubt, which many another maker of books has experienced. I should have liked to include everything I thought of relevance, and to have discussed at greater length many of the matters with which I deal. It was my original plan to do so. To this end I read and marked countless studies and books, but in the course of the years during which I have been at work on this book, it became apparent that were I to realize my original plan this work would grow to impossible dimensions—and my great desire was to make it readable and keep it within reasonable bounds. There remains, therefore, scarcely a sentence which could not be elaborated.

Meanwhile, I am aware of the risk I run of being accused of oversimplification. Faced with the alternatives of burying the reader under a mass of data and driving away a large number of those I most desire to reach, or attracting and keeping the attention of the widest possible number of readers at the cost of sacrificing some four fifths of the material which has actually gone into these pages, I have deliberately chosen the latter alternative.

I believe that the facts and theories here discussed are of the first importance for human beings at the present stage of their development. Hence I am interested in securing the widest possible discussion of these facts and theories. If the accusation of oversimplification (which I have heard before) is the result, I shall be sorry, for the necessary supporting evidence is abundantly available for most of the statements made in this book. I have simply been unable to cite more than a small part.

I should like to take this opportunity to thank all those workers who by their research and writing have contributed to my understanding of the nature of human nature and the direction of human development. This book owes as much to those who are not cited in its pages as to those who are. To Mr. Straughan L. Gettier of Princeton I owe thanks for his kindness in reading both the manuscript and page proof of this book. Professor Gerhardt von Bonin kindly read the manuscript of the first four chapters. To my wife I am greatly indebted for her care in reading page proof.

Thanks are due to the Columbia University Press for permission to quote from Margaret Ribble's *The Rights of Infants,* and to the Yale University Press for permission to quote from Miller and Dollard's *Social Learning and Imitation.*

Two publications which came to my attention too late for discussion in this book I would highly recommend to the reader. These are Izette deForest's *The Leaven of Love,* New York, Harper, 1954, and the late Gerhard Witt's "Primary love therapy," *Psychoanalysis,* vol. 3, 1954, p. 65-73.

The dedication of this book to J. C. Flugel expresses a debt to an inspiring teacher and great human being who, by his example taught me to know what a good human being could be.

A. M.

Princeton, New Jersey
Jan. 14, 1955

THE DIRECTION OF HUMAN DEVELOPMENT

1 INTRODUCTION

Central to the future, as it is of crucial significance for today, is the conception of man, of human nature, the potentialities of the human organism.   —LAWRENCE K. FRANK*

THE PURPOSE OF THIS BOOK

By what means and by what processes does man become socialized, that is to say, a social being? Or, to phrase the question in another way: What is man's original nature and how is that nature influenced and conditioned to assume a socially functional form?

This is the compound question that we will seek to answer in this book. It is perhaps the most fundamental question that the student of human nature and of society can ask—and attempt to answer. For man is not simply a social creature; indeed, he could never have become the kind of social being he is without the unique biological equipment which supplies the potentialities enabling him to undergo socialization. It follows, therefore, that in order to comprehend the nature of the processes whereby man becomes a social being it is essential to understand, as far as possible, not only the nature of these organic potentialities of human behavior but also the nature of their interaction with the socializing process. What, then, we wish to discover is the nature of the reciprocal interaction between the organic and the social, their mutual conditioning or organizational effects upon each other.

* Lawrence K. Frank, *Nature and Human Nature,* New Brunswick, New Jersey, Rutgers University Press, 1951, p. 12.

1

Socialization Defined

While it has justly been said that definitions are properly meaningful only at the end of an inquiry, it will be useful to give at the outset some definite, though arbitrary, measure of form to our subject by a definition. We may, then, take the term *socialization* to mean *the process of interaction between the organic potentials of the organism and the factors which serve culturally to differentiate and organize those potentials into a socially functioning whole.*

Socialization is a process which commences at birth and proceeds throughout the learning life of the person. Socialization is, indeed, the process by means of which the person acquires social experience and social habits. It is the process by means of which the organism forms social relationships through learning and becomes a person.

Socialization has been defined by Kluckhohn and Murray as the process of inculcating and learning the traditional patterns, until they become "second nature."[1]* Linton has defined the process of socialization as learning what one should do for other people, and what one is entitled to expect from them.[2]

The Learning Life of the Person

Here we may ask a question. How long is the learning life of the person? The evidence of neuropsychology is clear upon that point: As long as the person is capable of learning. Which is to say, as long as he is capable of increasing the strength of any act through training;[3] by training is to be understood more or less ordered repetition.[4] Perhaps, more generally, learning may be defined as the alteration in behavior that results from experience.[5] Making an omelette of these definitions we may say that learning is an increase in the strength of a response that comes about through *repetitions* of stimulus situations appropriate to the evocation of that response.[6] In sum, then, learning is the totality of those processes by which the organism utilizes experience to comprehend and manipulate the environment.[7]

* References for numbered footnotes can be found in Appendix C.

The training capacities of the person endure, albeit with diminishing strength, throughout his life span. For all practical purposes then, socialization is a term which may be taken to describe a process which affects the person throughout the greater part, if not the whole, of his life. In the United States (1954) the average life span of the white male is 66.6 years, of the white female 72.6 years. For nonwhites corresponding figures are 59.4 and 63.7 years respectively. Socialization is, however, not simply a matter of extension, but more particularly of intension. The intensive phases of socialization fall into the earlier period of the organism's development, the period of infancy, of childhood, of adolescence, and of young adulthood. These are the periods during which, with generally increasing ability, the organism learns to become a social being and in the process of which it becomes a person.

Approach

Commencing with the socially undifferentiated state of the newborn we shall follow the process of social differentiation through infancy and childhood. We shall refer to a certain amount of the comparative material from other groups of less complexly organized animals for such light as that material may be capable of throwing upon the relevant data in man. Indeed, before we introduce man upon the stage we shall discuss some of this material, as well as some of the fundamental concepts with which we shall be dealing, some of which have already been mentioned but neither discussed nor defined. Finally, when we have completed this part of our discussion, and before we proceed to consider the newborn, we shall have to discuss his prenatal history; for if it is true that the child is father to the man, it is also probably true that the developing fetus is to some extent father to the child. Without an understanding of the ontogeny of the child there can be no real understanding of the development of the man in all his subsequent sociobiological relationships. We shall therefore discuss the prenatal development of man, and the development of those organically based or biogenic

potentialities which prepare him for the process of social differentiation.

THE BIOLOGICAL AND THE SOCIOCULTURAL

However biological our discussion may at times appear, it is
always being conducted with reference to an integral of which
society and culture are essential elements. *Human beings function
within a framework from which the dynamics of the sociocultural
universe cannot be separated.* This is true of fetuses as well as
of philosophers. The difference is one of degree. Where man as a
functional whole is concerned it is never really possible to dissociate
the sociocultural from the organic or biological. When, for the purposes of discussion, this is sometimes done the procedure is arbitrary.
For methodological purposes it may be justifiable and, indeed, ad-
visable. It must, however, always be remembered that this procedure
is arbitrary, and that man, social man at any rate, is an amalgam
or better, an integral of the biological and the sociocultural. The
integration of the biological, the social, and the cultural variables
yields the functioning person. Kimball Young has expressed this
point in a simple formula.[8] If O is the organism, S society or social
interactional effects, and C culture, while P is the personality, then
the interplay of O, S, and C gives rise to P. Thus, the formula may
be written:

$$O\} \quad S\} \quad C\} \quad = \quad P \quad \text{or} \quad P = \int (O, S, C)$$

or more shortly

$$OSC = P$$

More recently Kattsoff has proposed a similar formula for behavior:

$$B = \int (G, C, E)$$

or more shortly:

$$G\,C\,E = B$$

where B is behavior, G is the goals of the organism, C is its capacity,
and E its environment. In other words, behavior is a function of
G, C, E.[9]

VARIABILITY

In the details of their structure the variates O, S, and C—or G, C, and E—must be taken as virtually infinitely variable. That is to say, for all practical purposes, in human organisms in interaction with one another in the universe of the sociocultural and physical environments, there is no measurable limit to the permutations and combinations which the processes of these interactive variates can assume. We do, however, make approximations to the measurement of many human behavioral functions; but with the exception of certain purely physiological functions our measurements are crude and rough approximations, even though they may have definite meaning for us. Such meanings are of a limited nature; our measurements of human behavioral functions are of limited meaningfulness, hence, for almost all human traits we may state this fact in what may be called *the principle of limited meaningful measurability*. This principle implies that in virtue of the enormous number, complexity, and variability of the processes and conditions of human behavior it is at best possible to obtain an approximate résumé of any form of human behavior.

No two organisms, no two societies, no two cultures, and therefore no two persons can ever be identical—not even so-called identical twins, as we shall see later. Practically infinite variability is the rule, and variation is the term which states the fact that no two things are ever exactly alike. The fact of variability is no occasion for despair but rather for congratulation, for variety constitutes not only the spice of life, but also—to the inquiring mind—a challenge to understand its origin and meaning.

POSSIBILITY OF SCIENTIFIC LAWS IN THE
BEHAVIORAL AND SOCIAL SCIENCES

Variability constitutes the most advantageous of systems for growth and development and the increase of further variability. The existence of such variability does not mean that the discovery or development of laws of sociobiology, of human behavior, or of sociology are rendered impossible. On the contrary, such laws, while perhaps more difficult to arrive at than in the physical and biological sciences, are not only possible but inevitable if scientific methods are pursued and rigorously utilized.[10] In the realm of the sociobiological there unquestionably exist statistically modal recurring series of phenomena, so that wherever one finds man living in groups, there one can always be sure of discovering certain uniformities of organized behavior as expressed in institutions. Such are, for example, the family, kinship, religion, magic, customary law, language, sexual division of labor, mythology, property, marriage, art, secular knowledge, science, and so on. Where such phenomena occur with the regularity with which they do in the human species the formulation of certain laws of society is not insuperably difficult.

By *law* we mean a generalized statement, verifiable within measurable degrees of accuracy, of the manner in which certain events recur under given conditions, from which a prediction can be made.[11] Thus, for example, we can predict from what we know of human behavior that when a child is born to a married woman within any human social group she will, other things being equal, nurse it and bring it up. We can make this prediction for a particular case from what we know of human behavior under such conditions universally. The possible variability of human behavior is so great as to prohibit the prediction that *all* married women will at all times and in all places behave in this way. But the total range of that variability is limited enough, and within that range constant enough to enable us to predict that *most* women in all cultures will nurse and take care of their children. An aboriginal married woman in Australia, for example, may have had a child ten months before the birth of her most recent one. Her inability to handle two such young children may, with the full approval of the group, cause her to suffocate the newborn infant.[12] This is not a universal pattern of behavior in parturitive married women. On grounds such as these it has been claimed that laws in the social sciences are impossible, at least in the sense of representing the precision and unrestricted universality of physical laws. This is an erroneous claim based, perhaps, upon a misunderstanding or possibly an ignorance of the modifying factors always at work in any social field. Such a modifying factor is present in the example of the Australian aboriginal woman who was forced to dispose of the newborn since she could not adequately take care of the older child with the added burden of the younger one on her hands. The modification of behavior here actually represents no variation from the law of maternal care; on the contrary it reinforces it, for the Australian aboriginal woman acts in this way because of her enculturated feeling of obligation to the older child, and because it is the customary belief that an unsocialized newborn is not really destroyed if it is killed, but will undergo subsequent reincarnation.

An understanding of the particular conditions underlying an apparent aberration from a particular social law often reveals, as in the above example, that it is not a departure at all but a good illustration of the functioning of the law. In most instances, if not in all, where the nature of the modifying factors is understood the resulting behavior is often found to be merely a special case of the law in question.

Because of the greater complexity of social as compared with physical phenomena, social laws should not be expected to be as precise as physical laws.[13] That the formulation of significant social laws is beginning to be possible we shall see later in the present volume. The expression of physical laws in mathematical form is suitable to the phenomena with which the physical sciences deal. Such mathematical expressions are only now beginning to be developed to meet the needs of the social sciences. When those needs become more refined and soundly based there can be little doubt that more refined mathematical methods will become available.[14]

As Miller has said, "Science is not any particular method or set of techniques. It is a way of reasoning. The standards are intellectual rather than procedural. The method of observation, formalization, and testing must vary with the nature of the problem."[15]

It is not its subject matter which makes a science, but the scientific application of efficient methods to the analysis and organization of that subject matter. In the study of human nature the humanity of the scientist is possibly the more important part of his equipment. Self-understanding is the best of all means toward the achievement of the understanding of others. The quality of the investigator is usually more significant than the methods he uses. As D. L. Watson has recently put it:

Of course, the student may easily be misled by his emotions, but equally by his *lack* of emotion. The road to success in handling human relations does not lie through the inhuman stolidity of the surgeon, but rather—as a first step—through the cultivation of emotional versatility and self-awareness. What is needed is not just participation, but a *critical* participation which holds fast to the thought that our self-regarding emotions deceive us.[16]

The scientific method, in Bridgman's words, is doing one's damndest with one's mind.[17] And as another Harvard physicist puts it, "the great moral which the progress of science teaches its students is: Faith in the marvelous ability of men to arrive eventually at truths by the free and vigorous exchange of intelligence."[18]

The old problem concerning the supposed difference between objective and subjective phenomena no longer exists. Objectivity, as Robert Seashore has pointed out, is simply verifiability, as judged by descriptions of equivalent samples of a given phenomenon.[19] When the subjective becomes measurable it is as objective as any other phenomenon. There is, then, no need to despair of our being able to apply scientific methods to the study of human behavior.

In spite of the tremendous variability and great complexity of the materials with which the social biologist, the anthropologist, and sociologist has to deal, there is every hope that the objective regularities observable in numerous aspects of social functioning will become increasingly more amenable to analysis and eventual statement in the form of laws.

THE "BIOLOGICAL" AND THE "SOCIAL"

It has been said that the human being is at once the terminal problem of biology and the initial factor of sociology, and that the last word of biology is the first of sociology.

If such a statement means that where biology ends and no longer plays a significant role in any social process it is unnecessary to consider biological factors but only social ones, then that is the sort of *as if* fiction which one may, for methodological purposes, justifiably accept. For that such a view is a fiction should be evident from the fact that interactive minds in society are functions of organic systems as well as social ones, and that there is therefore more than a doubt whether social phenomena ever occur without bearing to some extent, however imperceptible, the impress of the organic factor. Be that as it may, there are whole areas of social phenomena in which if an organic factor plays any part, that part is so minimal that one can safely proceed to deal with such phenomena as if organic factors played no part at all in their development. For instance, from the point of view of human relations and the organization of society, race prejudice is a social problem to be studied and dealt with by social means. In no way can the social fact of race prejudice be conceived as in any way biologically generated. Nor can the phenomena of bureaucracy, of business ethics, of annuities, of apprenticeship, of zoning, and many similar phenomena be so conceived. This is not to say that any of these phenomena is devoid of biological reference—which is always minds in interaction. But this does mean that such phenomena can be conveniently treated *as if* they were devoid of such a reference with considerable success, and under analysis yield results of great value.[20] The social biologist may be able to round out the value of these results by showing what part, if any, the organic factor plays in the genesis and expression of these phenomena, but at this stage of the development of social biology it must be his task to grapple with problems significantly more fundamental than these. He stands, as it were, in the middle of a continuum at the beginning of which the biologist labors while at the terminus the sociologist strives to reduce his less tractable material to some semblance of order. It is the social biologist's task to establish the most profitable relations between the one and the other. Thus, sociobiology, the study of the sociobiological relations of man, is at once a branch of biology and a branch of sociology. The social biologist is in a position to be able to avoid the occasional extremes of both the pure biologist and the pure sociologist, without himself making an extreme of his intermediate position. He will recognize that the life of man in society is a biological fact, but that that life is characterized by different and more or less interactive aspects, and that methodologically very different scientific techniques may best be utilized in the analysis of these various aspects of human life.

The social biologist recognizes in human culture something unique, but he finds it unnecessary to regard that culture as either superorganic or superpsychic. Here, indeed, he is in a position to supply the corrective to such points of view, and to point out the errors to which they lead. Yet when all this, and much more, has been said he can fully subscribe to the view, so well expressed by Hofstadter:

> . . . that the life of man in society, while it is incidentally a biological fact, has characteristics which are not reducible to biology and must be explained in the distinctive terms of a cultural analysis; that the physical well-being of men is a result of their social organization and not vice versa; that social improvement is a product of advances in technology and social organization, and not of breeding or selective elimination; that judgments as to the value of competition between men or enterprises or nations must be based upon social and not allegedly biological consequences; and finally, that there is nothing in nature or a naturalistic philosophy of life which makes impossible the acceptance of moral sanctions which can be employed for the common good.[21]

The study of man in his sociobiological relations embraces much more than the "merely" social and the "simply" biological. That study embraces also the psychological, the psychoanalytical, the psychosomatic, and the psychiatric analysis of the process of socialization. The social biologist, in short, seeks at once to bring about a unification of the scientific approaches to the study of socialization and an integration of the knowledge thus yielded for the better understanding and the more intelligent control of that process.

Orienting Concepts and Definitions

Before we can proceed much further there are several fundamental concepts the meaning of which must be clearly grasped. These concepts form the matrix or ground of much that we shall be considering. Two of the most immediate and important of these concepts are *social* and *cultural*. These terms are often used interchangeably and are not infrequently regarded as synonymous. Such loose usage should be avoided, for the distinction between the social and the cultural is real and useful, providing us with two helpful interdigitating concepts which, like all good concepts, serve as useful tools. Furthermore, through the medium of the processes for which these two concepts stand, the socialization of man is chiefly brought about.

What, then, do we mean by the "social" and the "cultural," what is the relation of these two processes to each other, and how may they be distinguished? An examination of the comparative material is here indispensable. Indispensable not so much because it is helpful in tracing the evolution of sociocultural behavior in man, but because the comparative simplicity of the more elemental processes in lower organisms gives us the kind of insight it would otherwise be difficult to develop into the nature of the more complex processes in man, and because it helps to confer greater sharpness of definition upon our understanding of those processes.

Origin and Evolution of Social Life

In the early stages of life upon this earth it is probable that the only forms of life were single-celled plants and animals. Such unicellular members of the plant and animal kingdoms are known to biologists as the *Protista.* Those organisms which belong to the plant kingdom are known as *Protophyta,* those belonging to the animal kingdom as *Protozoa.* In all these forms of life the single cell is a complete and self-supporting organism, which performs all the necessary functions for itself by means of the differentiated parts of its protoplasmic body. The amoeba and the paramecium are familiar examples. Such unicellular organisms always originate from a parent cell. In this fact, at this early stage, may be perceived the fundamental ground of social life, in the origin of one cell from another in the process of budding off or cleavage. In amoeba reproduction is achieved by simple fission of the parent body into two single cells. The plant cell haematococcus (which occurs in temporary pools of stagnant rain water or in the resting condition in dried-up mud or dust) multiplies itself by simple fission within the old cell wall, this process almost immediately resulting in the production of four new individuals (the same thing may happen in amoeba). Sometimes, however, another method of multiplication occurs in haematococcus. Instead of dividing into four relatively large zoöspores a restive individual may divide into thirty-two or sixty-four much smaller "microzöoids" which differ from the ordinary active form in the absence of the characteristic cell wall and its underlying vacuole.

The microzöoids freely swim about, propelled by their flagella, and sooner or later form a single individual. In so doing they provide an excellent illustration of sexual reproduction, the essential feature of which is the union or conjunction of two sexual cells or gametes (in this case the microzöoids) to form a single cell, the zygote, which is the starting point of a fresh series of cell generations.

Whether reproduction and multiplication is secured by fission or by conjugation of gametes, the process is always an interacting one between parent and developing organism. The parent organism supplies the vital tissues to the new organism and in the process of fission metabolic and other physiologic exchanges occur before parent and daughter cells become organically independent of each other.[22] This type of relationship in varying degrees is characteristic of all plant and animal life.

The fundamentally social nature of all living things has its origin in the reproductive relationship between parent and offspring; in the fact that the life of either one or the other is at some time dependent upon the potential or actual being of the other. Thus, for example, when the amoeba has reached a certain size the increase in tension becomes so great that it can only avoid death by dividing, and this it does. The original process of reproduction would seem, in part at least, to be a tension-reducing response. The new organism, during the period of division, is entirely dependent upon the proper functioning of its parent. In this dependency, brief as it may appear to our eyes, we may perceive the origins of infant dependency in the higher animals, and the obvious social, and in man cultural, consequences of that dependent relationship. In short, *the universal fact of reproduction constitutes the foundation of the social relationship which characterizes all living organisms.*

Where the offspring are born in a helpless condition and their postnatal care is more or less extended we have a setting for the development of more complex forms of social life. But of this more later. In the nature of the reproductive process we see, then, the basis for the development of social life, and the suggestion is that social life represents the response to organic drives, the expression of functions which are inextricably a part of the life of the organism. The universality of social life would seem to indicate as much.

It is the interstimulation of cells in the reproductive process which is the primordium of that subsequent interstimulation of organisms without which social life is impossible. This interstimulation has been called "trophallaxis."[23] The organism is dependent for its proper development upon other organisms, it being a product of the harmonic functioning of other organisms within the system. Organisms are environmental necessities of one another.[24]

Few living organisms are solitary either in their origin or in their lives. As Allee states: "The growing weight of the evidence indicates that animals are rarely solitary; that they are almost necessarily members of loosely integrated racial and interracial communities, in part woven together by environmental factors and in part by mutual attraction between the individual members of the different communities, no one of which can be affected without changing some or even all the rest, at least to some slight extent."[25] With few if any exceptions every organism from the lowest to the highest is engaged in some sort of social life. The solitary animal is, in most species, an abnormal creature.[26] Dobzhansky tells us that "A solitary individual wholly independent of others is largely a fiction. In reality, most or even all living beings exist in more or less integrated communities, and the ability to maintain these associations entails some cooperation, or at least 'protocooperation.'"[27] And Simpson adds:

"No animal or plant lives alone or is self-sustaining. All live in communities including other members of their own species and also a number, usually a very large variety, of other sorts of animals and plants. The quest to be alone is indeed a futile one, never successfully followed in the history of life."[28]

Animals that have been removed at birth from their mothers and raised apart from others of their kind do not know how to behave toward the members of their own kind when they are placed among them. A sheep so raised by J. P. Scott never became integrated into the group,[29] and a chimpanzee so raised was at first disturbed and aggressive when at nine months of age he was placed with another juvenile chimpanzee, although after several weeks good relations were established.[30] Dr. J. A. Reyniers of the University of Notre Dame has reported to me a similar but even more interesting series of events with respect to a monkey, *Macacus rhesus,* which was raised in isolation:

One young female which we reared germ-free for over a year and then deliberately contaminated for purposes of study, we eventually removed to the outside world. This animal had been reared alone in the confines of a germ-free cage and consequently had never seen anything of the outside world except a ceiling view and the face and arms, encased in rubber gloves, of the operator. When the animal was brought to the outside world, it seemed to be completely disoriented. If placed on a floor or table, it buried its head in its arms and remained motionless for hours at a time. When the animal was placed in a small container, it seemed to move about freely and to lose these inhibitions. This animal had never learned to make sounds. It was then placed on the opposite side of a glass panel one side of which was occupied by normal monkeys and in the course of several weeks, learned to accept its kind and to make animal noises.

Chickens which have been reared in isolation in a similar manner in Dr. Reyniers' laboratory have often "to be taught to eat." Dr. Reyniers writes, "we routinely in such cases teach it the proper head motions by manual operation."[31]

Certainly, social life is the rule among all mammals, the Class of animals to which man belongs, and no mammal is normally a solitary animal.

If the origin of social life owes its existence to the organic drives arising from the reproductive relationship, it is of more than passing interest to note that physically the multicellular organisms probably owe their origin to the same processes; that originally separate cells developed the habit of remaining attached together after division, as the spores in the encysted envelope of the parent amoeba might do to form a multicellular organism. Such an aggregation of cells would provide the means for the development of the multicellular higher animals. The interactive cells would, by their increasing ability to cooperate, develop specialized functions, and increasingly complex relations. The multicellular organism is therefore to be regarded as the expression of increasing intercellular cooperation, in which the interdependent cooperating activities of its cellular masses work together so that at all times the organism is able to function as a unit and as a whole.

ORGANISM AND SOCIETY

With the development of this interpretation of the facts we reach the view not that society is an organism, but rather that the organism is a species of society. The organismal conception of society is today generally discarded, yet, while the notion of society as an organism may be difficult to justify, a strong case can be made out for the organism as a form of society. Every word in Cooley's definition of society, for example, can be applied to the definition of an organism:

Society is a complex of forms or processes each of which is living and growing by interaction with the others, the whole being so unified that what takes place in one part affects all the rest. It is a vast tissue of reciprocal activity, differentiated into innumerable systems, some of them quite distinct, others not readily traceable, and all interwoven to such a degree that you see different systems according to the point of view you take.[32]

The system which a multicellular organism constitutes can also be so defined. But there is considerably more involved in human society than is stated in Cooley's definition, though that definition will do as a description of society in general. It will not do as a definition of human society in particular because it omits explicit reference to the fact that human society represents a development of mind, of interactive consciousnesses and the complex of relationships to which these give rise, in a sense different from that which might be conceived as possessed by the individuals or masses of cells which are the interactive elements constituting the organism. The units which make up human society are free, those constituting the organism are, for the most part, comparatively fixed. The greater part of a society can be destroyed without causing the death of its remaining units, whereas under similar conditions death would generally follow in organisms. A person in human society exercises his will and his being in thought, feeling, and action. This is not the case with regard to the cells which make up the organism. All this is not to say that there is no relation between the society of the organism and human society, but simply that there is a real difference between the two forms of society, and that one must not be identified or confused with the other. The organismal analogy as applied to human society is questionable, but the relationship of the behavior of the cells which in interaction constitute the organism and human society is a phylogenetic one, and this is far from being questionable.

Whatever the nature of the factors involved in the cooperation of cells cohering to form functioning many-celled organisms, such cooperation does exhibit the elements of a protosocial or social act, and our principal purpose has been to indicate the possibility that such acts originally represent the expression of a drive which has its origin in the reproductive-dependency relationship of parent cell and daughter cell, and that the tendency of living things to form aggregations or societies of however primitive a nature is coeval with life itself. Finally, we have tried to show that human society represents the culmination of this evolutionary tendency, and that in virtue of what seems to be the accident of the development of man's remarkable psychic potentialities human society has assumed a unique form: it has become culturalized.[33]

2 THE BIOLOGICAL BASIS OF COOPERATION

So advantageous are all forms of mutual service that the question may be fairly asked, whether after all Co-operation and Sympathy—at first instinctive, afterwards reasoned—are not the greatest facts even in organic Nature? —HENRY DRUMMOND*

THE UNIVERSALITY OF SOCIAL LIFE

The fact that such diverse groups as insects and mammals have developed social life strongly suggests the existence in organic life of deep-seated potentialities toward societization or rather toward what might more properly be called *sociality*, the tendency to be attracted to and exist together with other organisms. This drive toward sociality may be weak in some animal groups and strong in others, but in one form or another it appears to be universally present. Group life offers advantages of many kinds to the members of the group and therefore to the species.[1]

Having postulated an organic drive or basic need for sociality in living organisms, we have now to inquire into the manner in which those drives or needs are expressed in some typical organisms, and further, to discover, if possible, what are the biological advantages, if any, of social as compared with solitary life.

LIFE AND ORGANISM DEFINED AND DESCRIBED

Since we have been speaking about living organisms without having defined either life or organism, let us, before we proceed any

* Henry Drummond, *The Ascent of Man*, London, Hodder & Stoughton, 1894, p. 305.

17

further, offer a tentative definition of each. A minimum definition of life is that condition in which a body exhibits the functions of *irritability* (response to stimuli), *motility* (movement), *self-regulation* (control), and *reproductivity* (multiplication). An organism or living individual is that organization of interactive elements which displays the functions of life in a self-consistent manner. The activities of the organism constitute its behavior, and that behavior always represents an adjustment to environment. The environment is the totality of energy changes which may stimulate the organism and influence its behavior.[2]

What distinguishes the organism from inorganic matter is its directiveness and creativeness; the purposive building-up and maintenance of its structural-functional organization.

As E. S. Russell has pointed out, the activities of the organism and of its component parts are directed toward living, developing, maintenance, and reproduction. If the organism is to complete this life cycle of processes successfully it must maintain its structural-functional integrity, and satisfy its essential needs and requirements. To do so its environment must be functionally adapted to its needs and requirements for maintenance, development, and reproduction. It must be integrally adapted to its environment or environments, for it is upon its environment that the organism is dependent for the satisfaction of its needs. The organism must be an integrally harmonious structural-functional unity, in which its component parts cooperate to maintain the organism as a whole. Self-maintenance or homeostasis is the dominant drive of the organism, and in the realization of this drive it must cooperate with other organisms.[3] As Russell puts it: "A drive toward the actualization of potentialities, to which self-maintenance is a means, perhaps describes more accurately the essence of individual life—in Aristotelian phraseology, a movement from δύναμις or potentiality to ἐντελέχεια or actualization, 'the perfect realization of all that any creature or power is capable of becoming.'" In the words of Tinbergen, the key question is:

How do living things manage to survive, to maintain and reproduce themselves? The purpose, end, or goal of life processes in this restricted sense is maintenance, of the individual, of the group, and of the species. A community of individuals has to be kept going, has to be protected against disintegration just as much as an organism, which, as its name implies, is a community of parts—of organs, of parts of parts of organs. Just as the physiologist asks how the individual, or the organ, or the cell, manages to maintain itself by organized co-operation of its constituents, so the sociologist has to ask how the constituents of the group —the individuals—manage to maintain the group.[4]

THE COOPERATIVE BEHAVIOR OF LIVING ORGANISMS

From the enormous mass of data which now exists on the behavior of living organisms from the elementary to the complex let us select here a few representative examples of cooperative behavior.[5]

Sponges, which are made up of several different kinds of cells, may have their cells artificially separated and even passed through a muslin filter so that the cells become thoroughly dissociated and eventually form what appears to be a completely disorganized mass of cells. But interestingly enough, if they remain uninjured they will not long remain separated, for they regroup themselves in proper position and reform into a new organism.[6] Similar phenomena have been observed in hydroid, i.e., freshwater polyps.[7] Some of the original investigators of these phenomena have regarded them as due largely to random movements which bring the proper cells into appropriate relation with one another; if the random movements do not bring the cells into proper relation with one another they do not develop into an organism. This is, no doubt, true, but the important point is that the dissociated cells most frequently do establish the proper relations, and this must be due to something more than chance. To account for such behavior Wallin has postulated the principle of *prototaxis,* which is defined as "the innate tendency of one organism or cell to react in a definite manner with another organism or cell."[8] The reaction may be either positive or negative. Whether we regard prototaxis as being due to purely physicochemical factors or to a social appetite will depend largely upon the rigor with which and the degree to which we have made and analyzed our observations. It is easy to read into the behavior of cells purposes and motives which may in fact constitute no part of that behavior; on the other hand the fear of appearing ridiculous may deter some from drawing the clear conclusion. The fact is that no sharp line can be drawn between the behavior of cells forming an organism, the phenomenon of prototaxis, and the behavior of organisms in the process of association.

There most certainly exist the greatest differences in complexity in the relations involved; in these behavioral responses evolution has undoubtedly occurred in much the same manner as evolution has taken place in physical characters as between the simpler and the more complex organisms. Just as the single-celled organism stands physically in ancestral relationship to the human organism of some 60,000,000,000,000 cells, so does the single-celled organism's behavior stand in relationship to the behavior of a human being. Indeed, the physicochemical basis of the behavior of the human being bears the closest relationship to that of the single cell. This we shall clearly see when we come to the analysis of the basic or biogenic needs of the organism, whether it be a single cell or a multicellular organism such as man.

Examples of what has been called "the social appetite" in the lowest organisms have been known for many years. More than half a century ago, in 1894, the distinguished experimental embryologist Wilhelm Roux shook apart the cells of a frog's egg during an early stage of its development, placed the separated cells some distance from one another in water, and watched to see what would happen. The separated cells slowly approached each other until they established contact.

When an experimenter removes individual amebas some distance from a group of their fellows, the separated amebas immediately begin to make their way back to the group.

Deegener, in a series of experiments carried out on the caterpillar *Hyponomeuta,* found that these creatures actively seek out the company of their fellows when separated from them, and that even the isolated larvas tend to seek out their kind. He recognized a distinct need for association among caterpillars and spoke of a social instinct.[9]

Whether it is justifiable to speak of a social instinct with respect to caterpillars or whether it may not rather be that a tendency is present which under certain conditions leads to social behavior, the tendency to remain together is a fact.

It is a further fact that, with few if any exceptions, all animals maintain contact with their fellows unless, under certain conditions, such conduct happens to threaten them in some way. Under all other conditions, all animals exhibit a high tolerance for the presence of their kind. This does not for a moment imply that a type of social organization is developed by such elementary creatures, but rather that they exhibit potentialities for social life. In ascending the "scale of life" we are dealing with progressively increasing levels of integration,[10] progressively increasing degrees of complexity, terminating in the most complex of all, man. Nevertheless, in some elementary forms of life, such as in certain bacteria, remarkable resemblances to what can only be regarded as social organization are seen.

As long ago as 1892, Thaxter showed that *Myxobacteria* exhibit a remarkable specialization which consists in a striking division of labor in the maintenance of the group. Individual bacteria held together in slime join to form a common nonreproductive stalk at the top of which numerous other bacteria join together in cystlike forms to propagate themselves.

Even earlier than this, in 1880, Van Tieghem found a more advanced type of social organization in the myxamebas *Dictyostelium*. Here the myxamebas derived from spores wander about freely and multiply separately. Subsequently all the members of the population come together to form a single aggregate, with the cells still maintaining their individuality. Then some of the cells become immobilized and transformed into stalk cells which are organized into a reproducing mass at the apex. From this position the matured spores become subsequently dispersed.[11]

These are but a few of the examples which could be cited to demonstrate the existence of a social appetite throughout the kingdom of living organisms. Whether we are dealing with fungi, bacteria, slime molds, sponges, or higher plants and animals, the drive to form social aggregates usually seems to be present in one form or another.

Some insects, fish, and at least one mammal would appear to be exceptions to this rule. The solitary wasps and the praying mantis, pike and trout among fish, and the puma and hyena seem to prefer their own company and are frequently antagonistic toward members of their own species. As we shall later see from the special cases which have been studied (pp. 42–44), these seeming exceptions are not so in fact, but special cases which prove the universality of the rule that all living organisms are characterized by an innate drive toward association.[12]

Allee has presented the evidence which indicates that among the simpler plants and animals there exists a sort of unconscious co-operation or automatic mutualism.[13] This is primarily reflected in the tendency of such simpler plants and animals to aggregate together, while the biological benefits which follow from their activities is exhibited in the significantly greater survival rate of organisms living in fairly dense populations than of those living in sparse populations or in an environment in which they are isolated.[14] Varying with the nature of the environments the isolated animal will, in general, be retarded in growth or irremediably damaged or suffer death where the animal living in association with others will increase in size and in the speed of its physiological reactions, tend to recover quickly from wounds, and survive more often where the solitary animal would die. The planarian worms which have been exposed to ultraviolet radiation disintegrate more rapidly when isolated than when they are associated together. They survive exposure to ultraviolet radiation better when crowded while being irradiated, and there is a much higher death rate among those which are isolated a few minutes after irradiation than among those which are left together. Goldfish placed together in groups of ten in a suspension of colloidal silver survived much longer than those which were placed in similar suspensions alone. Allee writes as follows:

When exposed to the toxic colloidal silver the grouped fish shared between them a dose easily fatal for any one of them; the slime they secreted changed much of the silver into a less toxic form. In the experiment as set up the suspension was somewhat too strong for any to survive; with a weaker suspension some or all of the grouped animals would have lived; as it was, the group gained for its members a longer life. In nature they could have had more minutes for rain to have diluted the poison or some other disturbance to have cleared it up and given the fish a chance for complete recovery.[15]

The experiment involving the goldfish illustrates the physico-chemical basis of the advantage which lies in numbers, and presumably holds true for all other aquatic organisms. Allee's studies on the rate of cleavage of the fertilized egg of the common sea urchin *Arbacia* show that, with few exceptions, the rate is more rapid in the denser clusters of eggs than in associated but isolated fellow eggs. Protozoans, it has been experimentally shown, grow more rapidly when they are introduced in large numbers into a sterile medium of relatively simple salts than if the cultures are started with only a few organisms. The biological advantages are all in the crowding—not overcrowding—while separation or isolation would appear to be so fatal to the organism that we can be fairly certain that it rarely occurs in nature. The optimal population size for different groups in nature will depend upon the group and its environment, but thus far the evidence strongly indicates that optimal numbers present in a given situation have certain positive survival values and exert positive stimulating effects on the growth of individuals and the increase of population.[16] Thus, for example, Darling has found that among herring gulls the members of large colonies stimulate each other to commence sexual activities earlier than when the colonies are smaller, and furthermore, there tends to be a speeding-up of egg-laying, so that breeding activities are more intense while they last. The survival value of the short spread of time between laying and hatching lies in the fact that a greater number of young gulls survive under such conditions than do so where the colony is small and the spread of hatching time therefore longer.[17] The same holds true for asexual protozoans. It has been shown that when two protozoans of a certain species are placed together each one multiplies considerably more rapidly than when they are isolated.[18]

The unconscious kind of mutualism or cooperation which exists universally among lower animals, not commonly regarded as social or viewed only as partially social, undoubtedly represents an earlier stage in the development of social life among the higher animals. It is important to realize, with all its implications, the fact that this fundamental principle of mutualism, of cooperation, appears to have governed the relations of organisms from the first. The organic basis for this cooperation, the origin of mutualism, seems to be best understood in terms of the nature of the reproductive relationship, with the accompanying mutual interrelations which are for a time maintained between parent and developing organism. Whatever of truth there may be in this suggestion it is certain that the conception of nature "red in tooth and claw," which views animals as in a more or less constant state of warfare with one another, in which the "struggle for existence" and "the survival of the fittest" are the two cardinal principles of "natural selection," is one-sided and false. Activities which may collectively be called the competitive struggle for existence do characterize the behavior of most animals, but such activities are not all that characterize their behavior, the two forms of behavior often complementing rather than being in opposition to each other. In what might be called the tough Darwinian period of the nineteenth century the concept of natural selection through competition so completely dominated the thought of biologists and Spencerian sociologists—and practically every sociologist was a Spencerian in those days—that the existence of cooperative behavior on a large scale, though known to some biologists and certainly well understood by Darwin,[19] was virtually neglected in favor of the admittedly important principle of natural selection. Darwin's great book, published in 1859, was entitled *The Origin of Species by Means of Natural Selection, or the Preservation of Favoured Races in the Struggle for Life*. And that essentially is what throughout the last forty years of the nineteenth century most biologists were engaged in proving.[20] The voices which were raised in defence of cooperation[21] were drowned out in the one-sided din created by the proponents of natural selection. It was not that the natural selectionists denied the existence of cooperation, but that they passed it by and neglected it in favor of a crass competition. The extreme viewpoint of the natural selectionists was stated by Huxley in 1888 in his "struggle-for-life" manifesto.[22] The reply made by Prince Petr Kropotkin (published in *Nineteenth Century* in eight articles 1890–1896, and in 1902 published in book form as *Mutual Aid: A Factor of Evolution*) made and has steadily though slowly continued to make a deep impression upon all who read it.[23] It succeeded in drawing attention to substantial works which had already dealt with the subject, and in focusing attention upon an important and much underrated factor in evolution. As an economist and student of industrial civilization Henry George worked out the principle of cooperation for himself. He called it "the law of progress," and this appeared in his great book *Progress and Poverty* (1879). George formulated "the law of progress" as follows: "Men tend to progress just as they come closer together, and by co-operation with each other increase the mental power that may be devoted to improvement, but just as conflict is provoked, or association develops inequality of condition and power, this tendency to progression is lessened, checked, and finally reversed."[24] Giddings, in *The Principles of Sociology* (1896), was the first sociologist to emphasize the importance of cooperation in social evolution, and among English publicists Henry Drummond, for example, chose for his Boston Lowell Lectures, published in 1894 as *The Ascent of Man,* the exposition of the thesis that while in nature there was indeed a struggle for life there was also such a thing as the struggle for the life of others. A goodly number of works having the same theme for their subject have been published since the beginning of the second decade of this century.[25]

At the present time the principle of cooperation is in a fair way to becoming established as an important factor in the survival of living groups. Allee sums up the modern point of view as follows:

After much consideration, it is my mature conclusion, contrary to Herbert Spencer, that the cooperative forces are biologically the more important and vital. The balance between the cooperative and altruistic tendencies and those which are disoperative and egoistic is relatively close. Under many conditions the cooperative forces lose. In the long run, however, the group centered, more altruistic drives are slightly stronger.

If cooperation had not been the stronger force, the more complicated animals, whether arthropods or vertebrates, could not have evolved from simpler ones, and there would have been no men to worry each other with their distressing and biologically foolish wars. While I know of no laboratory experiments that make a direct test of this problem, I have come to this conclusion by studying the implications of many experiments which bear on both sides of the problem and from considering the trends of organic evolution in nature. Despite many known appearances to the contrary, human altruistic drives are as firmly based on an animal ancestry as is man himself. Our tendencies toward goodness, such as they are, are as innate as our tendencies toward intelligence; we could do well with more of both.[26]

The tendentious habit of thinking of evolution in terms of the struggle for existence, by means of which, it is believed, the fittest are alone selected for survival while the weakest are ruthlessly condemned to extinction, is not only an incorrect view of the facts, but is a habit of thought which has done a considerable amount of harm. It is understandable that in a warlike age men should confuse the survival of the fightingest with the survival of the fittest, but the two qualities are by no means the same. Only by omitting any reference to such an important evolutionary factor as the principle of cooperation, and by viewing evolution as a process of continuous conflict between all living things can men be led to conclude that survival or development depends on successful aggression. Omitting important facts and basing their arguments on false premises the tough Darwinians could only arrive at false conclusions. As Allee says: "Today, as in Darwin's time, the average biologist apparently still thinks of a natural selection which acts primarily on egoistic principles, and intelligent fellow thinkers in other disciplines, together with the much-cited man-in-the-street, cannot be blamed for taking the same point of view."[27]

Certainly aggressiveness in many different forms exists in nature, but there also exists a concomitant healthy non-ruthless competition, and there also exist strong drives toward social and cooperative behavior. These forces do not operate independently but together, as a whole, and the evidence strongly indicates that of all these drives the principle of cooperation is the most dominant, and biologically the most important. The coexistence of so many different species of animals throughout the world is a sufficient testimony to the importance of that principle. It is probable that man owes more to the operation of this principle than to any other in his biological and social evolution. Indeed, without this principle of cooperation, of sociability and mutual aid, the progress of organic life, the improvement of the organism, and the strengthening of the species, becomes incomprehensible. Cooperation constitutes a stabilizing, a cohesive, factor insofar as it makes for successful group activity, and thus ameliorates the environment so that the members of the group function more efficiently and the survival rate is increased.[28]

We may, by induction from the facts, arrive at a generalization to the effect that the greater the cooperative behavior exhibited by the members of any group the more harmoniously organized is that group likely to be. Interesting examples of this generalization are the social ants in which the principle of cooperation has been developed to the limit of fixity. Yet, as Schneirla has suggested, it were perhaps more accurate to speak of *biosocial facilitation* rather than of cooperation here because of the psychological limitations of social ants.[29] The distinction is, however, simply one of organization at qualitatively different levels. The principle of cooperation has been summed up by a group of distinguished biologists in the statement that the probability of survival of individual or living things increases with the degree in which they harmoniously adjust themselves to each other and to their environment.[30]

Today, contrary to the "nature red in tooth and claw" school of natural selectionists, competition, in the sense of conflict, opposition, or striving against other organisms, is not by any means regarded as the principal factor in evolution. On the other hand, the evidence increasingly indicates that natural selection acts primarily by favoring behavioral and organic variations which better adjust the organism to its environment. Competition of every kind exists in the state of nature and has, of course, played an important role in the evolution of the varieties of life, but so has cooperation. In the struggle for existence one group may be competitively more successful than another because it is more cooperative. Certainly, so far as the persistence or continuation of every group is concerned, natural selection favors the *cooperative* as opposed to the *disoperative* struggling for survival. As Burkholder has recently stated: "Though struggle, conflict and elimination have long been emphasized by the proponents of the Darwinian school, probably the most important basis for selection of fitness actually is the ability of associated components within organisms and in societies to work together harmoniously among themselves and in conformity to the physical environment."[31]

The modern concept of natural selection is that of differential fertility or reproductive efficiency. The fitness or adaptive value of a group is expressed or measured by its reproductive efficiency, by the number of surviving progeny it produces. In a population containing differences in the distribution of mutant genes (that is to say, in which some types or groups possess such mutant genes and some do not), if for any reason one type or group leaves a greater surviving progeny than others, certain of the hereditary particles, the genes, and associations of these will become more frequent in succeeding generations. To put it in other words, any group of a population which for any reason leaves a greater surviving progeny, will increase while others become fewer in numbers in succeeding generations. This is what is meant by natural selection—*differential fertility*, resulting in the perpetuation of new genotypes.

We have already seen that reproduction is greater in cooperative situations than in noncooperative ones. Social life is, among other things, a means of ensuring reproduction. Familiarity is more likely to breed children than contempt. To the extent, therefore, that any group is less social, less fully integrated than another, it is likely to be differentially less fertile. With all other factors being equal, the group in which its members are closely integrated and are often together is likely to leave a greater surviving progeny than the group whose members are less socially integrated. Compare the numbers of the comparatively solitary lions, tigers, leopards, and jaguars, with those of the more gregarious nonpredatory deer, cattle, rabbits, and the remainder of the harmless gregarious creatures of the land. Consider, in the air, the flocks of swallows, pigeons, ducks, gulls, and other birds; in the water the shoals of herring, cod, and mackerel and the innumerable big and little unarmed fishes; compare the numbers of these with the eagles and hawks of the air and the sharks and alligators of the waters. Those who have most efficiently learned to avoid destructive competition survive better by the association they have developed. The meek shall inherit the earth. It is in the methods of peaceful association that strength is accumulated, and it is in those of competition, struggle, and combat that it is dissipated and wasted. Getting along with one's fellows has great adaptive value, and in the evolution of man there can be little doubt that selective pressures have favored those possessing these adaptive qualities.[32] "In comparative or competitive life the peaceable would benefit more and live longer than the needlessly disputatious, and so among the most unintelligent creatures there would develop a more harmonious life by the operation of the law of survival, without any conscious sense of harmony or of duty."[33] As Gibson says: "the adaptation to closer association, by cultivation of its peculiar methods of cooperative life, will enable a continued increase, by reducing the evils of crowding and developing its benefits.

"Thus association begins to appear as a constructive force, while the mere competition of numbers for survival of the fittest, is a form of destructive contest."[34]

Evolution itself is a process which favors cooperating rather than disoperating groups, and "fitness" is a function of the group as a whole rather than of separate individuals. The fitness of the individual is largely derived from his membership in the group. The more cooperative the group, the greater is the fitness for survival which extends to all its members. Politically such conditions are best realized in a democracy, and most threatened in a totalitarian or "closed society." As A. E. Emerson has concluded, the dominant directional trend in evolution is toward a controlled balance of the important factors within the system. "Human society cooperatively brings the social environment under control for the better survival of the species."[35]

If we would seek for one word which would describe society better than any other that word is cooperation. Cooperation may be defined as interaction between organisms which produces mutual support and enlarging stimulations which confer survival benefits upon the interacting organisms. It is important for us to understand that, contrary to the beliefs of the Social Darwinists, man does not have to make war upon his alleged bestial innate nature by opposing it with a cooperative way of life of his own invention. Not in the least, for man is born with the strongest cooperative impulses, and all that they require is the proper support and cultivation. Man's innate cooperative impulses are notably strong, as might be expected of a species individually so defenseless and weak. With respect to any other kinds of strivings the infant of most birds and mammals is equipped with the ability to compete with the universe for attention, and it generally succeeds in eliciting cooperative behavior, usually from one or both parents. In the process of socialization a certain quantity of the energies of aggressiveness are transformed into cooperative processes. The reproductive process is a cooperative one, and in addition, development as one of a litter or group of siblings represents another early experience in the development of cooperation; development within a family represents a still further experience in the learning and practice of cooperation; but this is to anticipate.

Innate tendencies toward some sort of social life are present in even the lowest organisms, and such a thing as a completely asocial variety of animal probably does not exist. This seems to be the first point to grasp in arriving at any understanding of the nature of the social. The social behavior may be limited to the short mating association or to the period of *care* of the eggs, as in many insects,[36] or extended to the complexities of the social behavior characterizing human communities. A second point is that social life confers distinct biological advantages upon the organisms participating in it. Allee and Emerson, indeed, regard as at least partially social any group in which the organisms confer distinct survival benefits upon each other. Implying the same thing, but rather more ascetically, Tinbergen would regard as social the keeping together of organisms on the basis of their interaction, and he would even call much of the behavior in a pair of organisms social. Third, and most important, the dominant principle of social life is not competition or the struggle for existence in the competitive sense, but is cooperation—the process of interactive behavior between organisms in consequence of which they confer survival benefits upon each other.

Fourth, some form of social life, of aggregate existence or association, is probably coeval with life itself, otherwise life could not have become established and evolved, and finally, the organic basis of social behavior is to be found in the nature of the reproductive relationship between parent organism and offspring. Nothing would seem more appropriate than that the reproductive process, which is concerned with the creation of life, should constitute the fundamental social relationship, and that in the evolution of living organisms, from the simple to the complex, mutually beneficial mass physiological interactions continue to form the organic basis of social life. Man is no exception to this rule, but he is the one animal most capable of modifying it by means of his cultural devices.

SOME DEFINITIONS

SOCIETY. We are now, perhaps, ready for a tentative definition of society. *Society denotes that complex of fundamentally cooperative interactions or interrelations which exist between and among the members of a group.*

A SOCIETY. *A society, as distinct from society, is a group the members of which consciously or unconsciously cooperate to maintain a common life.*

THE SOCIAL. *By social we mean all those interactive relations between individuals or groups in which needs are satisfied.* The social is essentially a continuous relational reticulum in which the indispensable condition is interaction, the establishment or process of reciprocal relations and influences between and among the members of a group. The fundamental quality of social life is cooperation—the process of interaction between organisms during which they confer survival benefits upon each other.

These definitions apply to the whole animal kingdom including man. There is, however, one aspect of society which is by many students either held or implied to be peculiar to man, and that is *culture.*

CULTURE. *A culture is the particular form which characterizes the social activities of a group.* Society is the generic term and culture is a species of society; the cultural is the particular form of the social. Cooperative interaction between and among the members of a group is social behavior, and such behavior is more or less common to all animal groups. What is not common to such groups is the form which that behavior takes. This distinctive form constitutes the culture of a group. As Linton has written of human behavior: "the actual behavior observed will rarely if ever be identical for any two individuals or even for the same individual on two occasions. The variations will tend, however, to cluster about certain norms. The sum total of these norms together with their interactions, is taken to constitute the culture of the society."[37]

IS CULTURE UNIQUE TO MAN?

Warden, in an interesting book on this subject,[38] has attempted to show that animals do not have a cultural but are characterized by a social life. He has suggested a threefold criterion of culture, namely, invention, communication, and social habituation. Culture necessitates the development of some new form of behavior which is communicated to other members of the species so that it becomes the normal form of behavior to a large number of them. This type of behavior, Warden claims, is not found in any animal other than man. What appears to be cultural among lower animals is, according to Warden, "biosocial" behavior which is determined phylogenetically or by heredity, whereas culture in man is ontogenetic, developing during the lifetime of individuals as a result of the action upon them of more purely social conditions.

CULTURE IN NONHUMAN ANIMALS

Let us examine the facts. Are new forms of behavior ever invented or developed by animals and communicated by them to other members of the species so that the greater part of such a group will normally come to exhibit such behavior? There is some evidence that such modifications of behavior do occur among lower animals.

In the first place, it is known to most experienced field naturalists that separated local groups of the same species of animals will exhibit clearly recognizable differences in behavior, and in several such groups the development and establishment of a novel form of behavior within the group has actually been witnessed. Several instances of this may be given. All African lions belong to the same species. Throughout the greater part of Africa they customarily hunt alone or in pairs accompanied by their young. Occasionally several lions will combine to attack a wounded water-buffalo which would be more than a match for them singly. In Kenya Colony, however, lions have developed the habit of hunting in packs with a regular division of function. The pack spreads out in a surrounding movement and closes in, roaring; in this way driving the game within the surround to a place where one lion lies quietly in ambush. Old hunters, according to Linton, say that within the memory of persons now living Kenya lions used to hunt in the manner common to lions elsewhere in Africa. They suggest that the change in the lions' method of hunting is due to the diminishing supply of game. Whether this is the real reason or not, it would appear that a new pattern of behavior has been developed and established in this local group of lions as the normal form. Such behavior is transmitted to the young from generation to generation.[39]

If these lions have altered their mode of hunting, then culture as the social transmission of socially modified forms of behavior, by

Warden's threefold criterion or any other criterion, is certainly exhibited in the behavior of these Kenya lions.

The question arises whether the possession of culture would have been denied to all lions had they all exhibited the kind of behavior which is apparently peculiar to the Kenya lions. Such behavior, it would have been said by most students, is instinctive, "biosocial," being too uniform and invariant to represent anything other than the expression of a genetically determined pattern of behavior. This is the customary argument applied to the description of all animal behavior as noncultural. Behavior such as the rat-catching activities of cats has traditionally been discussed as clearly instinctive because of the regularity with which it is exhibited by cats. No one, until fairly recently, was inclined to ask how much of this behavior was due to hereditary predisposition and how much to learning and to cultural acquisition. The now classical experiments carried out by Kuo are in this connection illuminating.[40]

Kuo's Cats and Rats

Kuo reared three groups of kittens under the following conditions: (1) kittens reared with mothers who killed rats in their presence, (2) kittens reared without any contact with rats until they were several months old, and (3) kittens reared with rats as companions. In the first group 85 per cent of the kittens killed rats before they were four months old. In the second group only 45 per cent became rat killers. In the third group the cats lived amicably together with their rat companions, never molesting any one of them. What is more, they never molested any strange rat of the same variety, although 16 per cent of these cats did kill rats of other varieties.

Clearly, the process of conditioning plays a much more important role in determining the behavior of cats in relation to small animals than has been customarily allowed. A great deal of what has passed for the instinctive behavior of cats is proven to be due to enculturation or culturalization. Under wild conditions it may be necessary for cats to kill small animals if they are to survive, and they apparently inherit a disposition to do something of the kind, but even this disposition does not appear to be strong since only 16 per cent of the unconditioned cats in this experiment became rat killers—rather, killers of other varieties of rats. What seems clear is that the kind of development its behavioral potentialities shall undergo largely depends upon the kind of experience to which the animal is exposed. These potentialities can be developed, directed, or more or less completely inhibited by early conditioning. In this process the behavior of the parent in the presence of the offspring plays a significant role. The behavior potentials of the offspring become organized in terms of the pattern of behavior originally offered to them by the parent. When the kittens observed their parents killing rats 85 per cent of them became rat killers. In the finally established behavior of the individual, it is evident, early conditioning plays almost as large a part as predisposition and individual learning combined.

Indeed, as Kuo says: "Our behavior researches in the past have been in the wrong direction, because *instead of finding how we could build nature into the animal, we have tried to find nature in the animal*. Nothing is more natural than for the cat to 'love' the rat. And if one insists that the cat has an instinct to kill the rat, I must add that it has an instinct to love the rat too. In behavior nature is what can be built in and not what is supposed to unfold from within."[41]

Few more important words have ever been written in social psychology than are contained in that last sentence of Kuo: "In behavior nature is what can be built in and not what is supposed to unfold from within."

Cooperation in Cats and Rats

Much light has been thrown on the "love" of cats for rats by means of several studies conducted by Professor Loh Seng Tsai of Tulane University. In a first series of studies three domestic kittens about one month old and four alley cats about two months of age learned to live peacefully together with laboratory white rats. In a second series of experiments Tsai tried to discover whether a confirmed rat-killing cat could be taught to live amicably with a hooded or colored rat. For this purpose a special apparatus was used. This apparatus consisted of three sections, each separated by an electrically controlled screen. The first section was the entrance, where cat and rat met for each test. When the gate was opened the animals entered the second section—the reaction chamber. To enter the third section, where a dish of food awaited them—the goal chamber—cat and rat had to step on a floor button simultaneously. When they did this together the gate went down and they were free to enter the goal chamber and eat the food.

First both animals had to learn that the buttons were the keys to the food. They had to learn that neither would be rewarded when only one stepped on the button at any one time. They had to learn to cooperate, to step on the button at the same time, if they were to obtain satisfaction.

In his first experiment Tsai placed three domestic kittens and three young rats together in a cage where they learned to live together as they grew. From the first they exhibited no signs of aggression or fear. For two years they lived peacefully together in the same cage without a single "misunderstanding." They lived together, ate together, slept together, and played together. A movie record was taken of a cat with a rat riding on her back.

Tsai put the three kittens and rats in the apparatus described above. One of the cats began to play with his partner's tail and accidentally both pressed the two buttons simultaneously, in this way opening the gate. So the cat would continue to play with the rat's tail, imagining, apparently, that this tail playing would open the gate for him. But one of the rats was much more ingenious. He would attract the cat's attention with his tail, and, when the cat's paw was on the cat's button, he would scurry over to press his own.

In a short time all pairs were working together. In the beginning they averaged two or three successful trials a day, then five, then ten, then fifteen within half an hour. In a few weeks they finally took only two seconds from the time they left the entrance to the time they reached the goal. Their cooperation, at first accidental, became more and more deliberately cooperative.

But Tsai was not satisfied. Thus far his experiments had been made with animals that had lived together from shortly after birth. What could he do with alley cats?

In his second experiment Tsai employed four alley cats, born, he tells us, in New Orleans' French Quarter. These cats were already weaned and were more than two months old. Tsai writes:

Being alley-born and alley-raised, they should have had the experience of chasing after and killing alley rats. However, to my surprise, these alley cats also lived peacefully and cooperated with their rat-partners at least just as well as their domestic cat predecessors. They became friendly to the rats without much experience of living together with them in the same cage. One of the rats even sought protection from a cat and often stood right under the cat's belly, eating with him out of the same dish.

Alley-cats and rats learned to cooperate very satisfactorily in the experimental apparatus.

In his third experiment Tsai installed an extra key in the reaction chamber in front of the entrance gate. One member of the pair was put in the reaction chamber while the other was kept in the entrance compartment. Observing that his partner was confined and that he would be unable to open the gate alone, the released cat would refuse to go to the old buttons but instead would press the new key at once in order to release his partner. The rat, because of poorer vision, would tend to go forward to the old buttons. Failing to find his partner there, he would return to press the new key before the entrance door, thus releasing the cat. As soon as the cat was free the rat would run back to the old buttons to cooperate with him. Tsai points out that such behavior indicates that stereotyped position habits are not involved, but the responses are appropriately made to their partners as social simuli.

Tsai was still not satisfied, for although the alley cats were already weaned and assumed to have chased and killed alley rats, no authentic information could be obtained with respect to their actual rat-killing activities. The question was also raised whether these alley cats could cooperate with rats of another strain or color. Tsai therefore set out to discover whether a confirmed rat-killing cat could be taught to cooperate with a hooded or colored rat.

A ferocious rat-killing cat was obtained who, Tsai stated, "had enjoyed a long and glorious record of rat-killing." This female was eight months of age when she was brought to the laboratory.

In the course of training the apparatus was divided longitudinally into two sides along the midline by three pieces of glass, which were changed later into wire mesh partitions, thus separating the cat and rat all the way from the entrance through the reaction chamber to the goal. This was a safety device to prevent the cat from killing the rat, which past experience showed she would have done at the first opportunity.

After about 700 trials of training in 28 days distributed over three and one-half months, the cat finally cooperated with the hooded rat without any act of aggression. It took about 550 trials before the partition, first of glass, and later of wire mesh, was removed from the goal. From then on, the once ferocious rat-killing cat would be peacefully eating with the hooded rat face to face out of the same dish. Another 150 trials were taken before the last partition in the reaction chamber was completely removed. The cat was also trained to release the rat confined in the entrance compartment by pressing with his paw a tiny electric key of one inch in diameter, located on the right hand side of the reaction chamber mid-way between the two screen doors. This was to make him realize that he could not solve the problem without first bringing in the rat-partner. In other words, the rat has become a necessary instrument as well as an invariable sign of food to the cat.[42]

Tsai believes that his observations throw "overboard the traditional dogma in psychology that in animal nature there is an ineradicable instinct of pugnacity which makes fighting or wars inevitable. . . . My experimental results give the death blow to any such fighting instinct theory."

Quite obviously when the conditions of life are changed predators change their ways of life toward their prey, particularly when their own existence is dependent upon that change.

Evidence of Cultural Behavior in Birds

What appears to constitute a good example of the invention, transmission, and perpetuation of behavior is presented by the case of certain species of birds known as "tits" (*Parus*). In 1921 tits were first reported as opening the tops of milk bottles left on doorsteps and drinking the milk. This first report came from Swaythning, near Stoneham, Southampton, England. Since 1921 this practice on the part of tits has been reported from many parts of England and some parts of Wales, Scotland, and Ireland. To date eleven species of the genus *Parus* have been reported as engaging in this bottle-opening practice.[43] There are over four hundred records of bottle opening by tits, and observations to a lesser extent are also available on house-sparrows, blackbirds, starlings, robins, chaffinches, and hedge-sparrows.

Most British tits are resident, not normally migrating from their usual territory even in winter; they may move a few miles from their breeding place, but usually not more. This fact would support the suggestion that when the bottle-opening habit is observed in tits more than fifteen miles distant from any place where the habit has been previously recorded the discovery or invention of bottle opening has been independently made by individual birds. The distribution of the records is consistent with the view that the new source of food was discovered originally only by a small proportion of a local tit population and then passed on to other individuals. As Hawkins states: "In England and Wales, it seems likely that the habit has arisen *de novo* at least once per vice-county and may have arisen more often than this. . . . The evidence that the area in which the habit occurred, as well as the actual number of records, increased more rapidly each year, is enough to support the view that when the habit has been acquired by one tit it can then be spread through the population by some form of imitation or learning."

The tits usually attack the bottles within a few minutes after they have been left at the door. There are several reports of parties of tits following the milkman's wagon and removing the bottle caps while he is delivering milk to the houses. A great variety of bottle-opening methods have been reported. When the milk bottle is capped with a metal foil the bird usually first punctures the cap with its beak and then tears off the foil in strips. Sometimes the whole cap is removed and sometimes only a small hole is made in it. Cardboard tops receive a much wider variety of treatments. The whole top may be removed, or only the press-in center, or the cardboard may be torn off layer by layer until it is thin enough for a small hole to be made in it; the milk may be taken through the hole, or the bird may insert its beak through the hole and flick the whole top off. The records show that several different methods may be used in the same district, and that individual birds may employ more than one method.

Since 1949 opening of milk bottles by tits has been reported from Sweden, Denmark, Switzerland, and Holland. In Holland milk bottles disappeared in 1947–1948. It is unlikely that many of the tits which had learnt the habit of opening milk bottles in pre-war years still survived in 1948, the habit must, therefore, have originated in all recorded localities since 1948. Since Great Tits are relatively sedentary birds, it seems certain that the habit must have started in many different places, and that it was initiated by many different individuals.[44]

That birds are capable, within limits, of learning and communicating new forms of behavior has long been known.[45] Clear-cut cases of invention and transmission, perpetuation and individual capacity for variation in behavior have not, however, hitherto been available as they are for these European tits.

Scott's classical experiments on the song of young orioles, carried out in 1901, are of interest. Scott separated the young orioles from their parents before they had an opportunity to learn the usual oriole song from them. The orioles thus deprived developed a song of their own. When other young orioles were placed among these, they, too, learned this song.[46]

Conradi has shown that when sparrows are placed among canaries they imitate the song of the latter.[47] It is a well-known fact that these and many other varieties of birds will improve their song when afforded the advantage of listening to a "virtuoso" in their particular field, and that such accomplished songsters are kept by bird fanciers for this very purpose. Evidently, within certain limits, birds are capable of developing and communicating new forms of behavior, and clearly their behavior combines ontogenetic as well as phylogenetic elements; it contains cultural as well as innate predispositional elements.[48]

Lorenz has shown in convincing detail that jackdaws teach their young to recognize the enemy "by actual tradition by handing-down of personal experience from one generation to the next."[49]

The mothers of innumerable animal groups teach their young to perform a variety of acts. Birds teach their young to fly and also which enemies to avoid; dogs teach their young under domestication to open and close doors, ring bells, and so on; apes teach their young to walk. With reference to apes, Yerkes, our foremost student of their behavior, has given an excellent account of the acquisition, establishment, and transmission of new behavior in chimpanzees.[50] Years ago pushbutton water fountains were installed in each of the chimpanzee living cages at the Orange Park, Florida, laboratory. This was done with some misgiving since it was felt that the animals might never learn to use the device or that they might have to be taught individually. Except at the outset, tuition has proved unnecessary, and it is years since any individual has required other than the stimulus of seeing its companions obtain water by pushing the button. Social tradition carries the lesson.

Three generations of association with man in the Orange Park laboratories has produced many opportunities for these chimpanzees to observe and to develop forms of behavior such as spitting through the teeth, squirting water, clapping the hands, using such objects as balls, keys, and hammers. Any or all of these activities, Yerkes suggests, may become behavioral traditions in a chimpanzee group.

The use of these chimpanzees in experimental situations and their intimate and continuous association with man has resulted in the development of very definite cultural acts which are both persistent and cumulative, since they are passed along from individual to individual by imitation and from one generation to the next by social tradition. To the experimenters it is a boon to work with animals that increase in usefulness year by year by reason of their capacity for individual adaptation, and to have successive generations regularly outstrip one another as a result of social tradition. These chimpanzees are clearly exhibiting cultural behavior.

BEHAVIOR AND THE "SOCIAL FIELD"

At this point the fact perhaps requires to be emphasized that the discussion as to whether or not nonhuman animals are capable of culture is not simply an academic one. It is not merely a matter of understanding our relations to each other as human beings which may be illuminated by such a discussion, but what is in its way no less important, our relations to the so-called lower animals. The great importance of St. Francis of Assisi in the western world is that he was among the first to grasp something of the significance of this, although in the East this relationship has been well understood for several millennia.[51]

We have assumed, in our culture, that animals have a nature which is unalterably fixed by their heredity, that their behavior is predestined by heredity. To some extent this is, of course, true, but we appear to have overemphasized the extent to which this is true and permitted the lower animals hardly any potentialities for plasticity or educability. Hence, we speak of hereditary enemies among animals, "the nature of the beast," while the contrary examples which accumulate in increasing numbers tend to be dismissed as quaint aberrations, even though the example of domestic animals living together is constantly before us.

When we ask what the nature of the beast really is, we are likely to obtain an answer structured in terms of the question. That is to say, we go out into the field and observe, and return with a description of the behavior of the beast, and the description serves as an account of its behavior. But that is not a sound way of inquiring into what we really want to know, namely, what it is that has been built (and by what means) into the animal that has become its nature. This way of asking the question leads us to regard the animal as a function of its total environment, the environment within it, which may be called the *in*vironment, and the environment without it, of which the organism is quite as much a part as of its invironment. We know that when we alter the invironment we can often produce behavioral changes. May it not be that when we alter the environment similar changes might be produced—changes in what we call "the nature of the beast"? The fact is that the organism is but a part of a total field of energies which affect it. Change any part of the field and the change will be reflected in the organism.

It was, for example, for many years taken for granted that bass reared in breeding ponds of Departments of Fisheries in this country were instinctively cannibal, until it was noticed by Dr. T. H. Langlois in 1931 that the few successful ponds in which cannibalism did not exist were wide, shallow ponds with little or no vegetation. It was found that when bass are put into weedy ponds they tend to become separated by the vegetation and fail to form large social groups. Some of the fish take up lodgings in secluded spots and begin to prey on the smaller bass. Any small outsider unlucky enough to stray into these restricted territories gets eaten. The cannibalism does not stop when other food is thrown into the pond. The predators are unable to see the food owing to the vegetation. Langlois' solution was simply to remove the vegetation from the ponds before stocking them with young bass. Now when food was thrown to them they all ate together. With everybody well fed and everybody acquainted with everybody else, nobody tried to eat anybody. In some ponds it has been possible to bring about the cessation of cannibalism by introducing bass from other ponds who had learned to be dependent upon the food introduced by the fisheries men. These bass continued to be dependent upon the external food supply and appeared to influence the other bass to do likewise. But in some cases the introduced bass appeared to adopt the habits of the other bass in the pond and quit taking the offered external food.[52] In other cases it has been possible to induce individual bass that have claimed holdings to give them up, by causing a school of fish that have learned to follow the person who feeds them to swim repeatedly over the area which the individual bass is attempting to protect. In these cases the individuals have given up their holdings and joined the aggregation, but in some other cases this has not been possible.

We perceive, then, how slight changes in the environment are sufficient to change the behavior of creatures from a cannibalism that was erroneously thought to be instinctive to social behavior that is cooperative. When animals cannot see where their next meal is coming from they are likely to get it where they can. In this all animals are alike, and it seems now quite clear that under natural conditions some animals prey upon others simply because they would starve if they did not. Were such animals to develop under socially satisfying conditions in which an adequate amount of food were at their disposal it is doubtful whether more than a few of them would prey upon any other animal. Wanton killing is limited to a small number of animals, conspicuous among the latter being man.

Competition for Food

The competitiveness which animals exhibit over food is almost certainly influenced by the sparsity factor as well as by their conditioning. At least, such experimental data as we have bear out this suggestion. For example, Fredericson set out to test the hypothesis that a limited period of hunger-motivated competition for food during the infancy of mice will cause them in adulthood to show increased competition for food even when not motivated by hunger. Hungry infant mice were therefore trained to compete for food for a few days shortly after weaning. They were then permitted to grow into adulthood without having to compete. This experience in competition during infancy turned out to cause them to fight over food on a retest many weeks later when they were sexually mature; they were not hungry at this time. The littermates of the experimental subjects were raised without competitive experience during infancy. This control group did not compete for food when adult and not hungry.[53]

Calhoun has pointed out that as soon as animals begin to modify their environment through the elaboration of relatively permanent artifacts such as trails, nests, burrows, and the like, their biological conditioning assumes something of a cultural aspect. While it is true that such artifacts satisfy basic organic needs—dens and nests being places of retreat where the young are safe, trails leading to food or harborage, and food caches serving to make food more accessible—it is also true that in addition to their physical properties these arrangements serve as the physical molds in which the social matrix takes its form.

It is in relation to the construction and utilization of these physical artifacts that many patterns of behavioral relationships become established. Animals using the same trails order their behavior in relation to other familiar animals. Young animals in the artificially modified environment find life easier than the original colonizers. They not only find places of retreat, harborages, food sources, trails, and so on, already established for them, but they also experience a stabilized social structure within which their integration and development is facilitated.

"This alteration," Calhoun correctly states, "of the habits and social behavior of one generation by the activities of generations which precede it represents a cultural process, when culture is considered from a broad biological viewpoint."[54]

To the question, then, as to whether nonhuman creatures are capable of cultural behavior or not, the answer is that insofar as nonhuman creatures have been studied in any context relevant to our question they have been found to exhibit behavior which is indisputably cultural, satisfying the criteria of invention, transmission, and perpetuation of new behavior, and that this has been found in fish, in birds, and in mammals.

While the subject of animal culture has been far from adequately explored, sufficient has been said to show that at least some lower animals do possess cultural potentialities which under varying conditions can be, and often are, adaptively utilized to meet the requirements of particular conditions. It is probable that to a greater or lesser degree such cultural potentialities are possessed by a large proportion, if not by all, vertebrates; furthermore, that *to some extent* such social behavior as we observe many of them to exhibit constitutes, in reality, their adaptive cultural behavior, the *manner* of their social interaction, the expression of their acquired social heritage in interaction with their biological heritage.

ANIMAL AND HUMAN CULTURE

There is some ground for believing that there is really no sharp dividing line between animal and human cultural behavior. There *is* a difference, but this would appear to be one of degree rather than of kind. The degree or quality of difference is, however, great. The difference between the rudiments of culture characterizing some lower animals and the complexity and variety of human cultures is enormous.[55] What, then, are the limiting factors responsible for the rudimentary nature of animal as compared with human cultural behavior?

These limiting factors are unquestionably represented by a difference in genetic potentials for the development of cultural behavior. The system of genes which has permitted the development of the specifically human mental capacities enables man to adapt himself to his environment by calling upon the inventiveness which those genes make possible. Other animals adapt themselves to their environment by responses which are genetically both more limited and more fixed. So far as his psychological responses to the world are concerned man is almost wholly emancipated from dependence upon inherited biological dispositions, uniquely improving upon the latter by his ability to learn that which his social heredity (culture) makes available to him. Man possesses the genetic equipment which renders possible a much more efficient achievement of immediate or long-term adaptation than that possessed by any other species of animal—adaptation through learned responses or improvements upon these responses in the form of inventions and improvisations.

Two Types of Biological Adaptation

In general, two types of biological adaptation in evolution can be distinguished. One is genetic specialization and genetically controlled fixity of traits. The second is genetic plasticity, and consists in the ability to respond to a given range of environmental situations by evolving traits favorable in these particular situations. It is known, for example, that the composition of the blood which is most favorable for life at high altitudes is somewhat different from that which suffices at sea level. A species which ranges from sea level to high altitudes on a mountain range may become differentiated into several altitudinal races, each having a fixed blood composition favored by natural selection at the particular altitude at which it lives;·or a genotype may be selected which permits an individual to respond to changes in the atmospheric pressure by alterations in composition of the blood. Heredity determines in its possessor not the presence or absence of certain traits but, rather, the responses of the organism to its changing environment. The responses may be more or less rigidly fixed, so that approximately the same traits develop in all environments in which life is possible. On the other hand, the responses may differ in different environments. Fixity or plasticity of a trait is, therefore, genetically controlled.

Whether the evolutionary adaptation in a given phyletic line will occur chiefly by way of genetic fixity or by way of genetic plasticity will depend on circumstances. In the first place, evolutionary changes are compounded of biochemical changes in genes, of mutational steps, and consequently the kind of change that takes place is always determined by the composition of the store of mutational variability which happens to be available in the species populations. Secondly, fixity or plasticity of traits is controlled by natural selection. Having a trait fixed by heredity, and hence appearing in the development of an individual regardless of environmental variations is, in general, of benefit to organisms whose milieu remains uniform and static except for rare and freakish deviations. Conversely, organisms which inhabit changeable environments are benefited by having their traits plastic and modified by each recurrent configuration of environmental agents in a way most favorable for the survival of the carrier of the trait in question.

Comparative anatomy and embryology show that a fairly general trend in organic evolution seems to be from environmental dependence toward fixation of the basic features of the bodily structure and function. The appearance of these structures in embryonic development of higher organisms is, in general, more nearly autonomous and independent of the environment than in lower forms. The development becomes "buffered" against environmental and genetic shocks. If, however, the mode of life of a species happens to be such that it is, of necessity, exposed to a wide range of environments, it becomes desirable to vary some structures and functions in accordance with the circumstances that confront an individual or a strain at a given time and place. Genetic structures which permit adaptive plasticity of traits become, then, obviously advantageous for survival and so are fostered by natural selection.

Educability as a Species Character of Man

The possession of the gene system which conditions educability rather than behavioral fixity is a common property of all living mankind. In other words, educability is truly a species character of man, Homo sapiens, a genotype which is capable of a very wide range of phenotypes. It is this quality of educability or plasticity of his behavioral or mental traits which confers upon man the unique position which he holds in the animal kingdom. Its acquisition freed him from the constraint of a limited range of biologically predetermined responses. He became capable of acting in a more or less regulative manner upon his physical environment instead of being largely regulated by it. The genetically controlled plasticity of mental traits is, biologically speaking, the most typical and uniquely human characteristic. Man's suppleness, plasticity, and, most important of all, ability to profit from experience and education are unique. No other species is comparable to man in its capacity to acquire new behavior patterns and discard old ones in consequence of training.

Considered biologically as well as socially the limiting factor which prevents nonhuman animals from functioning at a level equivalent to that at which human beings function is the comparative genetic fixity of their behavioral potentialities, their comparative lack of behavioral plasticity or educability.[56]

Instead of having his responses genetically fixed as in other animal species, man is a species that invents its own responses, and it is out of this unique ability to invent and to improvise his responses that his cultures are born.

EDUCABILITY AND THE USE OF SYMBOLS

The most important vehicle through which educability is effected and expresses itself is speech or language. Again, man is unique in the degree to which he possesses this faculty.

Animals do communicate with one another by sounds, movements of the body of a meaningful sort, by gestures, facial and bodily expression, and various visible attitudes. Their communication appears to be limited mainly to matters of immediate import largely without reference to the past or future, and has principally if not exclusively to do with response to stimuli in the external environment.[57] Communication and language must be distinguished. Communication is a general term and refers to the behavior of an individual or of a group that influences others. Language is a specific term and refers to the utilization of a specific system of symbolic activities which is calculated to influence the behavior of others in a specific way. A symbol may be defined as a meaning or value conferred by those who use it upon anything, tangible or intangible. A sign, on the other hand, belongs to the physical world; it is, as White says, "a physical thing or event whose function is to indicate some other thing or event.[58] Or, as Cassirer says, "a symbol is part of the human world of meaning. Signals are 'operators'; symbols are 'designators.' "[59] Language is a species of communication.[60] Lower animals do not habitually make use of symbols. The chimpanzee has formed the subject of detailed study with regard to its ability to utilize symbols. Yerkes and Nissen concluded that the chimpanzee is occasionally capable of symbolic processes, but that those processes are relatively rudimentary and ineffective, and finally that there does not seem to be any increase in frequency and functional value of symbolic response with increase in experience and age.[61]

These findings are of the greatest interest, the more so in view of the fact that in the whole living kingdom the chimpanzee is probably the animal most nearly related to and most like man. It is quite unlikely that any other nonhuman creature (with the possible exception of the orang and gorilla) even approximates the chimpanzee in its very rare attempt at the use of a symbolic process. Rats under conditions of repeated training do show some evidence of a primitive symbolic capacity,[62] but this is extremely rudimentary. However this may be, the degree of symbol usage among chimpanzees and the kind of sociocultural behavior they exhibit, or are known to be capable of exhibiting, give us the clue to the essential difference both in the character of their communication and thought as compared with those of man, and in their lack of a developed culture. These differences are almost certainly due to the limited coefficient of educability of these animals and their consequent inability to make anything like an extended use of symbols. Here we perceive that we are, indeed, dealing with a difference in degree rather than of kind, a relative difference rather than an absolute one. It is, therefore, not correct to say as Dr. Leslie White has, that man alone uses symbols, and that there are no intermediate stages between a creature that does and one that does not use symbols.[63] Upon comparatively rare occasions chimpanzees are able to make rudimentary and inefficient use of symbolic processes, hence the rudiments of symbolic thought can be said to be present in at least one group of nonhuman primates. What distinguishes man from the ape is not that the one is able to use symbols and the other is not, but that man is capable of thinking and communicating with others almost exclusively by the use of symbols, by sounds and devices which stand for the thing represented. Such referred meanings and values man utilizes with great ability and increasing improvability both in the individual and in the group. In the chimpanzee not only are symbolic processes of thought rarely used, but when on occasion they are used it is with the greatest difficulty and most inefficiently, and, what is equally important, there seems to be no improvement in the use of such symbols through childhood to maturity.[64] In man, on the other hand, the growth and development of symbolic thought from childhood to maturity is considerable. It is these fundamental differences which explain the great gap between the cultural behavior of an ape and that of a man.

SYMBOLIC THOUGHT THE BASIS OF LANGUAGE

Without the ability to make free use of symbolic thought neither language nor culture can develop above the level which characterizes these activities in animals. Indeed, language is nothing but a system of symbols for producing action in specific ways. The meaning of a word is the action it produces. Language is the vehicle of human culture. There could be no human culture without language, and language is the inevitable correlate of symbolic thought. It is the tie that binds human society together.[65]

Given the structural vocal equipment with which man is endowed, organs of voice which, from the anatomical point of view, are far superior to anything of the kind possessed even by such animals as the apes,[66] articulate speech simply becomes a matter of finding sounds denoting symbols wherewith to express feelings, desires, and thoughts. The systematic use of such sound symbols constitutes spoken language, speech. No human being can ever develop the ability to use language or to become a cooperative member of a culture without the power of symbolic thought. The human child commences to speak meaningfully only when it has begun to master this power, and it is mainly through the use of symbols that it develops the ability to use more and more complicated relational systems of symbols. Human learning consists principally of the process of building up new systems of symbol relations and integrating them with already existing ones. Thought is essentially the process of educing relations from symbol correlates. In this symbolic type of learning and thinking lies man's uniqueness, and his ability to acquire and develop complex behavior of a cultural kind. Mind arises through the communication of such symbol-meanings in a social process or context of experience.[67]

Man has been described as the reasoning animal, *animal rationale*. But other animals can reason, too. As Oliver Goldsmith put it:

> Logicians have but ill defin'd
> As rational the human kind;
> Reason, they say, belongs to man,
> But let them prove it if they can.
> —from *The Logicians Refuted*

Reason is not peculiar to man, but the extended ability to learn to use symbols is, for all practical purposes, confined to man. It is this ability rather than the faculty of reason which distinguishes man from all other animals. Man should therefore be defined, as Cassirer has suggested,[68] as the *animal symbolicum*, the symbol-using animal. Becker has suggested *Homo loquens*, man the talker.[69] This suggestion has some merit, for the ability to utilize symbols is largely dependent upon language usage. The higher animals communicate through signals, by "mood convection," through the transmission and reception of sign stimuli which convey moods. Such signs are in no way comparable to spoken language, but are more akin to such expressions as yawning, wrinkling the brow, and smiling.[70] There is some evidence that human infants retain this capacity for interpreting sign stimuli, although in adults it seems to degenerate for want of practice. The more adept one becomes at symbol usage the poorer one becomes at sign reading.

Without symbol usage the objectification of subjective processes is limited to a narrow range of emotional cries, and the designation or description of objects is impossible.[71] Emotional "language," but not propositional language, is possible. Without propositional language and imagery the development of anything resembling human culture is beyond reach. Though language must be developed by every individual it is an error to regard language as something secondary. Language represents the development of a potentiality, it is something more than a mere acquisition. The potentiality is, of course, inherited in man, though what he shall say and how he shall use that potentiality is determined by the particular culture or segment of culture in which he lives. As a potentiality human speech is a matter of heredity, as a systematic performance it is a matter of culture. These are key points to remember. Just as the child has to learn to walk so he has to learn to talk, except that complex as the process of learning to walk is, learning to talk is vastly more complex. Whatever language man learns to speak, and however well or poorly he learns it, the process of learning involves an enormous number of organic changes necessitating the most delicate types of neuromuscular coordination and adjustment, as well as the establishment of innumerable complex interrelations within the body the character of which we have scarcely begun to know.

The so-called speech center of man is known as Broca's area. This is situated in the third frontal convolution. Injury to this region results in motor speech aphasia, that is, in an inability to express language vocally or to think linguistically. Since Broca's day several other areas of the brain have been recognized as being intimately concerned with the language functions. The roughly posterior three fourths of the superior and middle temporal convolutions are associated with the ability to recognize spoken words; injury to this area results in word deafness, a sensory auditory aphasia leading to disturbance of the ability to understand the meaning of words and language as heard. Both macro- and micro-scopically the structure of these areas of the brain is not known to differ in the apes and man. There is, however, a region at the posterior part of the second temporal convolution in man, adjoining the area for the reception of impulses from the organ of hearing, the development and great expansion of which is not approached by any other creature. This is the area of the brain which is associated with the ability to understand vocal symbols. Situated immediately above Broca's area is the region associated with the ability to write language, injury to which results in agraphia, an inability to write. In the paraoccipital region behind the auditory area is the region associated with the recognition of the printed word, injury to which results in word blindness or visual aphasia (alexia) or in disturbances of perception of the meaning of language as read.

We know today, from the study of thousands of brain-injured persons, that the process of learning language is the process of structurally organizing the nervous system in certain functional conceptual relations. Much more than structure is involved in language. Injury to the area of acoustic symbolism will reduce a human being practically to the level of an ape. Such a person loses his ability for understanding and using propositional language— the language of definite objects or actions, as well as relations between them, imagined by the speaker and guiding his understanding and speech. All that he will retain is the capacity for reactive or emotive language of the ejaculatory or automatic type. Examples of this are "Oh! dear me," "Yes," and "Hello."[72] To an unusual degree the behavior and thought of such an aphasic patient is centered about his own personality, and its relation to the world. He acts rather than thinks or speaks about the world.[73] On the other hand, as Markey has suggested, when symbolic thinking is well established and becomes automatic it appears that self-reference has greatly diminished or has reached a minimum.[74]

Words for the aphasic patient have lost all symbolic value; the same word can no longer be used for totally different objects, it can only be used in a concrete way and not in a general or categoric sense. Words have simply lost their character as useable abstractions, and the patient is unable to construct any sort of abstraction. Had he been born with such a potential deficiency the patient could never have become a functioning member of human culture. The ability to isolate relations, to consider them in their abstract meaning, independent of concrete sense data—visual, auditory, tactile, and kinesthetic—is the intellectual process beyond all others which characterizes man. "Language," as Wilhelm von Humboldt said, "never represents objects themselves but the concepts which the mind has formed of them in the autonomous activity by which it creates language." Without this autonomous activity, to which there seems no limit, man's life would be restricted to his immediate biological needs and interests, and he would be forever shut out from any experience of the "ideal world" which is opened to him by his culture.

From the brief reference to the evidence of the language disturbances exhibited by brain-injured persons it is clear that language develops as an integral part of the body–mind complex, and that a person is much more profoundly what he thinks than is customarily supposed. Thought is to a large extent subvocal language. Speech is thought made explicit. We need not go so far as Watson[75] and identify language with thought, nor align ourselves with those others who have attempted to reduce language to a system of conditioned reflexes.[76] There can, however, be not the least doubt that without human language there can be no human thought, and that language is the basis of thought whether vocalized or unvocalized. No more convincing proof of this relation can be had than that which is obtained from the study of the languages together with the cultures of nonliterate (so-called "primitive") peoples. Such studies reveal the amazing fidelity with which the culture is mirrored in the language. There is, indeed, no better nor more revealing way of commencing the study of philosophy and of scientific method, not to mention the study of culture, than submitting oneself to a good course in (comparative) linguistics. The great variety of ways in which different peoples view the world is very closely reflected in the categories of their language and the formal rules, the grammar, which govern their use. Therefore the study of the structure and functions of such language can be a very illuminating tool not only in the study of the cultures in which they function but of our own.[77] "Wer fremde Sprachen nicht kennt, weiss nichts von seiner eigenen,"[78] said Goethe.

But language is not merely an instrument or parallel process of thought or, as Malinowski put it, a duplicate of the mental reality of man in a secondary flow of verbal equivalents. It is also a very active ingredient of human behavior, one of the chief cultural forces and an adjunct to bodily activities,[79] a complex set of bodily habits.[80] Man learns much of his language in action situations where all sorts of personal physical as well as mental experiences are involved. This is, of course, particularly true of the periods of infancy and childhood. Malinowski is certainly largely right when he suggests that it is the pragmatic use of speech within the context of action which has shaped its structure and determined its vocabulary.[81] Ultimately, Malinowski suggests, the meaning of all words is derived from bodily experiences, from such experiences in the infant as hunger, dampness, painful position, and so on. The meaning of the cries or sounds emitted by the infant under such conditions may be variously understood by adults, but it produces action on the part of those adults which ministers in some way to the child, and it is this action which constitutes the meaning of the sounds it makes. The meaning of a sound is the response it produces. The child's sounds, its vocalizations, are a means of mobilizing its environment, and to a large extent this is the pattern which his language maintains throughout his subsequent life. The relation between the person and the environment in this respect is, of course, a reciprocal one; just as he mobilizes the environment by means of language, by the same means he, too, is mobilized.

We perceive, then, that in the integration of the self, the symbolic process through the use of language is basic. If the essential feature of thought is symbolism,[82] language, vocal or subvocal, is the vehicle or matrix of symbolism. Symbols represent stimuli not present to sense. As Deese says: "Symbols are stimuli which stand for or lead to other stimuli. The relation of symbols to the stimuli for which they stand is an artificial one that comes about through learning. Symbols have meaning as a result of learning. Thus, learning is of fundamental importance to symbolic behavior."[83]

It is clearly because man's learning capacity, his educability, is so much greater than that of any other creature that his capacity for symbol usage is so large. Man learns almost all his symbols through language, and by symbols he increases and deepens his language and develops additional and more profoundly operative symbols.

The Representative Function of Symbols

Through the use of symbols man is able within himself to bridge a gap in the absence of external stimulation. This type of representational symbol usage enables him to make the appropriate responses long after the external stimulus has been removed. The rat is limited to brief delays of little more than several minutes; higher animals do better. Man can bridge the delays over long periods of years.

By means of representational symbols man can solve complicated problems.

By means of linguistic or verbal symbols, by the use of words, the tools of language, man can control his environment symbolically, and practice the most highly developed form of *vicarious* trial-and-error behavior.

By means of verbal symbols the history of the person's experience, actual and vicarious, may be built up as a huge repository that can be brought to bear upon present and future problems. This function of symbols is largely limited to human beings. As Deese puts it: "Animals can 'remember,' but almost entirely only when they are faced with the appropriate conditioned stimuli. Humans, however, can draw upon a large number of linguistic symbols, which, in the last analysis, are the most important things that contribute to their high ability to solve problems."[84]

Human culture cannot be comprehended unless the parts which symbolic thinking and language play in its development are fully understood. The significant relationships between symbol, language, and culture must, indeed, be understood as interdependent and reciprocal.

Symbols necessarily arise in the context of the social situation, and in addition to integrating the self (of the person) within that context, symbols serve to integrate all the complex interrelations of the group. The significance of these facts cannot be overestimated for the past, present, and future development of man. Their full appreciation is basic for any sound analysis of the nature of culture.

There exist several fundamental differences between animal and human potentialities for cultural development. The first of these is the great plasticity or educability of man as compared with all other animals, and the second is man's great potential ability to make use of symbols and language, whereas the lower animals and even the higher nonhuman animals are unable to make more than an occasional and inefficient use of either. In these relative differences in potentialities lies the chief difference between the nonhuman animals and human.

Having arrived at these fundamental differences in educability and potentiality for cultural development between human and nonhuman animals, it will be in order to turn in the next chapter to an examination of the nervous system through which that education or socialization is largely secured. We shall then go on to consider the nature of those basic organic needs of the organism which through the instrumentality of culture become culturalized. Meanwhile, we may conclude that Warden's threefold criterion of culture: invention, communication, and social habituation, is applicable to many nonhuman groups, but that what distinguishes human beings from nonhuman animals is the marked degree to which human beings are capable of realizing the elements involved in this concept of culture.

The qualities of culture are: (1) It is transmitted and continued not by the mechanism of genetic heredity but by that of social heredity, through the interaction of educable organisms. (2) However it may come about in and through individuals, culture quickly tends to become suprapersonal and anonymous. (3) It falls into patterns or regularities of form and style and significance. (4) It embodies values.[85]

Culture Defined

Culture consists of patterns or regularities of and for behavior, overt (as mores) or felt (as folkways),[86] acquired and transmitted by symbols through the interactions of human beings, constituting the traditional (historically derived and selected) ideas and especially their associated values.[87]

In short, culture is whatever man learns as a member of society.[88] Culture is what remains of men's past working on their present, to shape their future.[89]

3 THE MEANING OF MAN'S NERVOUS SYSTEM

> . . . an enchanted loom where millions of flashing shuttles weave a dissolving pattern, always a meaningful pattern though never an abiding one. —SIR CHARLES SHERRINGTON*

THE INTEGRATIVE ACTION OF THE NERVOUS SYSTEM

In view of its fundamental importance for the development of human behavior and for the understanding of the role it plays in relation to the basic needs or drives of man, a brief discussion of the nervous system is in order here.

The nervous system is not an anatomically or physiologically distinct part of the body. When for the purposes of study we select, that is, abstract, a certain part of the body from a complex interrelated functional system, we sometimes forget that it is an integral part of a complex relational whole, and we tend to speak of it as a separate part of the body. The mind-body dichotomy is a good example of this unwarranted separation and distinction. There is no such thing as a mind *and* a body, there is only a living body, an organism, and mind represents but one aspect of its functioning. Similarly the separation between "structure" and "function" is arbitrary. Structure and function are interdependent processes, the organism forming itself structurally by function, and functioning through its form.[1] As Monné says, "Structure and function of protoplasm are intimately correlated with each other. Any function is accompanied by regular changes of the structure of protoplasm on the microscopical, submicroscopical and stereochemical levels."[2]

* Charles Sherrington, quoted by Grev Walter in *The Living Brain*, New York, Norton, p. 36.

The whole body is a system of differentiated interacting tissues directly or indirectly integrated with the nervous system. It is impossible to dissociate any functioning organ or part of the body from its nervous connections. When the organism acts it acts as a whole, and that it is able to do so is principally due to the fact that that body is, in a real sense, a nervous system. No act is ever performed without the integrative action of the nervous system.

THE NERVOUS SYSTEM

The nervous system is functionally the stimulus-responding system of the organism. The cells and nerve fibers which comprise it form an interconnecting network which links every part of the organism together. The fact of living implies stimulation and response, and it is the function of the nervous system to coordinate the activities of the body in the stimulus-response relations, that is, in response to internal and external environmental conditions. The harmonious response which the person is as a whole able to make to his environment is due to those innumerable fine adjustments which the coordinating or integrative action of the nervous system is able to produce. Many of these adjustments may be made through the agency of the lymph and blood, the vascular system, and the internal secretions circulating in the blood. The physiological nature of the reactivity of the nervous system at any given time can be altered by the action of substances circulating in the vascular system, such as metabolites (by-products of metabolism), internal secretions, gases, and toxins. Vascular and glandular activities are, however, essentially regulated by the nervous system. The principal function of the nervous system is the adjustment of the organism to its environment. This is achieved through (1) the coordination of the sustaining systems, (2) learning or habit formation, and (3) making possible reflective thought and planned adaptation.

Functional Divisions of the Nervous System

The functional divisions of man's, or of any other vertebrate's nervous system which are customarily distinguished are the following:

The central nervous system, consisting of the brain and spinal cord.

The peripheral nervous system, comprising the cranial and spinal nerves or cerebrospinal nerves with their respective ganglia.

The autonomic nervous system, consisting of the parasympathetic and sympathetic components.

THE CENTRAL NERVOUS SYSTEM

Twelve pairs of nerves arise from the brain or cerebrum, and thirty-one pairs from the spinal cord. The cerebrospinal nerves reach most parts of the body. They are composed of afferent and efferent fibers. Afferent fibers are those which receive stimuli and carry sensory impulses to the central nervous system. Efferent fibers convey outgoing or motor impulses from the central nervous system to the organs of response. The proper adjustment and coordination of the afferent and efferent impulses is the function of the central nervous system. The performance of this function requires the presence of billions of central or association neurons, and it is of these that the central nervous system, the brain and spinal cord, is principally composed. Donaldson has estimated that there are about 12,000,-000,000 neurons in the human brain, of which 9,200,000,000 are in the cerebral cortex;[3] Eccles gives the number in round figures for the cortex as 10,000,000,000.[4] Each neuron is composed of perhaps a million billion molecules and ions.[5]

The Neuron

The neuron is the basic functional unit of the nervous system and consists of a nerve cell and its processes, the dendrites and axon. The neuron is itself in constant process of chemical change.[6] The conduction paths of the nervous system are formed by chains of neurons. The length of some of these neurons may be such that they reach from the top of the head to the lumbar region, and from the nape of the neck to one of the toes. Since nerve impulses are conducted at rates varying up to 100 meters (approximately 328 feet) per second it will readily be understood with what speed the stimulus-response reaction can occur. Neurons are so arranged that the axon of one always establishes functional relations with the cell body or dendrites of many other neurons. The place at which such a relation is established is known as a *synapse*. There is no continuity of nerve substance between neurons; the relationship is one of contiguity, each neuron being separated from every other by a distinct plasma membrane. Something in the nature of the synaptic interval determines the propagation of the impulse in one direction only. This unidirectional transmission of the nerve impulse is resumed in the *law of dynamic polarity*, although under experimental conditions a nerve fiber may be made to conduct impulses equally well in either direction.

The manner of propagation of an impulse across a synapse is not fully understood. But as the result of Dale's and Loewi's work it is now fairly certain that such conduction will not occur in the absence of an excitor substance liberated by the axon terminals of the first neuron. This substance is believed to excite the second neuron and to initiate a nerve impulse in it. The electrical theory, in contrast to this chemical theory, suggests that the second neuron is excited by the action current potentials which have been generated in the axon terminals of the first neuron. The nerve impulse is not transmitted as such across the synapse.

Nerve fibers are axons with or without covering membranes. Axons which are covered with a fatty substance, myelin, supported by a reticulum, are known as *myelinated fibers* and are found in the spinal cord and brain. Myelin gives the nerve fiber a whitish color.

Naked axons or unmyelinated fibers are especially numerous in the central and peripheral nervous system, and, indeed, give that matter its gray color. The autonomic system is largely composed of unmyelinated fibers.

Myelinated axons which also possess a nucleated sheath, the *neurilemma sheath,* abound in the peripheral nervous system.

In myelinated fibers the conduction rate is rapid, in unmyelinated fibers it is by comparison slow. For example, one tenth of a second may elapse from initiation to completion in the myelinated fibers of the saphenous nerve (in the hind limb) of the cat, while it may take almost a minute in the unmyelinated fibers of the same nerve.[7] However, the usual rate in myelinated fibers is 100 meters a second as compared with 2 meters a second in unmyelinated fibers.

Conduction Rates in Myelinated and Unmyelinated Nerve Fibers

The fact that the cortex of the brain and the central associative system of the brain and spinal cord are made up chiefly of unmyelinated fibers is of great interest in the light of these differences in conduction rates. The central nervous system is the great integrating system of the organism; it is, therefore, advantageous in such a system that impulses shall travel at the rate which will assist the necessary coordinating changes to occur without the production, as it were, of a traffic-jam. In the peripheral nervous system, on the other hand, speed is desirable. Because of this the central nervous system is constructed of chains of neurons and their synapses, whereas in the peripheral nervous system single axons in large numbers, bound together and uninterrupted by synapses, are (with the exception of the autonomic components) the rule. Similarly, that part of the nervous system which is principally concerned with the processes of homeostasis or organismal stability, the autonomic, is constructed of nerve fibers which are often unmyelinated, and therefore have a slower rate of conduction than myelinated fibers.

With respect to myelinization there prevails a certain amount of erroneous and confusing opinion in much of the current literature, the "adhesion" of an earlier age. This consists in the belief that unmyelinated fibers are normally incapable of conducting impulses, or that a nerve fiber or tract of nerve fibers is not a "neurological pathway" until it is myelinated. Thus, in a well-known and deservedly popular book—to name but one—by two well-known psychiatrists we find the right advice against commencing early toilet training being given for the wrong reason: "because . . . the tracts of the spinal cord are not completely myelinated until the end of the first year. . . . it is rather futile . . . to ask the child to exercise a control over his organs for which he does not have the neurological pathways completely laid down."[8]

There are more recent works which make similar statements. But the work of Angulo y Gonzalez has demonstrated beyond any question that myelinization is not necessary for function and that the so-called "myelinogenetic law" is false.[9] It has already been stated that Gasser found that unmyelinated nerve fibers conducted impulses, the only difference being that they conducted them at a slower rate than myelinated fibers. Furthermore, there is some evidence which suggests, though it does not prove, that activity in a nerve stimulates, if it does not give rise to, the development of myelinization. Held, for example, found that if he opened one eye in kittens or puppies several days prematurely the optic nerve of that eye myelinized more rapidly than that of the opposite eye.[10]

Myelinization is accelerated at birth, whether full-term or premature. The fact that myelinization is prematurely induced in premature babies is good evidence of the importance of environmental influences upon the process of myelinization. The relationship would seem to be a reciprocal one between myelinization and behavior, rather than of dependence of either one upon the other.

THE AUTONOMIC NERVOUS SYSTEM

Those aggregations of neurons (ganglia) that lie outside the central nervous system and cerebrospinal ganglia, and that include the cells connecting such neurons with the central nervous system, are together distinguished as the *autonomic system*. There also exist certain centers in the brain stem itself which are autonomic in nature.

Functionally the autonomic system may be distinguished as comprising those parts of the neuron system which are primarily concerned with the regulation of visceral activities. In the execution of these functions both the central and peripheral nervous systems are involved. While the autonomic system possesses a certain anatomical and physiological autonomy from the cerebrospinal or somatic nervous system, nevertheless, the two systems are to be regarded as two aspects of the functioning of an integrated whole.

The autonomic system is the efferent (motor) system innervating smooth muscle and glands which are not under the voluntary control of the cerebral cortex. It is the motor system of the iris of the eye, the lachrymal, sweat, and digestive glands, the heart and blood vessels, as well as the bronchi, the gastrointestinal, and genitourinary tracts.

The nerve fibers of the autonomic system are separable on the basis of their origin into three streams or outflows:

1. *The cranial stream or outflow,* whose fibers pass through the third (oculomotor), seventh (facial), ninth (glossopharyngeal), and tenth (vagus) cranial nerves.

2. *The thoracolumbar stream or outflow,* whose fibers pass through the twelve thoracic and upper two lumbar nerves.

3. *The sacral stream or outflow,* whose fibers run in the visceral rami of the second, third, and fourth sacral nerves.

The Ganglia of the Autonomic System

Vertebral (paravertebral) or sympathetic ganglia, comprised of two ganglionated cords on each side of the vertebral column, extend from the level of the second cervical vertebra to the coccyx. There are three cervical, eleven thoracic, four lumbar, and four sacral ganglia, united together by nerve fibers.

Collateral (prevertebral) ganglia or sympathetic plexuses consist of three great ganglionated plexuses situated in front of the vertebral column in the thoracic, abdominal, and pelvic regions. These are, respectively, the *cardiac, coeliac,* and *hypogastric* plexuses. They are made up of nerves and ganglia, the nerves being derived from the sympathetic trunks and from the cerebrospinal nerves. The plexuses distribute branches to the viscera.

Terminal ganglia or visceral ganglia lie near, on, or within the walls of the organs with which they are associated. Little is known about them, and they may contain a mechanism for purely local reflex action. Cannon has described the sacral outflow of the parasympathetic as a mechanism for emptying, *i.e.,* it is motor to such hollow organs as the bladder and rectum and is concerned in the erection of the penis.

Both the vertebral and collateral ganglia are related to many smaller plexuses, and in each of these plexuses sympathetic and parasympathetic fibers are present.

The vertebral ganglia are associated with the cephalic (head) plexuses, cervical (neck) plexuses, and the collateral ganglia are associated with those of the thorax (chest), abdomen, and pelvis.

The fibers of the thoracolumbar outflow, the trunk of lateral ganglia which lie on either side of the vertebral column, join the sympathetic trunk, while the fibers of the cranial and sacral outflows do not, but run directly to the sympathetic plexuses. Furthermore, while the primary fibers of the thoracolumbar outflow end in the trunk or collateral ganglia (grouped around the aorta and some of its large branches), those of the cranial and sacral outflow end in the terminal ganglia, the latter lying close to the structures they innervate. Functionally as well as anatomically the cranial and visceral outflows belong together, being antagonistic in their action to the thoracolumbar outflow. When one is excited the other is inhibited. Hence, for these reasons the cranial and sacral outflows are grouped together as the craniosacral outflow or *parasympathetic system,* the thoracicolumbar outflow being distingushed as the *sympathetic system.* Since most of the structures innervated by the autonomic system receive their nerve supply from both divisions it will be readily understood how by the balanced opposition of their functions the organism is able to maintain the state of coordinated activity which is essential to its proper functioning. Thus, dilation of the pupil is brought about through the action of the sympathetic, contraction by the parasympathetic, balanced dilation by the action of both. The parasympathetic vagus (tenth) nerve slows the activity of the heart when it is stimulated, but the sympathetic cardiac nerve has exactly the opposite effect.

The autonomic is the system which performs for us the unconscious, involuntary, vegetative adjustments between our varying internal and external environments. The balanced coordination thus produced has been called by Cannon *homeostasis.*[11] Homeostasis frees the individual from the task of paying routine attention to the management of the details of bare existence.

In general the parasympathetic system may be said to be concerned with the functions of hunger, sex, and bodily elimination; while the sympathetic is concerned with those functions which express themselves in the form of the emotions. An emotion may be described as the set of internal physiological changes which assist the organism to return to normal equilibrium. The "epistemic correlates of emotions are neuronal events in circuits."[12] It is here important to observe that there is probably no behavior of which emotion does not constitute a part.[13] Myers finds that the sole objective distinctions between "emotional" and "intellectual" activities are those expressing the relative discreteness or diffuseness of segmental activity evoked in a given situation. Where the somatic and visceral activity of the organism is limited to relatively few neuromuscular segments, we may speak of it as relatively "intellectual" irrespective of whether it proves adaptive or not; and where wide participation of neuromuscular segments is apparent, we may speak of the activity as relatively emotional.[14] Obviously, from this point of view no activity of the organism can be considered as either purely emotional or purely intellectual, the distinction being quantitative only.

While the actual perception of emotion is largely cortical, consciousness of the functioning of the parasympathetic is, if anything, associated with a pleasant feeling of organic tone. On the other hand awareness of the operation of the sympathetic system is associated with an unpleasant feeling of organic tone. The sympathetic is roughly described as the preparer for emergencies, the parasympathetic the protector or supervisor.

The autonomic system is, therefore, closely associated with the satisfaction of the basic organic needs of human beings. The feeling tone of the organism as a whole of well-being or otherwise is produced through the action of this system, but awareness of that feeling tone is largely if not entirely cortical. The dominant component in such feeling as loss of appetite after tasting a bad egg or following the reception of bad news is due to cortical reflexes mediated through connections with the lower autonomic centers of the hypothalamus. Severe disturbance of the whole autonomic system may be produced by the consumption of spoiled food.[15]

The cortical representation of the autonomic is in the motor and pre-motor areas; parasympathetic and sympathetic being represented together and not separately, thus simultaneous adjustments in the activities of the autonomic together with other cortically integrated reactions become possible.

The Hypothalamus

The great shunting and coordinating center of the autonomic system is the hypothalamus. The hypothalamus is, however, always under the domination of the cortex. Removal of the cerebral cortex in animals removes all cortical inhibition, with the result that such decorticized animals exhibit, on the slightest provocation, all the signs of rage, including struggling, erection of the hair, dilation of the pupil, increased respiration, and heightened arterial blood pressure. Stimulation of the hypothalamus experimentally produces specific autonomic reactions of the same kind. These are, however, simply the motor accompaniments of emotion, not the emotion itself. Feeling is cortical. The hypothalamus is the center in which emotional expression is integrated into behavior patterns on its way to the muscles and glands.[16] Direct stimulation of the hypothalamus in the human subject under local anesthesia jumps the basal pulse rate from 55 to 145 beats per minute, with an accompanying increase in systolic blood pressure (the blood pressure due to the rhythmical contraction of the heart). Operative manipulation of the anterior part of the hypothalamus produced loud gastric peristalsis, nausea, and in one instance vomiting, and in 4 out of 8 patients abrupt loss of consciousness. Tumors of the hypothalamus in human subjects invariably produce disturbances in the autonomic system, and in particularly severe cases almost every function of that system may be involved.

In brief, the autonomic system is that system through which the emotions are *expressed*, while it is through the thalamocortical system that they are *perceived*. The central nervous system mediates the responses of the organism through the skeletal muscles; the autonomic through the visceral and vascular systems.

The experimental and pathological evidence also indicates that the hypothalamus is intimately associated with the regulation of the sleep-waking rhythm, of body temperature, and of the whole delicate involuntary adjustment to the external environment. "In addition, through its nervous connections with the cerebral cortex and the thalamus, it is the recipient of those vague and indefinable stimuli which arise in association with all sorts of visceral activities and metabolic processes. In this way it mediates the integration of visceral and psychic impulses, and plays an essential part in the control of the internal milieu of the organism."[17]

The Neurohumoral System

There is good evidence that the hypothalamus, through its hormonal secretions, initiates the activities of the pituitary gland and through the latter exercises a regulative effect on the endocrine system, and thus, in turn, upon the whole organism. Marked endocrine and other changes may be produced in the organism as a result, conscious or unconscious, of cortical activities, by thoughts or by dreams. Normally, such changes are of an adaptive nature, as in flight or fear reactions. Under abnormal conditions, such as prolonged emotionally disturbing states, states of anxiety, or repeatedly occurring stress,[18] the organism may exhibit a wide range of somatic disorders—a result of the overactivity of the *neurohumoral system*. The function of the neurohumoral system is to maintain the balanced physiological functions of the organism to produce general adaptation. The neurohumoral system may be described as that system which is constituted by the interaction of the nervous with the endocrine system through the fluid medium of the blood and its gaseous content. It is by inducing abnormal activity of this system that the pregnant mother's emotional states, for example, may affect the fetus.[19] It is through this system that severe physiological damage may be done to the depressed or unloved infant,[20] and it is through this system that the mechanism of shock works its effect, and similarly it is through the activities of this system that the exhaustion of the organism is produced as a result of prolonged or repeated stress and strain.

Attention has been paid to the autonomic system for two reasons: first, because it happens to be that part of the nervous system which operates below the level of consciousness and there is therefore a tendency to overlook it altogether; and second, because it is closely identified with the functioning of the sustaining systems of the body and therefore with the basic organic needs. Indeed, the socialization of the organism is so intimately bound up with the functioning of this part of the nervous system that understanding of an individual's behavior is assisted by a knowledge of the interaction that occurs between the socializing process and the autonomic system. To a significant extent the functioning of the autonomic is related to the functioning of the hypothalamus and that part of the nervous system which is situated immediately above the hypothalamus and beneath the end-brain. These and the immediately adjacent areas of the brain (gyrus cinguli, and the hippocampus) may be regarded as associated with the elaboration of central emotion and as participating in emotional expression.

Fundamentally, life consists in seeking experiences which will maintain the emotional tone of the organism at a satisfactory functional level. The thalamic and hypothalamic functions are organized at a high level of affectivity or feeling tone. Thus affectivity is not visceral but is induced by experience of the external environment and mediated chiefly by the central nervous system. It is believed that the thalamus and hypothalamus play a large part in the functioning of consciousness, and in some of the simpler affective processes such, for example, as protopathic sensibility, i.e., the ability to discriminate generalized sensations, and the discrimination of forms requiring synthesis of visual and tactile impressions.

Functioning under the control of the cerebral cortex through an extensive system of thalamocortical pathways, the thalamus serves as the center of integration for all those processes which cooperate in the development and functioning of the great variety of enduring attitudes and forms of reaction which give to the individual his peculiar character and personality and perhaps his feeling of identity. As Herrick says, "There is . . . a more closely knit assembling of all those internal processes, both inborn and acquired, which give the organism its sense of well being or malaise, its awareness of personal identity, and its distinctive disposition and character."[21]

Some evidence is available which vaguely suggests that there exist autonomic, cerebral, and thalamic types of personality. I say "vaguely" because it seems, in fact, that every part of the nervous system is involved in the responses of the organism, and at best one may perhaps attribute a dominance in the functioning of one part of the nervous system as compared with another, depending, probably on genetic and experiential factors. To identify the cortex with intellect and discrimination and the thalamus with emotion is no longer possible since both qualities represent a function of the activities of both structures.[22] However, the "vaguely" recognizable autonomic types tend to "internalize" showing their tensions in visceral types of upset, and they also incline to be free of more overt behavior difficulties. The cerebral types show their tensions in more overt behavioral disturbances, and tend to be less affected by visceral disorders;[23] while the thalamic types seem to live to a large extent on their affective or emotional capital. In this connection H. E. Jones has shown that in young babies a mildly disturbing stimulus will in some produce striped muscle responses, in others visceral responses; the one response tending to preclude the other.[24] The evidence for the existence of the thalamic type is now quite old and plentiful. This whole field, however, is largely unexplored, and awaits its Ptolemy before a Copernicus will be able to do anything with it. The brain functions as a whole and not in separate parts, but it may be that in functioning as a whole some parts of the brain play more important roles than others.

Something of a beginning in this field has been made by contemporary experimental psychologists. Mowrer, for example, has cogently suggested that by virtue of their different structural organization and functions the central (voluntary) and autonomic (involuntary) nervous systems are subject to very different learning processes. Mowrer points out that under ordinary conditions the autonomic responses occur in an autonomic manner, serving the "equilibrium-restoring" or "homeostatic" function. However, such responses can be made to occur not only to physiological needs but to conditioned stimuli or signals of many kinds. When the autonomic responses occur on the latter basis as *anticipatory states* they produce rather than eliminate physiological disequilibrium and are consciously experienced as *emotion*. The learning of such responses is quite distinct from the learning whereby ordinary habits are acquired—the latter being principally acquired through the central nervous system, the former through the autonomic by conditioning.

Autonomic learning is basic for the healthy development and survival of the organism, and hence it should be clear why such learning should become established in the form of automatic emotional responses. The emotional response puts the organism into a state of disequilibrium, being to some extent basically painful and constituting, as it were, a challenge to the organism which it must meet with the problem-solving, drive-reducing part of its nervous system (the central nervous system).

Trial-and-error or effect learning parallels the pleasure principle, conditioning more closely parallels the reality principle. Conditioned responses or emotions are acquired not because it is pleasant to do so, but because it is realistic. It is not pleasant to be afraid, but it is helpful for the purposes of survival. It is also biologically helpful to learn those responses which reduce drives. And as Mowrer points out, "it is apparently quite necessary that the neural mechanism which mediates this kind of learning be different from the mechanism whereby emotional, or attitudinal learning comes about."[25]

THE CEREBRAL CORTEX

The cortex is essentially the organ of inhibition, of delayed reactions, and of learning. It is not, on the whole, directly actuated by incoming nervous impulses from either the internal or external environments, but comes into play principally through activities going on in the lower correlation centers and in situations which those centers cannot adequately meet. Nervous impulses, therefore, which reach the cortex are to a large extent the overflows, as it were, from subcortical centers whose simpler reflex outlets are inadequate. The effect of cortical activity is the inhibition, the regulation, of lower nonadaptive reactions. A man "stops to think," an insect reacts at once. Where there is no interval between stimulus and response there can be no psychologic process.[26] The inhibitory potentialities of man's cerebral cortex are unique, and it is through the secondary functioning of these that all his characteristic qualities of self-control, poise, and deliberation are made possible. It is largely through the inadequately understood capacities of the cortex for inhibition that man can get outside himself and take a "second look" as it were. No other animal can do that. The cortex is, of course, much more than an organ of inhibition for among its principal functions is that of recombining every possible kind of stimulus, including lower reflex units, into patterns determined not only by the stimulus-complex acting at the moment, but also by the relevant, personally acquired mnemonic vestiges of previous allied reactions. This mnemonic capacity of the cortex is that highly developed faculty which enables the human being to accumulate experience and to act in the light of that experience—that is, to predict the consequences of action.

Experimental and clinical evidence indicates that specific functions are not located in any particular part of the cortex, that habits and memories are not stored in any limited area, but rather that there exists a multiple representation of every function, operating through some sort of reduplicated network of equivalent functional reverberatory circuits, constantly active. The excitatory effects of this multiplicity of interacting circuits are transmissible around various types of cortical interruption.[27] It is quite possible that the elaboration of cerebral functions may depend largely not so much upon the number of cerebral units as upon the richness of their interconnections.[28]

From the physiological point of view the mind may be regarded as a pool of reverberating electrical circuits which are built up in patterns to a large extent influenced or determined by exposure to certain configurations of experience. Learning may actually represent the process of establishing new relations between neuronal electrical circuits.

THE PHYSIOLOGY OF LEARNING

Precisely what the mechanism of learning is we do not know, "but the assumption which best fits the observed facts," Herrick suggests, "is that every cortical association pattern when once actuated leaves the synaptic thresholds (or whatever may be the apparatus of facilitation of path by use) in a different structural arrangement or 'set' which makes the reactivation of these neurons in this particular pattern easier than it was before. The thing which is preserved is static, a changed structural arrangement of parts."[29] A more microscopic and complementary explanation has been offered by Monné, who points out that synthesis of new proteins within the cytoplasm of various cells is induced either by internal or external agents. During development of the embryo synthesis of new proteins is brought about under the influence of internal agents, the nuclear genes. "Nevertheless, the cells are also able to 'learn' to synthesize new proteins under the influence of external agents. . . . By synthesizing new enzymes the cells are able to 'learn' to induce new chemical reactions. It may be," says Monné, "that neurones are particularly 'intelligent' and consequently able to 'learn' with particular ease, to synthesize new proteins within their cytoplasmic fibrils. Only the amazing variability of proteins can explain the fact that all that we experience during our life is stored in our memory."[30]

Within the nerve cell there are certain macromolecules or Nissl bodies known as chromidia. These chromidia contain proteins, ribonucleic acid, lipoids, calcium, magnesium, and also certain respiratory and hydrolizing enzymes. The chromidia may be the sites of cytoplasmic genes (plasmagenes). Monné suggests that the cytoplasmic proteins are synthesized by the chromidia, and that at any moment when new perceptions and concepts arise in the mind chromidial mutations causing synthesis of new proteins within neurons may occur.

It is known [writes Monné] that mental functions are intimately associated with physiological functions of the neurones of the cerebral cortex. For this reason our mental functions must also be accompanied by regular structural alterations of the cytoplasm of the neurones at the microscopical, submicroscopical and chemical levels. It is obvious that memory must be associated with some permanent structural changes of the cytoplasm (cytoplasmic fibrils) of neurones. These postulated alterations are called engrams. Chromidial mutations, synthesis of new specific proteins and new connexions between various chromidia and between various neurones may be the structural changes of the brain associated with all intellectual activities. Some alterations of this mechanism may be associated with clever and others with pathological thinking. It may be that a high mutation rate of the chromidia is characteristic of clever thinking. Instincts are inherited because the specific mode of protein synthesis and structure formation within the nervous system are also inherited. Inherited behaviour seems to be determined by protein synthesis within the nervous system under the influence of nuclear genes, and acquired behaviour is determined by protein synthesis within the nervous system under the influence of exterior agents. Feeling is possibly associated with changes in the colloidal properties of the lipoid-protein compounds of the cytoplasm.[31]

Learning, according to Monné's hypothesis, may be a matter of protein synthesis within neurons and in relation to other neurons. This view is independently supported by Halstead, who, in discussing protein organization and mental function, points out that the nucleoprotein gene acts as a template on which replica molecules are formed. If instead of the biologically inherited templates of the genes we postulate the formation of templates as a result of individual experience we have a mechanism for memory. It is suggested that the template molecule organizes the available neural proteins into protein lattices which register the particular memory trace.[32] According to Hydén and Hartelius the protein-producing system is poorly developed in mentally disordered persons.[33]

The cortical system of neurons, it is necessary to point out, is not constructed like an automatic telephone exchange, one which is constructed to give identical responses to repeated stimuli. It resembles rather an extensive electrical network or lattice of neuronal chains and circuits in a state of fluctuating equilibrium. What response will be made to a particular stimulus depends upon the system's state of equilibrium at the moment an impulse enters it. The system is therefore eminently one which makes for great plasticity.[34]

An outstanding characteristic of the human cortex is this great plasticity, a plasticity which enables a human being to make free and multiple associations of innumerable kinds without necessarily ever repeating them, and potentially allowing the maximum of freedom and originality in thought and behavior. In short, the human cortex is so educable as to be the single phenomenon in the animal kingdom of which it seems uniquely possible to be able to say that it can develop (increase in complexity) almost without limit. It is, of course, true, as Lawrence Kubie points out, that "Unfortunately these same human beings who have inherited this adaptive plasticity also limit their own freedom through certain rigid psychologic mechanisms, which confine closely their instinctual patterns." But, as he goes on to add, "it is reasonable to expect that in the course of time it will be within our power to alter our limiting compulsions and phobias by processes of emotional education."[35]

The cortex, more than any other part of the brain, is a forecasting mechanism. It forecasts its own efferent messages for its own use, and this the cortex is able to do by converting a spatial into a temporal sequence. There is a continuous process of correcting and improving while the forecasted messages pour forth. When talking, for example, we have a dimly grasped or vague outline of what we are about to say in our head, but the precise formulation of our words and sentences proceeds as we talk.[36] The function of the cortex is to oppose and make order out of randomness, to organize the unorganized. This is to say that the function of the cortex, among other things, is to provide the organism with an analogue of the external environment or situation, and thus to enable the organism to adjust its behavior accordingly. In this respect it operates very much—though, with much more complexity—like an analogue computer fed by sensory clues.[37]

Any further discussion of the human mind beyond what has thus far been attempted would scarcely be fruitful until we examine the materials presented in the pages which follow. At this stage it will possibly suffice to say that the human mind represents the social organization and patterning of the potencies of the neuronal net. Unless the potencies of that neuronal net undergo such social organization and patterning, mind cannot develop.

Mind as we know it phenomenally, as a process of behavior, is knit into the whole network of living as a natural event. Organically the nervous system is the adjusting system of the body as a whole, the fundamental equipment for the adjustment and control of behavior. It is the system which serves to adjust the parts of the body to one another and the body as a whole to the pressures of the internal and external environments. It is in this process of adjustment that, as Murphy suggests, the clue to personality lies.[38] Intelligence, reason, abstraction, idealization are also part of man's equipment for the adjustment and control of behavior, but on a new and qualitatively higher plane, a plane regulated and determined by the interaction of man's organically determined potentialities and the cultural processes in which they undergo development.

4 HEREDITY AND ENVIRONMENT

Heredity determines what we can do and environment what we do do.
—J. McKEEN CATTELL

Heredity provides the possibilities and environment determines which of them shall be realized. —C. M. CHILD*

THE HEREDITY–ENVIRONMENT FALLACY

Among the concepts concerning which it is necessary to be clear in studying the process of socialization is that of heredity, especially in its customarily dichotomized form, heredity *and* environment. It has sometimes been asserted that many, if not all, cultures assume the particular form they do as a consequence of the differences in the hereditary biological composition of the groups giving rise to them. Since it has also been claimed that the genetic composition of the individual constitutes a definite limiting factor so far as his achievements as a personality are concerned, it becomes necessary to clarify our thinking on this subject before proceeding further.

There are few ideas concerning which more widespread misunderstanding exists than the generally held idea of heredity. This misunderstanding or fallacy is the bogus distinction between heredity and environment. Here again we see the danger which is associated with all abstract reasoning. When for the purposes of analysis and experiment we abstract the ordinates from some interacting co-ordinate system, the procedure is a perfectly legitimate one, but one falls into grievous error when one then begins to speak of those ordinates as if they were self-sustaining autonomous variables. This

* C. M. Child, in E. Dummer (editor), *The Unconscious*, New York, Knopf, 1927.

is what has been done in the case of the concepts of heredity and environment, both of which are complex variables which are always part of the same functioning coordinate system determined by the mutual interaction of their physicochemical properties.

Some biologists still think like preformationists: as if they believed that the ultimate character is unalterably determined at conception. The quanta of heredity, as they may be called, the "genes" or "determiners" of the organism, so say such thinkers, are present in the sexual cells of the parents, and when these combine they do so in a definite pattern, this pattern developing part by part, organ by organ, into the predetermined individual. The environment is spoken of as if it were merely superimposed upon the genetically predetermined characters, not as a condition of their development.

Such a view of the nature of heredity is widespread, and it is false.

The primary agents of organic development are the genes. In the fruit-fly *Drosophila melanogaster,* in which there are four pairs of chromosomes, it has been estimated that there are between 5000 and 10,000 genes. Man has 24 pairs of chromosomes, so if we tentatively award him the same number of genes as *Drosophila* is believed to have on at least one chromosome—1250—then man has at least 30,000 (1250 $\times$ 24) genes in the chromosomes of his sex cells[1] and trillions throughout his body. In a single mating the possible combinations between the 24 chromosomes of the male and those of the female are 16,177,216, or 2 raised to the twenty-fourth power, and the chance of any one such combination being repeated more than once is 1 in 300,000,000,000,000 (three hundred thousand billion). The different combinations which a 30,000 gene system can assume reach a stupendous figure. This is on a purely quantitative basis. When the physicochemical factors and those of the environment are introduced as modifying agencies the possible differences in human development become practically infinite.

THE NATURE OF GENES

Genes are enzyme proteins or giant self-duplicating protein molecules or catalysts (estimates of size vary between 4 or 50 millimicrons in diameter—a millimicron is one-millionth of a millimeter, estimated gene size is therefore between one 250,000th and one 20,000th of a millimeter). Each of these protein molecules is susceptible to chemical change under varying conditions. The development of the body occurs under the influence of these enzyme proteins, *in interaction with one another*. Enzymes, and therefore genes, are organic catalysts that accelerate essential chemical reactions of living systems.[2] The genes do not represent unit characters—as even the most distinguished of biologists may still believe[3]—that is, chemical packages which control the appearance of specifically determined characters in the offspring. There is no gene for eye color, tallness, shortness, or hair color. The belief that each gene is a specific unitary determiner for some particular character came into being as a result of inadequate observation and its natural associate, invalid inference.

HEREDITY AND DEVELOPMENT

In the early stages of genetic experimentation it was observed that certain characters were transmitted as if they were regulated by single units or representative particles. These representative particles were conceived to be the genes, and it was thought that each one represented such unit characters as head shape, eye color, and so on. Later research showed that except in the case of two parents who differ in but a single pair of genes affecting the character in question, there is no such thing as unit character inheritance. On the other hand, the interaction of many genes enters into the development of any character, and every gene affects many characteristics. The development of the individual is determined by the manner of interaction of the genes and what they produce will depend upon the conditions under which they interact, their environment. This is the critically important point to grasp. A genetic type per se, which has developed in the absence of an environment, or of an environment that has affected that type, does not exist. The organism always develops in an environment. The environment varies to some extent for every individual, and apparently affects various genes differently, some genes being less affected by the environment than others. Such, for example, are the blood-group genes which under all known environments appear to remain unaffected and express themselves in the same way. On the other hand the genes involved in the development of skin color, height, and weight, are much subject to the influence of the environment, which may modify their expression considerably.

Interaction Between Genes and Environment

The cumulative effect of environmental changes may produce changes in the structure of a gene, known as mutations. Mutations can be produced by radiation, and some scientists believe that the accumulated effects of solar or cosmic radiation may produce mutational changes in genes. However, the changes in the expression of genes we are here considering are those of a developmental nature brought about by the interaction of the gene system with the environment. The environment influences the process of interaction between genes in all sorts of ways, so that the final expression of that interaction, depending upon the requirements prevailing in any given environment, may be judged as either more or less advantageous or disadvantageous. The character or trait which is the final expression of that interaction is rarely in itself either advantageous or disadvantageous, but only in relation to a particular environment. It is of the utmost importance to understand that this truth applies no matter whether the environment be a socially accepted norm or a purely physical condition. Thus, a tall member of a pygmy group would be at a positive disadvantage in some situations and at a definite advantage in others. The same would apply to a dwarf living among ordinarily tall men. He would be at a distinct disadvantage in many ways, but there are certain environments—in airplane factories, for example—in which the advantages, for certain types of work, would be all with him. A negroid skin under certain conditions is considered desirable, and under tropical conditions of sunlight is certainly an advantageous trait; but under certain other entirely social conditions, a negroid skin may have a high negative social value. It thus becomes associated with an environment which is capable of exerting a tremendously depressing influence upon the hereditary development of the person. Under different conditions the same organism will develop differently. In one environment a plant will grow tall and narrow, in another the same plant will grow short and wide. In sunlight a plant will grow green leaves; in the absence of sunlight the same plant will grow etiolated (pale or white) leaves. Similarly, a sailor exposed to sunlight will develop a highly tanned skin; the same sailor in solitary confinement will tend to lose most of the pigment from his skin. Plants raised in the mountains and others of the same generic stock raised in the valleys are so different in appearance that they would be classed as belonging to different genera by those unacquainted with their history. Alpine plants transferred to the rich soil of the valleys have undergone the most spectacular transformation, so that they would not have been recognized as belonging to the same species by those who had not witnessed the transformation. When, after thirteen generations, these plants were removed to poor and stony soil they reverted to the characters of their Alpine ancestors of thirteen generations earlier. The same alterations occurred when the seeds of plants grown in the rich soil of the valleys were transplanted to the poor Alpine soil.[4]

Whether the expression of the interaction of the genes in some particular form of a character is due to a change in the structure of the gene itself (mutation), or to the modifying influence exerted by the environment (modification), it should be clear that we can never speak of the purely genetic development of any organism, for every organism develops in and is influenced by an environment. The genes make adjustive responses to the environmental factors acting upon them. Hence, the organism, or any part of it, is best regarded as the *physiological* form of a particular genotype. Latent gene potentialities express themselves differently in different environments.

Characters, then, are the product of the interaction between a particular genetic composition and a specific group of environmental conditions, and what precisely may be due to the one and what to the other can, in the final analysis, only be decided by experiment.

Heredity is not a disjunctive but a conjunctive process, not a process in which the inherited factors operate independently of environmental ones or to the mutual exclusion of the one by the other, but one in which both factors are more or less continually interacting.

Potentialities and Heredity

It would be more helpful to everyone, and a more correct picture of the nature of heredity would emerge if instead of using the word "heredity" we were to use the word "potentialities." The newborn organism, so far as its heredity is concerned, is best regarded as a complex of specific potentialities that have a controlling and directive influence on the vital synthetic process.[5] These potentialities are developed and assume their functioning form under the regulative influence of the environment. The expression of heredity, therefore, is a function of two interacting variables, the organic potentialities and the environment. The heredity of an individual is constituted by the interactive effects of the organic potentialities for development with which he is born, and of the environment in which those potentialities have undergone development.

Those who would object to including the environment after birth as a part of heredity, would logically find themselves in the position of having to object to its inclusion at any time after conception.[6] The reason why neither of these positions can be maintained is that the facts show, beyond any question, that the expression of the elementary particles of the organic potentialities is always a function of both their nature and the environment in which they interact. In other words, the expression of genes is both a function of their nature and their nurture. *The organic potentialities do not develop at all in the absence of environmental influences.* This is true of physical potentialities; it is even more true of mental ones. The development of the mental potentialities presents virtually infinite possibilities under the action of varying environments. We can, of course, say that no two persons are ever born with quite the same potentialities, and that at birth those potentialities may be said to exist apart from any significantly influencing environmental factors, and thus recognize that on the one hand there exists a complex of potentialities which may be called the heredity of the individual, and on the other a complex of environments which must be distinguished from heredity. For the purposes of abstraction and analysis this is often done and is a perfectly allowable procedure, but the fact is that we know and can only know the potentialities of any human being in their environmentally influenced expression. A physical or mental character is the expression of a potentiality or group of potentialities under the influence of an environment or group of environments. The environmental influence may be small or it may be large. In the environments in which human beings live differences in many features of the organism are mainly due to the action of the genes, in other features the differences are mainly due to the influence of the environment upon the expression of the potentialities determined by the genes, but whether little or much, the environment—internal or external or both—is always involved.

Physical and Mental Characters

The basic physical characters of human beings are to a large extent determined while the child is being carried by the mother. Basic physical characters are color and form of the eyes, the color of the skin and hair, and the form of the body. The differences between individuals in these respects are principally the result of differences in genic structure. Monozygous (one-egg) twins, having the same genes, are usually closely alike in their physical characters, while heterozygous (different-egg) twins, having different genes, are very much more diverse in their physical characters. On the other hand, the development of man's behavior, his psychical or mental potentialities, is to a considerable extent influenced by environmental factors. In fact, the mental potentialities of human beings remain undeveloped in the absence of the necessary environmental factors, the stimulation which the interaction with other human beings makes possible.[7] Mind, indeed, represents the cultural organization of those potentialities. And the hereditary background of a person's mind must be considered to be as much the environmental factors which have influenced his potentialities as the quality or properties of the potentialities themselves. As Dobzhansky has cogently pointed out:

> . . . A Negro, or for that matter anybody having a slightly pigmented skin, may be different or aggressive in a social environment in which his pigmentation subjects him to discrimination and handicaps. This "psychology" may correctly be called inherited, just as the skin color is called inherited, although in some people the skin color is greatly changed by exposure to sunlight. Heredity which causes the skin to be black and behavior self-conscious may result in a quite different behavior in an environment in which discrimination is absent.
>
> Non-geneticists may feel disinclined to regard as hereditary a trait so plastic that it appears in some environments but not in others. Yet all degrees of environmental plasticity occur. . . . Behavior is influenced so much by environmental variables, particularly training, social conditions and accumulated experience, that the genetic variable is frequently masked. The designation "hereditary" can not be restricted to traits which show a certain degree of constancy of expression. The degree of constancy is itself inconstant. . . . Theoretically, the action of any gene may be controlled. To say that man's psychology is inherited does not, by any stretch of the imagination, mean that it is fixed and unalterable. We cannot change our heredity directly, but heredity is not implacable destiny to which one must submit in resignation. We should seek for ourselves, and contrive for others, environments in which our heredities respond most favorably.[8]

THE CONTROL OF HEREDITY THROUGH ENVIRONMENT

Where we control environment, we to some extent control heredity. Heredity determines what we can do, and environment what we do do. Genes do not make a mind, but the environmental, the cultural, organization of the potentialities which they determine, do. We know that in their gene potentialities all men differ, and are equal only in that they possess such potentialities for mental development. We know that differences in the possibilities for development of those potentialities are already present in the infant at birth. But however variable those potentialities are in any human group, they do exist, and they constitute the material out of which society weaves mind—the social development of the person. Society reaches those potentialities through the responses it makes to the basic needs of the infant and subsequently by the responses it induces in the person through its institutional controls. Hence, from the point of view of socialization it may be said that heredity represents the social organization of the potentialities of the individual according to the patterns of organization prevailing in the culture into which he is born. Heredity is not something static or immutable; on the contrary, it is a dynamic process in which the limited predetermined capacities for performance, the potentialities, are made to undergo development in relation to the conditions with which they interact.

The process of learning the traditional cultural patterns is called *socialization,* and is essentially cultural in character. We may, then, call the natural endowment of human potentialities *primary human nature,* and the socialized development of those potentialities *secondary human nature.* Human nature, therefore, consists of both primary and secondary elements, the innate and the acquired. Where most errors are committed is in the identification of the latter with the former.[9] What is customary should not be mistaken for what is natural, for custom is man's own extension of what is natural.[10]

The Genetic Unity of Humanity

All the evidence we possess indicates that there are no really discontinuous differences in the variability of the genic potentialities to be found in any group of mankind. No two individuals are ever alike in the genic potentialities which they inherit, nor—within the range of the normal—are they ever so unlike as to exhibit the absence of any potentiality. From the point of view of the capacity for social development every individual possesses all the necessary potentialities, and this is true for human beings in every ethnic group and has certainly been true of our species for many hundreds of thousands of years. In their capacity for social development, within the range of the normal, all men fall within the range of equality at birth. This is our basic assumption, while at the same time it is recognized that appreciable individual differences in this and in other respects exist in every case.

Scott has pointed out that because of man's greater learning powers organic heredity as such has smaller effects upon his behavior than it does in lower animals.[11] This is perhaps equally significantly stated the other way round: because organic heredity plays so small a role in man's social development, what he learns through the socialization process plays a vastly more important part in his development than it does in nonhuman animals.

In man, the evidence indicates, there does not seem to have been any significant differential selection for mental characters. There is no good evidence that any human group differs from any other in the nature of its gene potentials for mental or social development.[12] Hence, until evidence to the contrary is forthcoming, we may rule out any effect of a genetic factor in differentially determining any of the cultures in the great range of human society known to us. It is not genes which determine culture, but the organization of the genic potentialities through the medium of the basic and derived needs, by the particular conditions of the social environment in which man lives. These conditions condition the character of the person's social development, and they arise not from any genic differences between groups but from the difference in the history of their experience.

5 LIFE IN THE WOMB AND THE TRAUMA OF BIRTH

Yes,—the history of man for the nine months preceding his birth, would, probably, be far more interesting, and contain events of greater moment, than all the threescore and ten years that follow it.

—SAMUEL TAYLOR COLERIDGE*

The question may be asked—is it important that we should concern ourselves with the details of birth or earlier pre-natal experience? If we are interested in tracing the early patterns of consciousness we must needs turn our attention to the phenomena occurring in that pre-natal period which, through their very presence, would seem to influence and color the child's emotional and personality patterns after birth.

—M. E. KENWORTHY**

THE PERIODS OF DEVELOPMENT

The developmental history of the individual is separated by the act of birth into two distinct periods: the one preceding birth, *the prenatal period,* and the other following birth, *the postnatal period.* On physiological grounds these two periods are again customarily subdivided into the following periods:

Prenatal Life

PERIOD OF THE OVUM: From fertilization to the close of the second week of prenatal life.

PERIOD OF THE EMBRYO: From the end of the second week to the end of the eighth week.

---

* Samuel Taylor Coleridge, *Miscellanies, Aesthetic and Literary* (collected and arranged by Thomas Ashe), London, Bohn Standard Library, 1885, p. 301.
** M. E. Kenworthy, "The pre-natal and early post-natal phenomena of consciousness," in E. Dummer (editor), *The Unconscious,* New York, Knopf, 1927, p. 181.

PERIOD OF THE FETUS: From the end of the eighth week to birth at the tenth lunar month.

Postnatal Life

BIRTH: The period during which the organism passes from its uterine shelter into the external world.

NEONATAL PERIOD (or period of the Newborn): From birth to the close of the first month.

PERIOD OF INFANCY: From the beginning of the second month to the close of the first year, or until the habitual assumption of the erect posture (during, on the average, the sixteenth month).

PERIOD OF CHILDHOOD: (1) *Early childhood*: From the end of the period of infancy to the end of the fifth year. (2) *Middle childhood*: From the commencement of the sixth year to the end of the ninth year. (3) *Later childhood or pre-pubertal period*: From the commencement of the tenth year to about the middle of the fourteenth year in females, and toward the end of the fifteenth year in males.

PERIOD OF PUBERTY: The middle of the fourteenth year in females, and toward the end of the fifteenth year in males.

PERIOD OF ADOLESCENCE: From puberty to about the twenty-first year in females, and about the twenty-fourth year in males.

EARLY MATURITY: From the end of the adolescent period to about the thirty-fifth year.

LATER MATURITY: From about the thirty-fifth year to 55 or 60 years of age.

TERMINAL AGE: From about 55 or 60 years of age to death.

Psychological Phases of Development

The psychological phases of development of infancy, the dependency period, do not correspond to the physiological developmental periods, except very roughly. The following psychological postnatal phases may be recognized:

Psychological Phases of Infancy

BIRTH: The period during which the organism passes from its uterine shelter into the external world.

PERIOD OF INFANCY: From birth to the end of the sixth year. This period has three phases: (1) From birth to the commencement of the sixth month; (2) From six months to the third birthday; (3) From the third birthday to the end of the sixth year.

PRENATAL LIFE

From the point of view of the total social development of the person the prenatal life of the organism is not without some relevance. There is no direct connection between the nervous system of the mother and that of the fetus. Hence there can be no direct mediation of the mother's experiences to the fetus through the nervous system. There exists no avenue through which the mother's mental states can, as such, be transmitted to the fetus. On these grounds the belief in "maternal impressions," for example, is generally held to be nothing but a myth. So far as the blood stream is concerned we know that no blood normally passes from mother to fetus. The placental barrier, in fact, is normally so effective that not even the smallest red blood corpuscles can pass through it. The placenta will not even pass substances which are completely soluble in the blood plasma if their molecules are larger than .0004 of an inch. Such protein molecules must be broken up chemically into components of smaller molecular size, either simpler proteins, protoeses, or still smaller amino acids.[1]

It is, however, well known that maternal hormones are capable of reaching the fetus, and it is highly probable that the physicochemical changes accompanying certain mental states in the mother may reach and act upon the fetus. Indeed, the "common endocrine pool" of mother and fetus forms a neurohumoral bond between them. Even such physical changes as occur in the mother as a result of cigarette smoking, or the inhalation of a small quantity of amyl nitride, are reflected in the fetus by an increase, or less frequently a decrease, in heart rate.[2] The gases absorbed by the mother must clearly pass through the placenta to the fetus. It is now also well established that from the end of the eighth uterine week the fetus becomes progressively more capable of responding to tactile stimuli,[3] and that within the last three months of intrauterine life it is capable of responding to sounds outside the mother's body. For example, striking the side of a bathtub in which a pregnant woman was lying induced a sudden jump on the part of the fetus 31 days before it was born. Concerts attended by another woman toward the end of pregnancy resulted in vigorous movements of the fetus.[4] Sontag and Wallace found marked increase in fetal movements from the thirteenth week onward when a doorbell-buzzer was held opposite the fetal head.[5] The responses, according to these observers, were somewhat convulsive in nature. Subsequent work has shown that the human fetus in utero is capable of being stimulated by, and responding to, a wide range of tones.[6]

Sontag and his co-workers have found that emotional disturbance or fatigue of the mother produces a marked increase in the activity of the fetus.[7] Several mothers reported that the vibration of a washing machine and also concerts of piano music during the last two months of pregnancy resulted in marked increase of fetal activity. Fetuses that were very active during the last two prenatal months tended to be light in weight in relation to length; such fetuses also tended to have a more advanced motor development. Sontag has also observed an association between prenatal stimulation of the fetus and postnatal feeding difficulties. The drugs used by the pregnant woman, her nutrition, endocrine status, emotional life, and activity level may very likely contribute, Sontag concludes, to the shaping of the physical status, the behavior patterns, and the postnatal progress of the child.[8]

The Fels Institute workers have found that if the pregnant mother undergoes severe emotional stresses, especially during the latter part of her pregnancy, her child is likely to be born and develop as a hyperactive, irritable, squirming, crying infant who cries for his feeding every two or three hours instead of sleeping through the four-hour interval between feedings. The irritability of such infants involves the control of the gastrointestinal tract, causing emptying of the bowel at frequent intervals, as well as regurgitation of food. As Sontag puts it, "He is to all intents and purposes a neurotic infant when he is born—the result of an unsatisfactory fetal environment. In this instance he has not had to wait until childhood for a bad home situation or other cause to make him neurotic. It has been done for him before he has even seen the light of day."[9]

In this connection Halliday mentions the clinical impression that "patients who develop recurring depressive states in adult life frequently provide a history . . . showing that the mother was grievously emotionally disturbed during the intrauterine phase of the patient."[10]

Phyllis Greenacre suggests that the evidence indicates the possible existence of pre-anxiety reactions in fetal life without, necessarily, any psychic content.[11] She suggests that traumatic stimuli such as sudden sounds, vibrations, umbilical cord entanglements, and the like, including the "trip through the birth canal" may produce a predisposition to anxiety which, combined or not with constitutional and traumatizing birth experiences, might be an important determinant in producing the severity of any neurosis.

Converging evidences at the present time would tend to lend strong support to Greenacre's suggestions. Much further research, however, is required. Meanwhile, it would seem quite likely that Samuel Taylor Coleridge was not far off the mark when, more than a hundred years ago he wrote: "Yes,—the history of man for the nine months preceding his birth, would, probably, be far more interesting, and contain events of greater moment, than all the threescore and ten years that follow it."[12]

The Psychoanalytic View of Uterine Life

Freud originally, and many psychoanalysts since, have claimed that their psychoanalytic experience convinces them that prenatal existence is normally supremely pleasurable. The satisfactions and security of intrauterine life, according to Otto Rank, the principal proponent of this theory,[13] constitute a blissful state which is rudely destroyed by the experience of birth. That experience is, according to this theory, a tremendous psychic shock, and constitutes the trauma or injury of birth, from which the person is all his life endeavoring to recover by a symbolic effort to return to the paradisial bliss of the womb. Birth is the primal separation and the cause of the primal anxiety. Anxiety is the apprehension of separation. With birth there is not only a cataclysmic change both in environment and modes of functioning but also a loss of the intrauterine state of security and freedom from effort. The experience produces feelings of helplessness and anxiety. The severance of the physical and psychical attachment to the warming, nourishing, protecting mother is something which the deepest levels of the person never accept. The whole of later existence is, in fact, a reaction to extrauterine suffering and loneliness, an attempt to make the whole world a substitution for the womb—a womb with a view.

According to Rank, all later pleasure-seeking impulses have as their final goal the re-establishment of the prenatal pleasure state. The resentment of the child during sphincter training represents the child's expression of its claim to intrauterine freedom. Thumb-sucking is an attempt to replace the mother's body by the child's own. Toe-sucking re-establishes the intrauterine position of the body.

Freud, while agreeing that "the act of parturition appears to be the first individual anxiety experienced to give the characteristic traits of the expression of an anxiety affect" (through the motor innervations of the respiratory organs and the heart), objects to the notion that every anxiety reproduces the original birth situation. He can see no justification for such an idea.[14] Freud, however, accepts intrauterine security and pleasure as a fact, but the concept of the trauma of birth he can accept only in a much modified form. The experience of birth he regards as producing a sense of physical and psychic helplessness rather than of severe shock.

In criticism of the psychoanalytic view of the uterine state it has been said: (1) that no real evidence has ever been produced which would even suggest that such a state exists; (2) if such a state does exist then it can at most be a thalamic state, it can have no cortical content, since—it is alleged—the evidence at present indicates that cortical activity of any really functional kind does not begin till almost three months after birth. Furthermore, there is some evidence that the quality of an affective state is to some extent dependent upon the existence of a functioning cortex and the development of pathways between it and the thalamus.[15] Any discriminative act of feeling or affective awareness by the fetus must be assumed to be dependent upon the existence of corticothalamic pathways the very existence of which at this early stage of development is questioned. It has therefore been argued that on neuroanatomical grounds the state of uterine bliss of which the organism is said to be aware or to recall during the allegedly cataclysmic process of birth must be doubted.

To such objections the reply may be made that it is far from established that corticothalamic pathways do not exist in the late fetus, but that on the contrary there is every reason to believe that they do. Furthermore, there are now some grounds for believing that the thalamic reticular system, connected with the cortex through ascending sensory (afferent) and efferent connections, "may be actually the primary physical basis of the background of conscious awareness."[16] However, the thalamic reticular system has not been investigated in the newborn. We do know that the organism is capable of experiencing and functioning in the absence of a cortex. Such an organism is capable of exhibiting fear, rage, and other emotional forms of behavior. This is one of the most firmly established facts of neurophysiology. The fact that a six-week-old baby is able to recognize whether a person is hostile or friendly by responding to inspissating or klucking sounds with sustained laughter, strongly suggests that cortical activity with psychic content is possible at this early age. Furthermore, as we shall see, conditioning of the newborn to respond to the sign of an original stimulus would suggest neurological activity through the intermediation of the cortex. It has long been known that in the three-month-old fetus the cortex is already laid down in its essentially permanent form. Whether the fetal cortex is capable of registering its experiences must, however, remain an open question until the unequivocal researches have been carried out that alone will enable us to return an answer to that question.

BIRTH TRAUMA

Not all psychoanalysts agree that the process of birth is as shocking an experience as some have claimed. Ferenczi, for example, an early and particularly sensitive psychoanalyst, denies the existence of such a phenomenon altogether. "The more I observe," he wrote, "the more I realize that none of the development and changes which life brings finds the individual so well prepared as for birth." Physiological preparation, reflexes, and the intuition of the parents, he believed, go to make the transition from the womb to the external world as smooth as possible. On the other hand Fodor, who has made a long-time clinical study of this subject, states that "The change-over from pre-natal to post-natal life involves an ordeal as severe as dying. Hence the fear of death begins at birth and is based on a maelstrom of bewildering experiences that are covered by infantile amnesia but break through in nightmares or become converted into symptoms."[17]

The child's cry is not, as it has often been taken to mean, a cry of distress, but purely a reflex activity, a necessary one, following immediately upon the filling of its lungs with atmospheric air. Physiologically the first cry is an emergency form of breathing, a bellows-like action of the diaphragm which serves alternately to expel fluids from the lungs and suck in oxygen. "The sound element at this time is largely incidental and is in all probability due to a wavelike action of the vocal cords as the air passes in and out."[18] With its first cry the newborn announces the functioning, the primitive functioning, of his first and enduring basic need, oxygen hunger. He does not "cry" because he suddenly realizes what a vale of tears he has entered, but rather because he is satisfying a want. The newborn has no tears, and his "crying" is not what at a more mature level it is often subjectively misinterpreted to mean. Far from constituting one of the evidences of the traumatic nature of birth, the newborn's crying is but a proof of the fact that the primary basic need of the newborn is being satisfied, that the organism is receiving what it wants.

An important piece of evidence for the theory of birth trauma insofar as the trip through the birth canal is concerned, would be what Kenworthy has claimed as having been noted, that "the Caesarian sectioned child is prone to be less sensitized—he cries less, is markedly less irritated by the contacts of handling, etc.—than the first-born child delivered through the birth canal."[19] Such data would, however, not have any bearing on the effects of the separation of the fetus from the womb. An interesting and important piece of research is indicated here. Mothers who have had Cesarean babies with whom I have discussed this matter are very positive about the following two facts: First, that the head shape of the child is noticeably roundheaded as compared with the molded head of the normally born child, and second that the skin appears to be much less wrinkled than that of normally born children. These facts would lend support to the notion that the birth process is at the very least physiologically hard on the infant. Opinions seem to be divided as to whether Cesarean delivered children are more or less sensitive than normally delivered children.

Kenworthy has suggested that the birth trauma is apt to be more excessive with the first-born child; as we shall see there seems to be some evidence for this suggestion.

Prematurely Born Children

Of interest here are Shirley's findings that premature children exhibit a significantly higher sensory acuity than term children, and in comparison are somewhat retarded in lingual and motor manual control, as well as in postural and locomotor control. Control of bowel and bladder sphincters is achieved later and with difficulty. The attention span is short, such children being highly emotional, jumpy, anxious, and usually shy. In interpreting this prematurity-syndrome Shirley points out that "Premature births often are cataclysmic; unduly prolonged or precipitant, both of which conditions subject the baby to birth trauma." At birth the premature suffers a more prolonged weight loss, and an arrest in development that writes its permanent record in the growth of bones; may it not also write a permanent record in that much more impressionable material, the nervous system? "Thus," Shirley adds, "it seems possible that, through a less favorable prenatal environment, or through the too early loss of intra-uterine media, or through the lack of adequate time for the birth preparatory responses, or through birth injuries that sometimes are so slight as to be unrecognized or through a combination of these factors, the premature may be predisposed toward the development of a higher degree of nervous irritability than the term child."[20]

In England, Drillien, studying English prematures, has fully confirmed Shirley's findings on American prematures. In addition, Drillien found that the prematures showed a significantly higher incidence of nasopharyngeal and respiratory infections, especially during the first year. Behavior disorders, particularly with regard to feeding, were more frequent among premature infants.[21]

These observations have been confirmed by American investigators who have found a higher incidence of behavior problems of various sorts and a variety of affections of the nervous systems in children at school age and in later life who had been prematurely born.[22]

Birth Trauma, Dependency, Neurosis, and Culture

Freud maintained that it was through its sense of physical and mental helplessness that the dangers of the outer world become of greater importance to the newborn, "and the value of the object which can alone protect from these dangers and replace the lost intra-uterine life is greatly enhanced." The need for love is created which, Freud says, "will nevermore leave the individual." Birth, since it is the first dangerous situation through which the infant must pass, establishes a physiological anxiety pattern which the ego (the organized personality) makes use of in later danger situations to give the "pain signal" to the id (the aggregate of basic drives or urges).[23]

It should be reasonably clear that it is the birth process which produces the major reinforcement of the dependency needs; the infant is mortally afraid and desires to return to the womb; thus death, fear, womb, and birth remain closely related in the infant mind. Rank suggests that from the point of view of the average healthy adult one can designate the person's childhood as his normal neurosis. In neurosis this infantile condition may continue into adult life.[24] The neuroses, according to Rank, represent futile attempts to overcome the birth trauma, whereas man's cultural adjustment represents man's largely successful attempt to overcome the birth trauma.[25]

Evidence as to the Reality of the Birth Trauma

The nature of many fantasies and dreams, upon analysis, lends strong support to the views of both Freud and Rank with respect to the psychic consequences of the birth trauma. Fodor, who for many years has investigated the fantasies and dreams of his patients from the psychoanalytic point of view, finds evidence not only for the reality of the trauma of birth but also for the existence of a state of positive "uterine bliss." Patients whose dreams and fantasies indicate that their illnesses stem from the experience of birth and the subsequent exacerbation of that experience, have been cured by what Fodor calls "birth therapy." Demonstration of the prenatal character of an abnormal urge "cancels the patient's resistance to the therapeutic effort and permits a speedy integration of personality."

Fodor claims to have traced a genetic connection between the experiences of the fetus *in utero,* between the trauma of birth, and various forms of behavior which he interprets as a desire to return to the state of fetal bliss, and also certain anxiety states such as nightmares of suffocation, claustrophobia, insomnia, nightmares of falling, of water, fire, and so on.[26]

Fodor's study is the first intensive clinical investigation of the trauma of birth to be published. But while it is suggestive it cannot be said to have proved anything. However, additional support for Fodor's views has come from independent investigators in England and in the Netherlands. Kelsey has reported upon a number of patients who, under hypnoanalytic treatment, were regressed to what could only be interpreted as uterine stages of development. One of these patients even regressed to the period of conception! Here is an extract from a case report of an unmarried woman of 44 years of age:

She says "I am very tiny. I seem to be lying on something very soft and white. I am very comfortable but somehow it is not right. I used to be a part of a 'oneness,' and now I am separated." At this I [Kelsey] told her that at "ten" she would find herself again part of the "oneness." As I reached "ten" she said quite calmly and quietly and positively, "This is the womb." She went on: "There is something beating in me and through me—my mother's heart. I can't see—and it feels as if I've got no mouth." I asked her in what position she found herself. She replied, "Curled up," and immediately assumed the foetal position.

After some time I told her that at the count of "ten" she would start to leave this place. At "ten" she arched her back, put one hand on her head, and an expression of severe suffering appeared on her features. She was portraying in fact exactly what one can imagine that the foetus feels when the first contraction of the uterus clamps down upon it. In a moment or two this attitude was relaxed, only to be repeated a few moments later. At length I told her that at "ten" she really would leave this place. At "ten" she began to moan from the pain in her head, and then, just as one felt that the head must soon emerge, she suddenly gasped, "I can't breathe," and she appeared to be fighting for air. Then came a short period of gasping and gulping, interspersed with cries that she could smell blood. It was distressing to witness. Then she suddenly gave a great sigh of relief—"That's better"—and appeared to fall asleep. She retained the foetal position. . . . At a subsequent session I regressed the patient back to the "oneness" and then asked her to go back where she was before she reached the "oneness." There followed half an hour of extraordinary material. She appeared to find herself in a place which she described in incompatible superlatives. It was dark, yet filled with heavenly music; it was still, yet everything was quivering. And so on. . . . This patient had had opportunities in her life of acquiring obstetrical knowledge.[27]

However, other patients were, at least on the conscious level, utterly ignorant of such knowledge. Of course, such knowledge may have been repressed and then recovered under hypnosis. Kelsey describes many other extraordinary cases in his remarkable report, and in the Netherlands Peerbolte has published an account of similar findings.[28] Quite clearly further investigation in this field will be necessary. Meanwhile, it will be desirable to keep an open mind. One cannot help but be impressed by the recurring theme in the dreams of children which takes the form of finding themselves in a dark narrow chimney, through which they are struggling to descend, often accompanied by a terrifying feeling of imminent suffocation.

Convincing evidence for the reality of the birth trauma has been provided by Sontag and his co-workers. This evidence indicates that the severity of the "trip through the birth canal," the shock of birth itself, is even capable of affecting the growth of the infant's skeleton. These workers have shown that certain fine white striae which develop in the tarsal bones of some neonates are highly correlated with the severity of the birth process which such children have undergone. Severity is measured by length and difficulty of labor, forceps delivery, primiparity, and the influences of such factors as might enable the infant to withstand the shock of birth, such as nutrition, persistent vomiting or nausea during pregnancy, and economic status insofar as this may reflect the action of nutritional and similar factors. The facts are set out in Table 1.

TABLE 1. COMPARISON OF FACTORS OF GESTATION AND BIRTH FOR
MOTHERS OF INFANTS WITH STRIAE AND THOSE OF INFANTS
WITHOUT STRIAE

Factor	Incidence in Mothers of Infants with Striae (*per cent*)	Incidence in Mothers of Infants without Striae (*per cent*)
Forceps delivery	31	6
Precipitate delivery	31	15
Primiparity	39	19
Long labor	8	9
Basal metabolic rate below 0%	26	19
Persistent nausea and vomiting	25	8
Poor health	6	0
Hemoglobin control below 70%	42	36
Inadequate economic status	10	0

SOURCE: L. W. Sontag and L. M. Harris, "Evidence of disturbed prenatal and neonatal growth in bones of infants aged one month," *American Journal of Diseases of Children*, vol. 56, 1938.

The authors' conclusions, in their own words are as follows:

Our findings lead us to believe that the tarsal striae frequently found in the roentgenograms of 1 month old children are the result of disturbances in growth produced by the process of birth itself and influenced by such factors as maternal health and nutrition. We believe that the shock of birth is an important factor and that it is determined by the severity of the birth process plus the physical condition of the infant. We consider the mechanism comparable to that involved when striae are laid down in the long bones of growing children as a result of a surgical procedure or of severe illness.[29]

If the severity of birth is capable of producing such marked effects upon skeletal growth, it will not be unreasonable to conclude that normal birth is to some extent shocking to the child.

Wile and Davis have investigated the relation of manner and order of birth to behavior. They studied children who were instrumentally delivered and compared these with children who were spontaneously born.

Every nonspontaneous birth involves some trauma and physical compression regardless of birth order. Nonspontaneously born children were found to be more frequently hyperactive and distractable than the spontaneously born. First-born children have, in general, a harder time getting born, as measured by duration and complications of labor, than later born children. Such children are more frequently behavior problems than the later born. This is a fact of some importance, but whether the behavior problems of many first-borns are due to birth trauma or to subsequent experiences is an open question. The percentage frequencies of the types of behavior problems presented by the two groups are set out in Table 2.

"The children with instrumental birth" write Wile and Davis "appeared to show a general reduction of personality energy rather than a mere increase in sensitivity and irritability, although the physical element was generally noted as a restless, distractible, irritable hyperactivity. We may conclude, therefore, that behavior reactions are not to be interpreted as shock of birth, with a per-

TABLE 2. PROBLEMS PRESENTED—TOTAL: 380 SPONTANEOUSLY
BORN (A), 120 INSTRUMENTALLY DELIVERED (B)

	A (per cent)	B (per cent)
Aggressive types of behavior (rages, tantrums, pugnacity)	65	33.3
General hyperactivity (restlessness, irritability, distractibility)	25	50
Submissive types of behavior (fears, unhappiness, fantasy life, no friends)	40	25
Tics, nail-biting, food fads	70	33.3
Peculation	12	6.7
Infantile home relationships	55	20
School difficulties	45	22.3
Intersibling conflicts	30	15
Physical ills	10	3.3

sistence of fear and pain and an anxiety state that later might become a source of neurotic behavior." These investigators point out that "the process of birth offers environmental factors whose impact upon personality may modify structure and possibly may shift and even alter some of the genetic bases of accomplishment by limiting their growth." Birth trauma in the Rankian sense they believe has comparatively little meaning in the light of the behavior exhibited by their two groups.[30]

It would seem, however, that this investigation does throw some light upon the crucial problem of the relation of the trauma of spontaneous birth or nonspontaneous birth to anxiety. Greenacre has pointed out that "the forerunner of anxiety exists in a condition of irritable responsiveness of the organism."

[What is] important in the development of anxiety potentials in any human being, is the degree of tension existent, dependent on the sensory-motor balance, i.e., the ratio between the sensory stimulation and the capacity (development and opportunity) to effect some sort of motor discharge. Where there has been considerable disproportion between an increased sensory stimulation and a limited motor discharge over a period of time such tension may conceivably be incorporated into the working balance of the individual, and becomes temporarily or permanently a characteristic of his makeup. Where this is true a sudden in-

crease or decrease in the established tension level of the individual contributes to symptoms of anxiety. There is, however, in each individual a
unique primary organization and level of tension that is determined, in
some measure, by the birth experience, furnishing an important element
in the patterning of the drive and energy distribution of that individual.[31]

Irritability and reduction in personality energy are two among
the cluster of traits characterizing the anxiety state. These were the
traits which Wile and Davis found more frequently in the nonspontaneously born children. It is a likely suggestion that these
traits are significantly correlated with the greater traumatization
which these children are known to have suffered at birth.

Schroeder found that distractibility and hyperactivity were characteristic personality traits of children who had been instrumentally
delivered,[32] and Despert found that out of 35 "anxious" children
of nursery school age 19, that is 54 per cent, were instrumentally
delivered.[33] Finally, Boland has found a significantly greater number of instrumental births among a group of 209 stutterers than
occurred among other large samples of the general population born
in hospitals.[34]

Summarizing the best available evidence we may conclude that
it appears to be reasonably certain that the prenatal experiences of
the fetus are to an important extent capable of affecting the subsequent psychic development of the organism. The evidence indicates
that the organism constantly seeks the state of relative stability
which is enjoyed in the womb, a state which was so rudely interrupted by the separation and experience of birth. Birth, the evidence
suggests, constitutes the first major anxiety-producing experience.

Whether such statements be regarded as facts, theories, hypotheses
or opinions, it must be conceded that the prenatal life of the
organism can no longer be disregarded if the development of the
person as a whole is to be understood.

THE TRAUMA OF BIRTH AND THE FEAR OF SEPARATION

We have already observed that birth may be regarded as the first
separation which the organism experiences, a separation which is
productive of the first anxiety. Any separation which the organism

experiences thereafter, whether it be at weaning, or physically from the mother, or from an accustomed environment or state, tends to re-evoke the anxiety of the original separation. Anxiety could be defined as the expression of the repressed fear of separation. Separation is here understood to include the idea of separation in any part from oneself, as in threats to the integrity of one's ego, challenges to one's belief or security, the fear of falling either psychologically or physically, and the like. Love, conversely, could be described—in this respect—as the maintenance of the organism in a manner such that all anxiety-producing situations are kept at a minimum, principally by ministering to the dependency needs of the organism in a satisfactory manner, but distinctly *not* by helping to cover up existing fears. To resolve conflicts by facing fears and critical situations is the road to maturity and character.[35]

It may well be that the suffering and psychic disordering of the separated child (see pp. 200-243) is ontogenetically related to the suffering and disordering of the newborn. The function, it may be suggested, of the disordering produced at birth in this previously highly organized creature is to enable its re-ordering to proceed upon a higher level of organization than that which it vegetatively underwent during the prenatal phase of its existence. The vegetative process gives way to an increasingly active participating role on the part of the organism in its own development. It is in this sense that from complete dependency the organism develops postnatally to increasingly larger degrees of freedom in self-actualization.

6 THE BASIC AND ACQUIRED NEEDS

Man, like the generous vine, supported lives:
The strength he gains is from the embrace he gives.
—ALEXANDER POPE, *Essay on Man*

MAN BORN A SOCIALLY UNDIFFERENTIATED ANIMAL?

Like all other mammals man appears to be born a socially un-differentiated animal. The experience of the developing fetus in the womb may be regarded as a prenatal protosocial preparation of the developing organism for the experience of postnatal socializing life. The many months of "comfortable" dependence of the fetus upon its intrauterine environment reinforces the conditioning of the unborn fetus to the habit of dependence and the maintenance of an optimum state of comfort. As we have seen, it is believed by some students of the subject that the process of birth constitutes the first major discomfort suffered by the fetus, the first real disturbance of its intrauterine security. Hence, the re-establishment of the newborn infant in its extrauterine environment in some sort of security, in which the expression of its needs receives more or less satisfactory attention, constitutes a social process which may be linked with the newborn's generalized consciousness of the immediately ante-cedent conditions of intrauterine life and birth.

Man Born a Culturally Undifferentiated Animal

With respect to the question whether man is born a socially un-differentiated animal, it is possible to argue that the elements of a social process exist under intrauterine conditions in the cooperative

105

interaction of the fetus with its environment. For our immediate purposes, then, it is strictly more accurate to say that man is born a *culturally* undifferentiated creature. We are not for the moment concerned with returning an answer to the question: How is this culturally indifferent animal differentiated as a sociocultural being? The answer to that question is reserved for a later section of this book. Here we are concerned with the answer to the more fundamental question: What are the basic needs of man the satisfaction of which constitutes the end to which culture is the means?

THE BASIC NEEDS

Malinowski has cogently argued that if we are ever to develop a sound scientific theory of culture which will yield efficient general laws, that theory must start from the organic needs of man and attempt to relate to them the more complex, indirect needs of the spiritual, economic, or social type. All behavior that relates to human nutrition, to sex, and to the cycle of life, including birth, growth, maturation, and death, is fundamentally and invariably associated with physiological changes in the body, in the nervous system of the person, and in that of his fellows. The problems and complexities of cultural behavior are, then, best approached, as Malinowski says, by attempting "to relate them to organic processes in the human body and to those concomitant phases of behavior which we call desire or drive, emotion or physiological disturbance, and which, for one reason or another, have to be regulated and coordinated by the apparatus of culture."[1]

This is essentially the view adopted in the present volume. Man as an animal must breathe, eat, excrete, sleep, maintain adequate health, and procreate. These basic needs constitute the minimum biological conditions which must be satisfied by any human group if its members are to survive. These physiological or biogenic needs and their functioning interrelations constitute the innate nature of man. As will have been concluded from an earlier chapter, these needs cannot be exercised without the integrative action of the nervous system, and it should be evident that it is through the agency of the nervous system that those needs can be controlled, socialized, and culturalized. In the socializing process the nervous system itself becomes organized into the controlling mechanism of an interrelated system of bodily habits of which symbolic thinking and language are perhaps the two most important.

A basic or biogenic need may be defined as any urge or need of the organism which must be satisfied if the organism or the group is to survive.

Malinowski has defined the concept of basic needs as "the environmental and biological conditions which must be fulfilled for the survival of the individual and the group."[2]

Reduced to the form of elementary impulses these needs and the behavior which they determine are set out by Malinowski in a table representing the permanent vital sequences which are invariably incorporated in every culture.

TABLE 3. PERMANENT VITAL SEQUENCES INCORPORATED
IN ALL CULTURES

(A) Impulse	(B) Act	(C) Satisfaction
Drive to breathe: gasping for air	Intake of oxygen	Elimination of CO_2 in tissues
Hunger	Ingestion of food	Satiation
Thirst	Absorption of liquid	Quenching
Sex appetite	Conjugation	Detumescence
Fatigue	Rest	Restoration of muscular and nervous energy
Restlessness	Activity	Satisfaction of fatigue
Somnolence	Sleep	Awakening with restored energy
Bladder pressure	Micturition	Removal of tension
Colon pressure	Defecation	Abdominal relaxation
Fright	Escape from danger	Relaxation
Pain	Avoidance by effective act	Return to normal state

SOURCE: Bronislaw Malinowski; *A Scientific Theory of Culture and Other Essays,* Chapel Hill, University of North Carolina Press, 1944.

THE SUSTAINING SYSTEMS

The vital sequences listed in Table 3 constitute forms of behavior that together form a complex of conditions constituting the irreducible minimum of vital functioning necessary for the survival of the individual and of the group. Intimately associated with the functioning of these vital activities are the sustaining systems of the body. These sustaining systems are the *respiratory* sytem, which controls the intake of oxygen as well as the utilization and elimination of carbon dioxide; the *circulatory* system, which conveys the oxygen through the blood vessels to the capillaries to supply the cells, and, in turn, to take up the gaseous waste products and return them to the lungs; the *digestive* system, which is concerned with the ingestion and chemical breakdown of solid foods and liquids; the *eliminative* systems, which carry the waste products from the alimentary tract, from the urinary tract, and from the skin through the sweat glands; the *reproductive* system, essential for the propagation of the group; the *nervous* system, which enables the organism to make the proper responses to the stimuli it receives through that system; and the *endocrine* system, which, in addition to the important part it plays in growth and development and in behavior,[3] assists in the functioning of all these systems. The *neurohumoral* system is constituted by the interacting nervous and endocrine systems acting through the fluid medium of the blood and circulatory system.

The harmonious operation of these sustaining systems is dependent upon the ability of the organism to perform the acts leading to the satisfaction of the impulses to which functioning of the sustaining systems partly give rise. The acts, listed in the second column, which lead to the satisfaction of the basic impulses are organically determined in the sense that they are performed principally as the result of certain organic conditions and that they are acts *which do not require to be learned*. In other words, the original impulses arise in consequence of the existence of certain states representing a disturbance of physiological equilibrium which is expressed in a certain state of tension. The acts leading to the restoration of physiological equilibrium, that is to say the reduction of tension by the satisfaction of the needs (which are the basic impulses), follow more or less automatically from the presence of such physiological states.

The Criteria of Dependability

Klineberg has suggested a threefold criterion of dependability which must be satisfied by any form of behavior if it is to be regarded as a fundamental tendency of the organism.[4] The first requirement in man is the existence of continuity between a particular form of behavior and that found in other animals, particularly the anthropoid apes. The second is a biochemical or physiological basis for such behavior. The third requirement is the universality of such behavior. Malinowski's list of permanent vital sequences fully satisfies these criteria, and may be accepted as the minimum complex of basic urges or needs necessary for the survival of the individual and the group.

NEEDS AND SATISFACTIONS

These vital sequences of behavior must further be reduced to the states which condition them. "Impulse," "act," and "satisfaction" inadequately define the conditions. While the conditions described by Malinowski as impulses can quite properly be described by such a term in the sense of an influence or force acting upon the body, it would be less confusing and more accurate to describe the basic states of disequilibrium in their functional relation. The states called "impulses" by Malinowski are all characterized by a certain tension or, better, urgency. Their conditioning factors may therefore be said to give rise to a state of urgency, and these states may therefore best be described as *urges*. It will clarify our thinking to realize that Malinowski's impulse is an urge or drive, and that the urge or drive is the need. Fatigue is an urge to rest, somnolence an urge to sleep, thirst an urge to drink, and so on. The acts of resting, sleeping, and drinking are the actual processes of satisfaction of the urges, while Malinowski's "satisfactions" really describe the end effects of those processes or acts. Thus, the terms *urge* and *need* may be used interchangeably. It is not that the physiochemical or physiological states give rise to an urge that produces a need, that is then followed by an act that produces satisfaction, but rather that the urge *is* the need, while the activity that satisfies the need is the process or act of satisfaction, the end result of which is the restoration of the disturbed part of the organism to a normal state of balance. From the point of view of the end results the urge-needs can be described, and often are described, as desires. We shall adhere to the terms *urge* and *need,* and we shall use them as synonyms.[5]

The *impulse* of hunger, then, may be better described as a positive physiological tension that is expressed in the form of an urge or need to ingest food. The physiological tension of hunger leads to satisfaction by the appropriate activity, in this case the ingestion of food. According to Malinowski, satisfaction consists in the restoration of the organism to a state of equilibrium or homeostasis, through the process of food ingestion and its end effect satiation.

What Malinowski has failed to note is that the acts which lead to satisfaction are in themselves tension-reducing, satisfying, pleasurable, and may be indulged for their own sake. That satisfaction consists of a process comprised of (1) the satisfying acts, and (2) the restoration to equilibrium. In a schematic form this may be represented as follows:

			Satisfaction	
Physiological *tension*	$=$	*Urge or* *need to* $\longrightarrow$	*Which leads to* *the act of* $\longrightarrow$	*Homeostasis*
Hunger (tension)	$=$	ingest food (imperative need) $\longrightarrow$	ingesting food (act of satisfaction) $\longrightarrow$	satiation (restoration to equilibrium)

This diagram may be read as follows: The *physiological tension* of hunger represents the *urge or need to* ingest food. It is an imperative need, one which must be satisfied if the organism is to survive. This need usually *leads to the act of* ingesting food, a satisfying act in itself, and this usually results in satiation, a replenishment of energy and a restoration to equilibrium, *homeostasis*. It is to be noted that the act of ingesting food is part of the process of satisfaction, and that satiation is the end effect.

These physiological tensions which are experienced (by the organism) as urges or needs can be described in terms of anatomy, physiology, biochemistry, and physics. From these points of view the cultural reference is for all practical purposes taken as absent. Culture plays no part in the original basic structure of such physiological tensions. Nor does it play any part in the performance of the basic physiological acts calculated to bring about the appropriate adjustments. But culture does, to a varying extent, play a part in bringing about modifications in the character of those physiological tensions, and in the performance of the physiological acts. The point is that theoretically a cultureless individual would exhibit all the basic vital sequences of behavior in their primary states, and would do so under cultural conditions, but that ultimately culture would serve to influence and modify the character of some or all of those sequences of behavior. Normally, the physiological tensions or needs begin to be culturally influenced from the moment of birth, and even before; however, before continuing with the discussion of this aspect of the subject it will be necessary to inquire into the nature of physiological tensions or basic needs.

THE NATURE OF BASIC NEEDS*

Three components probably enter into the structure of every basic need. These are (1) a biochemical, (2) an inherited but modifiable network of nerve cells (neuronal net), and (3) the complex of cultural psychic experience which Kubie describes as "a complex psychic superstructure of fantasies and of obligatory and phobic patterns which together shape the derivative instinctual drives."[6] The degree to which the latter will enter into the structure and functioning of any basic need will vary in different cultures, in different persons, and in different needs.

* This section owes much to the work of Lawrence S. Kubie and G. L. Freeman.

Basically, any tissue deprivation musters the organism as a whole to secure its restoration. The tissues are so organized that any deficiency (or excess) in them will give rise to states of internal excitation or physiological need within the body as a whole. This excitation affects the neuromuscular system in such a way as to induce overt behavior calculated to produce alleviation of the basic tissue disturbance.[7] This is the process of *homeostasis* which may be defined as consisting in the coordinated and cooperative physiological processes which maintain most of the steady states in the organism.[8] The degree of psychological craving associated with the internal excitation or physiologic need will vary under different conditions, but it will always be present whether the organism has been culturalized or not. In short, a basic need is at once a biochemical, neuromuscular, and psychological state, and these three interwoven components of the need can be dissociated arbitrarily only for the purposes of investigation and analysis. The relative importance of any one of these components may vary in the constitution of each basic need. By constitution is meant the combination of what is inherited and what is acquired. Hence the possibility of normal and pathological development within the area of any basic need.

Homeostasis

Homeostasis means "steady state." Every organism possesses systems of physiological mechanisms each of which function to return to a steady state any part of the organism which has become unbalanced or disturbed. Many enduring and apparently constant or static states of the organism are the product of a processual interaction of forces, an interchange of substances, a constant building up and reducing. The living organism is in a constant state of inconstancy in innumerable respects. It is the function of each organ system, alone or in interaction with others, when there has been any departure from the balance of interacting forces to restore that balance.[9]

Homeostasis is not a cause but an effect of the functioning of various qualitative processes in the organism. The balance restored in the organism is not most illuminatingly described as "equilibrium," but rather, as Maze states, by "some specific amount or concentration or intensity of a particular property." Thus, it is the *kind* of change that we must recognize as significant—for example, electrolytic activity of the kidney in relation to the heart and vascular system, the carbon-dioxide content of the blood in relation to the respiratory rate, the water-sodium balance, the pH of the blood, and the like.

As both Maze and Mace[10] have independently pointed out, homeostasis is not properly a descriptive term applied to the functioning of the organism as a whole, but to the functioning principally of parts of the organism. The concept of homeostasis is most useful when it is applied to the case, as Mace says, in which (1) the norm is defined in terms of some internal condition of the organism, (2) this norm is merely maintained or restored, and (3) it relates to some specific need as contrasted with the general welfare of the organism or the personality as a whole.

A need is a tension, resulting from an alteration in some state of the system and expressing itself in activity which continues until that state is restored. The expressed activity may be said to be *goal-directed,* and the state the activity seeks to secure—freedom from tension—is its end or goal or satisfaction.

The Interval Between Stimulus and Response

Kubie has pointed out that the generalization that there can be no psychologic process without a time interval between stimulus and response applies to a tissue need and its alleviation.

In unicellular organisms the absence of such intervals makes impossible any psychologic development; because in such organisms under favorable circumstances all processes of exchange go on continuously at the surface membrane; and only unfavorable circumstances which interpose some barrier to this exchange can cause a delay between tissue requirements and their satisfaction. In differentiated multicellular organisms, however, even under optimal conditions such a delay must always occur; since it takes time to gather in the essential substances from the environment and distribute them through the body; and since it takes additional time to gather up tissue waste, to transport it, and get rid of it. Thus the higher organism's structural complexity interposes unavoidable delays which make possible the entire superstructure of psychologic evolution.[11]

Kubie points out that in each primary or vital process there is a time-consuming series of overlapping component steps, as follows:

1. Intake of raw material
2. Assimilation and temporary storage of material
3. Release of new material from body reservoir
4. Transport of raw material throughout body
5. Neutralization and destruction of metabolites; and/or the production of specialized tissue products
6. Transport of waste
7. Storage of waste
8. Evacuation of waste

Kubie uses the phrase "primary or vital instincts." If we substitute for this, in our own terminology, "basic needs or drives," then we may agree with him that basic needs or drives are patterns of behavior which are built upon the intake and/or output ends of the above series, "since only the first two steps and the last two can give rise to behavior which is goal-directed towards the external world. Consequently only these initial and terminal steps are subject to psychologic representation and elaboration, the intermediate phases being wholly internal."[12]

WARNING MECHANISMS

Lashley has shown that every instinct is associated with a warning mechanism,[13] and Kubie has pointed out that man's basic needs are similarly associated with warning mechanisms.[14] It would seem clear that the warning mechanism has a direct relation to the mechanism of anxiety,[15] and comes into play before there is any actual tissue depletion.

In respiration, for instance, we do not normally experience air-hunger. Nor is there a state of oxygen-want in the tissues at the onset of each normal respiratory cycle. This occurs only in states of acute or chronic interference with the exchange of gasses in the body. Therefore oxygen-lack is not the immediate stimulus which sets off the normal respiratory mechanism. This is done rather by the accumulation of carbon dioxide and the attendant tick-tock oscillations of the acid-base equilibrium, which set the threshold of the respiratory center for its response to proprioceptive impulses from vagus endings in the lungs (the Hering-Breuer reflex). Consequently it is not strictly accurate to say that we breathe because we need oxygen; but only that we breathe because if we did not breathe then we would very soon begin to need oxygen, whereupon we would have to breathe or else die.

Actually in normal life we breathe for psychologic reasons before we have to breathe out of physiologic necessity. There is a faint phobic stir underlying every breath we take, as the breath-holding Yogis well know.[16]

The same holds true for all other basic needs. We are warned long before there is any actual tissue depletion or experience of excess. The intervals between the warning activity and biochemical depletion or excess vary, the margin of safety varying from a few seconds in respiration to hours in water balance. The longer this interval the greater are the psychological complications which can be developed. The extent to which psychological processes can influence the various warning mechanisms varies widely.

The warning mechanism, then, is a minimum physiological change which provides the organism with cues which enable it to anticipate the high pressor effects of depletion or excess. Thus, we generally drink before we become conscious of intense thirst, or indulge in activity long before we feel any intense need for it, and we breathe long before we are aware of the "faint phobic stir" which precedes every breath. The warning mechanism or minimum physiological cue enables the organism to anticipate its needs before the latter become too disturbing. Forestalling behavior therefore becomes possible.[17]

Since the warning mechanisms operate through a phobic-like anxiety, failure to obtain the necessary satisfaction of the need which develops serves to increase anxiety. And as Kubie remarks, "every instinct [basic need] functions between the pressure of normal phobic and normal compulsive psychologic processes which are the anlage of all pathologic distortions."[18]

Under certain conditions the warning mechanism and the basic need may become detached from each other. So that the warning mechanism in the form, for example, of a sense of dryness, may continue to operate even though the tissues are thoroughly hydrated. Or vice versa, there may be a considerable degree of dehydration without any sense of dryness or thirst. Such dissociations are usually pathological. Anorexia or chronic lack of appetite is a well-known example.

It will now be readily understood how differences in conditioning and learning may affect the character of the basic needs and therefore, to some extent, the person's patterns of adjustment to the environment. This may be seen to be a matter of the interaction of excitations or physiological tensions in the organism and the varying degree of frustration or conditioning imposed upon their expression by the environment. This process is further complicated by the warning mechanism interval, which in relation to the need is also subject to cultural conditioning. The phobic aspect of the warning mechanism has a genuine physiological substrate in the biochemical changes of which it is constituted.

The warning mechanism itself arises out of afferent impulses which are set up by a series of biochemical changes in the tissues with respect to such processes as carbohydrate metabolism, hydrogen ion concentration, hydration, salt balance, oxidation, and so on. Both by local action and reflex paths these produce local vascular, glandular, secretory, and neurohumoral changes, and eventually smooth and skeletal muscle adjustments. So long as adjustment is not made to these changes the phobic excitation remains. Inadequate satisfaction of basic needs or satisfaction of such needs when the margin of safety has been exceeded may therefore produce a paradoxical condition in which anxiety is experienced whenever a particular need is satisfied. This is, of course, a pathological condition, but it occurs with great frequency.

THE BASIC VITAL SEQUENCES

We may, then, reschematize the basic vital sequences as follows:

TABLE 4. THE BASIC VITAL SEQUENCES

Warning Mechanism →	Physiological Tension =	Urge or Need to →	Which Leads to the Act of →	Satisfaction / Homeostasis →
Accumulation of CO_2	Oxygen hunger	intake air	breathing	oxygenation of tissues
Periodic gastric waves	Hunger	ingest food	ingesting food	satiation
Dryness of mucous membranes	Thirst	Intake liquid	intaking liquid	quenching
Tumescence	Sex	conjugate	conjugation	detumescence
Reduced organization	Fatigue	rest	resting	restoration of muscular & nervous organization
Excess energy	Restlessness	action	activity	reduction of energy to equilibrium
? Tonic disturbance	Somnolence	sleep	sleeping	awaking with restored energy
?	Bladder pressure	micturate	micturation	tension removal
Peristalsis	Colon pressure	defecate	defecation	tension removal
Autonomic activity	Fright	escape	escaping from danger	relaxation
?	Pain	avoid	avoidance	return to normal state
Activator	Internal Excitation = Craving		→ Neuromuscular Act →	Equilibrium

Nonvital Basic Needs

In addition to the vital basic needs the satisfaction of which is necessary if the individual and the group are to survive, there are also several nonvital basic needs which must be satisfied if the organism is to develop and maintain adequate mental health. These nonvital basic needs have their origin in the same kinds of physiological states as do the vital basic needs. Two of these nonvital basic needs may be schematized as follows:

		Satisfaction	
Physiological tension =	*Urge or need to* ⟶	*Which leads to the act of* ⟶	*Homeostasis*
Feeling of non-dependency or aloneness	= be with others ⟶	physical contact or association ⟶	feeling of security or interdependency
General need or tension	= expression ⟶	communication ⟶	social recognition

The tension of nondependency or aloneness is doubtless phylogenetically connected with the genitor-offspring relationship which is in one way or another characteristic of all living things, and ontogenetically in man is associated with his prolonged intrauterine existence. During these phases of its existence, that is, *in utero* and during infancy, the organism is *dependent* upon the maternal organism for the satisfaction of its needs, a fact which in man establishes a pattern which requires the maintenance and satisfaction of those dependency needs throughout life. Social life, as we shall see, further reinforces the strength of these dependency needs.

Dependency

Dependency may be defined as the state of reliance of an organism upon objects outside itself for the satisfaction of its needs.

In other words, dependency is the state of striving to obtain support from sources external to the ego. The directiveness of drives is, therefore, outward in order to obtain gratification of needs from objects stimulated by the appropriate acts.

All needs are dependent, even such needs as bowel and bladder tensions, fatigue, and restlessness. These are obviously dependent upon the proper functioning of the sustaining systems of the body, which are external to the ego, in much the same sense as are air, food, and such socially emergent objects as have become need-satis-fiers. Bowel and bladder tensions are dependent for their satisfaction upon the proper functioning of the eliminative system; fatigue, upon the functioning of the neurohumoral system; and restlessness upon the proper functioning of the respiratory, circulatory, and nervous systems. It is the business of the ego, as Freud says, to discover "the most favorable and least perilous method of obtaining satisfaction, taking the external world into account."[19]

Expression

Every tension constitutes a need which requires to be satisfied. From the earliest age all needs are made known by some expressive act. Within the limits set by the organism's capacities such acts may take any form. Vocal expression is one of the earliest and most con-sistent forms which such acts take. It is through this form of expres-sion that the infant learns of his ability to make an impression upon the world outside him, to stimulate others to recognize his needs. The development of speech comes about as rapidly as it does because it is so highly rewarded. Speech becomes the most expressive of the acts of which any human being is capable. It is the principal agency through which needs are made known. Muscular acts which produce pleasure-giving vocalizations, or sounds which are identified with pleasure-giving objects, are associated with pleasure and come to be repeated under similar either existing or desired conditions.[20] Speech, at all age levels, is perhaps the greatest of all tension-reducers. In speaking of the physiological tension of general need or general tension giving rise to the urge to expression, it should be obvious that any form of expressive act which leads to "contact" with another object may be experienced by the organism as a communicative act. Infants almost certainly establish such "contacts" with their clothes, the parts of their cribs which they can either touch or see, and their toys. The animistic approach of the child to his world enables him to communicate with inanimate objects of every sort not only by speech, but by touch, and in imagination.

Clearly, if the physiological tensions of nondependency and general need are not the same things they are very closely related. The urge to expression is an urge to be with others, and physical contact or association is but a form of communication. Recognition and the feeling of security or interdependency obviously have the most intimate genetic kinship.

Ian Suttie has pointed out that expression is not merely an outpouring for its own sake, but an overture demanding response from others. It is the absence of this response, he believes, that is the source of all anxiety and rage, whose expression is therefore wholly purposive.[21] Linton has stated that perhaps the most continuously operative of man's psychic (nonvital basic) needs is the need for emotional response from others—not simply behavioral response, but response with positive emotional quality.[22]

The reason for supposing that nondependency and general tension are not the same things is that while it is possible, at least as an adult, to survive without physical contact or association with other human beings, it is doubtful whether it would be possible to survive without being able to express oneself, however elementarily, in some communicative manner. Deaf-mutes as well as isolated children are endowed with such communicative potentialities, and even though they may never be subjected to culturalization, they nevertheless perform communicative acts, however rudimentary. Touching, for example, may be such a rudimentary communicative act, or even hearing the sound of one's own voice. The suggestion is that any act which is conceived by the actor to establish contact with an object (whether that object be oneself or another object) is a communicative act.

CUTANEOUS STIMULATION

The mention of "touching" brings us to the consideration of yet another extremely important nonvital basic need. For all we know it may be a vital basic need, but until that is established one way or another it had best be considered as nonvital. I refer to tactile or cutaneous stimulation.

Whether touch or cutaneous sensibility is the earliest sense to develop we do not know. We do know, however, that in the human fetus as early as the 8-week stage, when the crown–rump length is no more than 25 mm., reflex movements are easily elicited by tactile stimulation with a hair bristle.[23]

It will have been noted that the mothers of many mammals spend a good deal of time after the birth of their young licking or nuzzling them. This is always seen in such domesticated animals as the horse, cow, cat, and dog. The act is popularly described as "washing." The young seem to enjoy being "washed" greatly.[24] However, the universality and invariability of this act in these animals, as well as other considerations, would suggest that a much deeper biological significance is to be attached to this act of licking than simple washing. The evidence indicates that such licking acts as a stimulus to development of the nervous system and thus to the organism as a whole. There is good evidence which indicates that when young nonhuman mammals are removed from the mother before they have been licked they tend to die from what appears to be a functional failure of the gastrointestinal and genitourinary tracts. The suggestion is that the newborn must receive a certain adequate amount of cutaneous stimulation if the proper reflexes are to be mediated to the autonomic nervous system. Failure of such stimulation appears to result in a failure of the autonomic to be properly activated. The manner in which the young of all mammals snuggle and cuddle against the body of the mother and against the bodies of their siblings or any other introduced animal strongly suggests that cutaneous stimulation is an important biological need of the organism.[25]

Since this is a subject which up to the present time has received very little attention we may devote some space to it here.

When one makes inquiries among animal breeders, husbandrymen, veterinarians, and any other persons who have been much associated with lower animals, those who have any positive observations to offer reveal a significant unanimity in the kind of effects they report. The substance of their observations is that if the newborn animal is for some reason unlicked,[26] particularly in the perineal region, it is likely to die of a failure to function of the gastrointestinal and/or the genitourinary system.

Here, then, we have a hint concerning some of the possible functions of cutaneous stimulation. The indication is that such cutaneous stimulation serves in the activation of the gastrointestinal and genitourinary tracts. It would seem that peripheral stimulation of the sensory nerves of the skin constitutes a necessary part of the process of activating the gastrointestinal tract through the connection of the peripheral and sensory nervous systems with the autonomic. It would appear that when cutaneous stimulation is inadequate the autonomic is inadequately stimulated and there is a failure of activation of the gastrointestinal tract.

So far as the genitourinary system is concerned the evidence indicates that this will simply not function in the absence of cutaneous stimulation. The most interesting evidence I have on this point I owe to the kindness of Professor James A. Reyniers of the Laboratories of Bacteriology of the University of Notre Dame. At the Lobund Laboratories at Notre Dame Professor Reyniers and his colleagues have been interested in raising germ-free animals.[27] In the early days of their experiments it was found that the experimental animals apparently died from a functional failure of the genitourinary and gastrointestinal systems. Fortunately, an ex-worker in a zoological garden brought her own experience to bear upon the solution of this problem, advising the Notre Dame group to stroke the genitals of the young animals after each feeding until urination and defecation occurred.[28]

Professor Reyniers writes:

THE BASIC AND ACQUIRED NEEDS

With respect to the constipation problem in hand-reared newborn mammals the following may be of some interest: Rats, mice, rabbits, and those mammals depending upon the mother for sustenance in the early days of life apparently have to be taught to defecate and urinate. In the early period of this work we did not know this and consequently lost our animals. The unstimulated handfed young die with an occlusion of the ureter and a distended bladder. Although we had for years seen mothers licking their young about the genitals I thought that this was a matter largely of cleanliness. On closer observation, however, it appeared that during such stimulation, the young defecated and urinated. Consequently, about twelve years ago, we started to stroke the genitals of the young after each hourly feeding with a wisp of cotton and were able to elicit elimination. From this point on we have had no trouble with this problem.[29]

Motherless kittens, and I doubt not other animals, have been successfully raised by similar means.[30]

The human fetus is capable of urination and defecation *in utero*,[31] and apparently its external genitalia require no external cutaneous stimulation in order to function properly, but whether this is also the case in all other members of the Order Primates, the order of mammals to which man belongs, we do not know.

Thirty years ago Hammet quite inadvertently found, in the course of a series of surgical experiments, that "gentled" rats—rats which had been stroked and gently handled—were far better operative risks than those which had not been so "gentled." In the ungentled rats he found the picture as a whole to be one of constant high irritability and neuromuscular tension in contrast with the rather friendly behavior of the "gentled" rats. In the "ungentled" series 79 per cent died in parathyroid tetany within 48 hours of thyroparathyroidectomy, whereas only 13 per cent of the "gentled" rats died after the same operation within the same period. The same ratios were maintained when the rats were parathyroidectomized alone. "Ungentled" rats when "gentled" underwent a reduction in mortality rate to zero in the relatively small series studied.[32]

Subsequent experience and observations at the Wistar Institute (where Hammet did his work) have shown that the more rats are handled and petted the better do they seem to thrive in the laboratory situation.[33] More recently Weininger found that rats which had been gentled for 3 weeks for 10 minutes a day following weaning showed a significantly greater mean weight, more activity and less fearful behavior in an open field situation, and sustained, as adults, less physiological damage to the endocrine, cardiovascular, and gastrointestinal systems under prolonged emotional stress than did a comparable group of ungentled controls. Weininger suggests that the physiological damage seen in the heart and vascular system, as well as in the gastrointestinal system, may be considered an end product of the action of the adrenocorticotrophic hormones (ACTH) from the pituitary in releasing hormones from the adrenal cortex. "The relative immunity to stress damage on the part of the gentled animals may, therefore, have resulted from a decreased ACTH output from the pituitary in response to the same alarming situation that also faced the nongentled animals. If this were the case, it could be expected that a comparison of adrenals from gentled and nongentled rats following stress would show the latter to be heavier, after being stimulated by more ACTH output. Such was indeed the case."[34]

Hammet's and Weininger's independent observations indicate something of the possible importance of "gentling" or cutaneous stimulation for the viability of the organism under conditions of stress. The effects recorded are produced through the activities of the neurohumoral system. We may recall here Osler's aphorism: "Taking a lady's hand gives her confidence in her physician."[35] We may also recall the fact that taking almost anyone's hand under conditions of stress is likely to give both the taken and the taker a feeling of greater security by reducing anxiety. Contact has a soothing effect.

The relation between cutaneous stimulation and breathing has received insufficient attention.[36] For several thousand years, at least, it has been known that if the newborn fails to breathe a hearty slap or two on the buttocks or massage or dipping it alternately into warm and cold water will often be sufficient to initiate breathing. It has long been known that a shower of cold water over the nude body causes one to "catch one's breath." Throwing water in the face of a person who has fainted is often sufficient to restore him to consciousness. Cold water stimulates to activity, warm water to relaxation. Similarly with the cutaneous stimulation of cold air and warm air. Most human beings like to have their backs scratched, and most human beings enjoy the soothing effect of having their skin stroked. To stroke a child on the cheek or head is a common act of affection. We stroke people the right way, and rub them the wrong way, we pat them or hit them on the back, and sometimes we get under their skin.

It is probable that the proper development of the respiratory function is to some extent dependent upon the amount and kind of cutaneous stimulation which the infant receives. It is not unlikely that persons who have received inadequate cutaneous stimulation in infancy develop as shallow breathers, and become more susceptible to upper respiratory tract and pulmonary disorders than those who have received adequate cutaneous stimulation. There is some reason to believe that certain types of asthma are, at least in part, due to a lack of early tactile stimulation. There is a high incidence of asthma among persons who as children were early separated from their mothers. Putting one's arm around an asthmatic while he is having an attack may interrupt or alleviate it.

May it not be that the contractions of the uterus during labor represent, in addition to their other vital functions, a series of massive cutaneous stimulations calculated to activate such vital systems as the respiratory, gastrointestinal, and genitourinary? This is a question which can to some extent be answered. Cesarean-delivered and some prematurely born infants ought to throw some light on this. If there have been no or few contractions of the uterus or delivery has been precipitate, the amount of uterine cutaneous stimulation the infant will have undergone will be minimal. According to the present theory such infants should exhibit a higher frequency of respiratory and gastrointestinal difficulties than normally born children. Unfortunately the data for Cesarean and prematurely born infants at birth are not available on these points. The Cesarean-delivered child seems to be virtually unstudied. The only evidence of possible relevance I have is that Cesarean-delivered children have a higher mortality rate during the first year than normally born children, and there is some evidence that their heads are rounder and their skin less wrinkled than that of normally born children. Better evidence is available for prematures during the first year of life and also for their later years.

Dr. Mary Drillien, we have already seen, found that prematurely born children showed a significantly higher incidence of nasopharyngeal and respiratory troubles than normally born children, and that this difference was especially marked in the first year.[37]

Dr. Mary Shirley found that, among other things, prematurely born children achieve bowel and bladder sphincter control later and with greater difficulty than do children born at term.[38] Both Shirley and Drillien observed that prematures as children presented more frequent and greater feeding problems than children born at term.

These observations suggest the possibility of inadequate cutaneous stimulation playing a role here and, in some cases at least, resulting in a greater susceptibility to infection and disorder of the respiratory and gastrointestinal systems. Margaret Ribble has pointed out that the tactile experiences of the infant may be registered in improved breathing.

Respiration which is characteristically shallow, unstable and inadequate in the first weeks after birth is definitely stimulated reflexly through sucking and through physical contact with the mother. Infants who do not suck vigorously do not breathe deeply and those who are not held in the arms sufficiently, particularly if they are bottle fed babies, in addition to breathing disturbances often develop gastro-intestinal disorders. They become air-swallowers and develop what is popularly known as colic. They have trouble with elimination or they may vomit. It seems that the tone of the gastro-intestinal tract in this early period depends in some special way on reflex stimulation from the periphery. Thus, the touch of the mother has a definite, biological implication in the regulation of the breathing and nutritive functions of the child.[39]

Love has been defined as the harmony of two souls and the contact of two epidermes. A truth spoken in jest, it hits off at least one fact which is too often overlooked, the contact of epidermes. Cutaneous contact between infant and mother is obviously of some organismic value to the infant. I say "obviously" because it is obvious to anyone who has ever observed an infant snuggling up to its mother's body that it derives pleasurable sensations from that contact. Cutaneous contact between infant and mother usually constitutes the first act of communication between them, and cutaneous contact would seem to be the language which for some time the infant best understands. It may, perhaps, be recalled here not altogether without relevance that it was through the skin that Helen Keller and Laura Bridgman were first reached and through which they learned to communicate with the rest of the world. Perhaps it should also be noted here that the skin and the nervous system are derived from the same embryological blastocystic ectodermal layer. The skin would appear to be the largest and least understood sensory apparatus which the nervous system presents to the external world.

The application of the baby's lips to the mother's nipple and breast is undoubtedly one of the most pleasurable of such early experiences, and much of the cutaneous stimulation which the individual subsequently experiences is largely associated with stimulation of the lips. The lips are, of course, eversions of the oral mucous membranes and are not strictly speaking cutaneous at all—the relationship is, however, close. As is well known, the representation of the lips in the cerebral cortex is simply enormous as compared with other parts of the body. In fear, shock, worry, or weeping, the hand is frequently applied to the lips, as if to secure succor and support, and under conditions of stress persons often go into labored breathing reminiscent of breathing at birth. Stroking, caressing of the skin under such conditions will often serve to restore the sufferer to equilibrium. It is of great interest to observe that paranoics suffering from asthma when in the non-asthmatic paranoid state dislike being touched, but when in the asthmatic state are anxious to be touched.

When a baby is put to nurse at the mother's breast shortly after birth, the involution of the uterus is accelerated, and there is a resulting significant reduction in bleeding.[40]

Lóránd and Asbót have shown that slight stimulation of the nipples in pregnant, parturient, and nursing women results in a marked increase in the contractions of the uterus. Near term the usual slight spontaneous contractions double in intensity, last longer, and continue for some time after the stimulus has been discontinued. In most of the parturients the contractions are only moderately increased. In the nursing woman the contractions are strong, often as painful as during labor.[41]

The benefits which the nursing infant receives from both the sucking and perioral stimulation are seen in the comparative rarity of gastrointestinal disorders in the breast-fed baby as compared with the bottle-fed baby. Further investigation will probably reveal that the breast-fed baby is respiratorily more efficient than the bottle-fed baby.

Human beings do not lick their young, but in all cultures a certain amount of caressing is normally given the infant by the mother. Breast feeding brings the infant into close physical contact with the mother, resulting in much labial and facial tactile stimulation in cultures where infant and mother wear clothes,[42] or total body stimulation where infant and mother habitually remain nude. It is possible that such cultural differences in raiment or nudity in the nursing situation, apart from other incidental nursing practices, have some effect upon the subsequent development of the infant. This is a subject which has thus far received no adequate study. However this may be, the fact is that in all human cultures physical contact between persons plays an important role in their interpersonal relations. Hand-shaking, nose-rubbing, kissing, putting one's arm round another person, holding hands, walking arm-in-arm, nuzzling, and the like, are evidences of affection or friendliness. Avoidance of such acts indicates the withholding of affection or social nonrecognition. In western cultures it is still the practice of well-bred persons to apologize to a stranger whom they may accidentally have touched, and to do so even to a friend or close relative. To establish contact with another constitutes an act of communication, of social recognition. If there has been no formal or other occasion for such social recognition the act is considered out of place. "Touch," Bain has said, "is both the alpha and omega of affection."

Children want to touch everything. It is only gradually that they learn what and when they may or may not touch. There is a strong tendency on the part of human beings to take nothing for certain unless they can touch it. We want "tangible," "palpable" evidence. What we perceive through our other senses as reality we at best take to be nothing more than a good hypothesis subject to confirmation by touch. We believe nothing that we cannot "grasp."

Spurgeon English has stated that love and touch are inseparable and indivisible, that love cannot arise in the human being without touch and sensuous arousal, and that the cooperation necessary for social conformity is not possible without affection and tactile stimulation. What we love we want to touch. The supreme act of touching is the sexual act with its physiological relief of tension through orgasm.[43] Physical proximity insofar as it approximates tactile association tends towards social homeostasis. Separation tends to produce disequilibrium.[44] As English says: "Misunderstandings which arise through wide separation are cleared up on close contact."[45] When people "get together," "into touch," or "contact," they "stroke" each other the right way, when they remain apart they are more likely to "rub" each other the wrong way.

Charlotte Wolff points out that "In protective affection tenderness has a 'tactile' quality, expressed chiefly by cautious and subtle gestures of the hands which satisfy both the pleasure of contact and an unconscious physical curiosity. By touching the object of affection the child gains his first emotional and sensuous knowledge of others."[46]

Tactile stimulation during infancy, and especially during the first months of nursing, is extremely important for the subsequent development of the person. Inadequate stimulation may retard and mar the development of the person in a variety of ways which, though not yet investigated or demonstrated, nevertheless can be conjectured. On the physical level persons who have received insufficient tactile stimulation in infancy are frequently shallow breathers and are more susceptible to disorders of the gastrointestinal and respiratory tracts and possibly the genitourinary tract than those who have received an adequate amount of cutaneous stimulation. Behaviorally it may be that such persons are abnormally preoccupied with securing cutaneous stimulation in all sorts of ways. These are but conjectures about possible relationships which remain to be investigated. Schematically the need for cutaneous stimulation may be analyzed as follows:

		Satisfaction	
Physiological tension	$=$ *Urge or need to* $\rightarrow$	*Which leads to the act of* $\rightarrow$	*Homeostasis*
General tension	$=$ be caressed $\longrightarrow$	contact $\longrightarrow$	soothing effect

It is possible that we need to caress, to massage, infants rather more than we have recognized as necessary in the past. If it is true that cutaneous stimulation is a way of communicating with the infant, should not the infant receive more assurance through his skin than he has customarily been given? May it not be that if we massage the skin in infancy it may in many cases later be unnecessary for a physician to massage his psyche?[47]

7 NEEDS, CULTURE, AND VALUES

If there is any harmony between our instinctive preferences as living things and any standards of value established in nature, its basis lies in the organized stuff of life. —EDMUND W. SINNOTT*

THE INTERRELATION OF NEEDS

The primary basic needs and the secondary or nonvital basic needs together form a fully integrated system of the whole functioning organism. Each need represents but an aspect of the functioning of the whole organism. Together these needs represent the drive system of the organism as a whole. Each of the basic needs is, therefore, closely interrelated with every other. It will have been gathered, for example, from the last chapter, that the need to be with others, the need for expression, the need for tactile stimulation, and restlessness, are very closely related to and dovetail with, as it were, one another.

NEEDS AND CULTURE

The basic needs determine sequences of behavior which must be incorporated into every human culture. Given man's peculiar potentialities it may, indeed, be said that the response which he makes to these needs is the basis of all culture. It is the organization of such responses to his basic needs which constitutes the basic structure of every human culture. The organic needs of man set up a sequence of imperative demands which must be met. The manner in which these demands are met constitutes the culture of the group. Man gives a particular, and in different groups a variable, form to his basic responses, and in so doing creates a novel, secondary, or

* Edmund W. Sinnott, *Cell and Psyche, Chapel Hill,* University of North Carolina Press, 1950, p. 85.

131

artificial environment. That secondary, artificial, or man-made part of the environment is culture. What men do, what they think, and what they make is a broad description of culture. It is novel because it is an environment which is peculiarly human, it is secondary because the biological environment is prior to it, and it is artificial because it is essentially made by man. It is not, however, something separate from man but grows out of the satisfaction of his basic biological needs. The biological responses made to those needs in the process of their satisfaction are cultureless in their basic character. But since cultural factors begin to operate on the human infant from birth with respect to the satisfaction of (responses to) most of his basic needs, it is not for long that those responses remain without cultural content. Nor do the basic needs those responses are calculated to satisfy go altogether unmodified. Specific associations are established between these·physiological tensions and the mode of their satisfaction, and these modifications and associations are as much the effects of the process of socialization as is any other form of socially conditioned or canalized behavior.

THE PERPETUATION OF CULTURE

The cultural environment has to be reproduced and maintained. Its reproduction and maintenance depend upon two primary factors, the physical reproduction of the group and the organized transmission of specific forms of behavior. These processes immediately give rise to other conditions which become necessary forms of behavior if a culture is to maintain itself. Methods of socialization must exist in every culture, and these must exist by mutual agreement. All this at once implies *organization,* arrangements of various sorts for the sanctioning of various forms of behavior.

Before all else man has to live. He must have organized forms of behavior at his disposal which enable him to satisfy all the needs of his organism. Feeding, heating, housing, clothing, and protection from cold, wind, weather, and noxious animals are activities which are dependent upon some form of organized social service or economic organization,[1] as is the maintenance of the culture as a whole.

These primary problems are solved for the individual by organization into cooperative groups, by artifacts, by the development of knowledge, of a sense of value, and of ethics. From all that we know of prehistoric and living man it can safely be said that these are the means by which human beings have always met the demands of their basic needs and those which are derived from them.

DERIVED NEEDS AND INSTITUTIONS

The responses which human beings make to their needs, basic and derived, are to a greater or lesser extent cooperative, and it seems fairly clear that the responses in a cooperative group to the basic needs give rise to the derived or socially emergent needs, and these in turn to the responses calculated to satisfy them. In all human societies the form of such responses is determined by the accepted traditional values, the institutions of the group. An institution, then, is an organized circumscribed system of purposeful values, an organized type of activity. In order to achieve any purpose, reach any goal, human beings have to organize. Those segments of experience which they have organized as the system of values or norms by which their behavior shall be regulated constitute their institutions.

Man's institutions are based fundamentally on the satisfaction of his basic needs, though the structure of his institutions is made up of those derived needs which arise out of the cooperative process of satisfying the basic needs. These derived needs have been called, by Malinowski, *instrumental imperatives*—arising out of such types of activity as economic, normative (setting up a norm or standard), educational and political—and *integrative imperatives*—knowledge, religion, and magic.[2] As Malinowski points out, the self-sufficiency of each culture is brought about by the satisfaction of its basic, instrumental, and integrative needs.

The conditions arising from the satisfaction of man's basic needs form the basis of the development of his institutions. It is obvious that the whole sequence of vital functions (function = the satisfaction of an organic need) always operates in a cultural setting, and that the integrative interaction between man and his institutions is what constitutes culture. Those institutions always act through human beings and, as we have said, ultimately arise out of the satisfaction of their basic needs. Thus, the family, courtship regulations, marriage, kinship, and so on, are ultimately traceable to the satisfaction of the sex urge or need. The clan and tribe, age-grades, and systems of classificatory relationship are some of the institutions which arise out of the derived needs which come about in the satisfaction of the basic needs. The satisfaction of hunger gives rise to such institutions as food gathering, hunting, agriculture, food preparation, production, and distribution. Fatigue—to bodily comforts and all that implies by way of clothing, housing, and furniture. Right—to safeguarding protective activities. Pain—to health and hygienic activities. Restlessness—to movement and activity of various sorts. Visceral pressures—to toilet arrangements and stylized forms of behavior commensal with them.

THE PLASTICITY OF NEEDS

Each need is, of course, to some extent modified by culture. Such a statement implies the fact that the basic needs are plastic, that human nature is plastic. And this is the observed fact, for the members of different human groups can learn to make the same responses to their basic needs in a large variety of ways. Such apparently organically based processes as laughter, weeping, sneezing, walking, sleeping, and love-making assume a different character in different cultures. Each culture teaches the satisfaction of needs by different culturally specific forms of activity, so that the *forms* of the responses determined by canalization and conditioning come to vary as between different cultures, and to a lesser extent even between the members of the same culture. This being so, an indispensable approach to the study of personality must consist in the analysis of the specific ways in which the child learns to become a socially integrated being in a particular culture. This will involve not only the study of his culture, but of his family, and the subgroup or subgroups within the culture which have participated in his culturalization. Learning theory, therefore, should constitute a significant area of interest for the student of socialization and personality. Unfortunately, learning theory is in no condition at the present time to be very helpful to the student of socialization and personality, so that what there is to be said on this subject has been relegated to an appendix in this book.

To repeat a statement from Linton, already quoted: "the actual behavior observed will rarely if ever be identical for any two individuals or even for the same individual on two occasions. The variations will tend, however, to cluster about certain norms. The sum total of those norms, together with their interrelations, is taken to constitute the culture of the society."[3] It should be remembered that culture is originally something outside the organism, a processual continuum *into* which the organism is born. Because culture is originally outside the organism it is something which must be learned. By learning the norms of the culture into which it is born the organism becomes a person, and personality, therefore, means the internalization of cultural process in terms of the organization of the unique potentials of the organism for being human. The logic of a culture consists in the sequence of necessary responses which the group has devised to meet its needs, the needs of the parts (its members) and of the whole (the group).

THE CULTURAL MODIFICATION OF NEEDS

Under cultural conditions no basic need can ever function as a purely physiological state. Needs function in a culture and culture modifies them. It is evident, therefore, that the vital sequences of behavior, while constituting a very necessary point of departure in the analysis of man as a cultural being, cannot alone, however well analyzed, tell us much about man unless we analyze them in their cultural setting. Each vital sequence has to be considered with reference to the individual, the organized group, the traditional values, norms, and beliefs, and also to the artificial environment in which most of the urges are satisfied. Each sequence, then, is part of a total configuration of events in relation to which it must be considered. Thus, the concept of *need* in its cultural setting becomes the state of the human organism in which culturally and environmentally modified basic physiological urges (which must be satisfied if the organism or the group is to survive) express themselves.

Let us briefly consider something of the variety of ways in which a few selected basic needs are handled in different cultures.

Breathing

Immediately following upon exposure to atmospheric air the newborn's previously unexpanded lungs fill with air and the various changes in pressure which occur at the moment of birth help to initiate the postnatal type of respiratory movements which continue throughout the life of the person. The urge to breathe is so compelling that a three-minute denial of it is often sufficient to cause death. It is the most imperative of all man's basic urges, and the most automatic. The process of learning to breathe is an anxious one. As we have already seen (p. 124), with every breath we take even as adults there is a faint phobic stir. Under conditions of stress many persons go into labored breathing reminiscent of breathing at birth. Under such conditions the person often regresses to fetalized activities and assumes fetal positions. In fear or anxiety one of the first functions to be affected is breathing. Yet in spite of its automaticity breathing or respiration is under voluntary control and under conscious control for short periods of time, as any person who has ever taken singing lessons knows, and for very durable periods of time as every Yogi well knows. This control is actually exerted during the ordinary activities of daily life, such as speaking, swallowing, laughing, blowing, coughing, and sucking. Breathing, indeed, is not simply a physiological process but part of the way in which an organism behaves.

Stertorous breathing probably occurs more frequently among members of the lower classes than it does among those of the upper, just as sipping or rather inspissating one's coffee or soup with an "accent" does. Differences in the rate of breathing and oxygen-combining capacity of the lungs, as Dill has shown, are closely correlated with occupational status.[4] Insofar as breathing serves the function of speech it is utilized in an enormous variety of different ways. Even in the same culture the "tone" of the "voice," the "accent," may be very distinctive of class, rank, caste, and locality. Depth of breathing may be altered by differences in occupational activity, and activities resulting from differences in social status. In such cases the influence of culture is indirect. On the other hand, the modifying action of culture is direct where the various forms and aspects of speech are concerned. The adjustment of deep breathing to performances in oratory, debate, whispering, the utterance of formal statements, the recital of magical formulas, and singing all represent forms of cultural breathing which significantly differ from one another. Malinowski points out that the interaction between magical and religious beliefs and those connected with etiquette and breathing, would supply another co-determinant of behavior to that of physiology in cultures in which the exhalation of breath, especially at close quarters, is regarded as dangerous, impolite, or noxious, while the deep, noisy intake of breath is regarded as a sign of respect or submission.[5]

In the process of developing the power of vocal communication the child learns to control its breathing by conscious effort. Anyone who has ever observed the infinite patience with which the American Indian parent repeats the correct pronunciation of a word, in teaching the child to put the glottal stop in just the right place and to pronounce the vowels clearly, will not need to be told with what effort in the control of breathing man's speech is acquired.

Much earlier than this in many cultures it is highly probable, as Rosenzweig has pointed out, that in addition to its natural tendency to react to unpleasant situations by crying, the infant learns to cry in other, not necessarily unpleasant, situations as a means of commanding attention when its other signals go unheeded.

The common belief that it is natural for a baby to cry when it wants something leads parents to disregard the many other ways in which babies attempt to make their wants known, such as brief

lip-licking or lip-sucking, and to *expect* the baby to cry. This practice soon causes the baby to learn that he must cry in order to be
understood. The learning process, as Rosenzweig puts it, is as
follows:

> In situations of real distress at the beginning of life, the infant cries or
> screams as an unconditioned response to pain. Ordinarily he then expe-
> riences relief, since the attending adult hurries to his aid. In other situa-
> tions requiring the attention of an adult, the child may emit various
> *other* unconditioned responses closely related to the need in question.
> For example, he may smack his lips or protrude his tongue as a signal
> that food is desired. If, however, the parent fails to respond to this type
> of signal, the baby soon finds himself in a situation of distress in which
> crying becomes a natural mode of expression. He yelps and the parent
> comes. In this way the child learns to substitute for the more direct
> smacking of the lips—or other comparable response—the response of
> crying.
>
> Since the parent takes it for granted that the child *has* to cry in order
> to make his wants known, there is ordinarily no effort on the part of
> the parent to look for other cues. After a short time the various responses
> alternative to crying as a means of communication tend to drop out and
> are superseded by crying as the preferred mode of communication left
> to the baby.[6]

Hunger

Hunger is satisfied by eating. But *how* one eats, and *what* one
eats, and *when* one eats is to a large extent determined by the traditional ways in which these things are done in the group. Among
the Australian aborigines anything that is edible is food. Cooking
with the use of hot water is unknown. There are no cooking or
eating utensils. In France and England certain land snails are regarded as a great delicacy. In America the stomach is outraged at
the thought. In the lands bordering the Mediterranean Sea octopus
is a common food. In England and America it is only the occasional
gourmet who eats it. Though availability and nonavailability has
much to do with the food habits of people, it is tradition—the
heritage of ideas and practices, and the canalization to which these
lead—which is the determining factor.[7] Milk-giving animals are

abundant in mongoloid Asia but innumerable Asiatic Mongoloids regard milk as disgusting. Sheep's eyes are regarded as a great delicacy by many Arabs; practically all other sheep-raising peoples discard them. What one may eat is determined according to what the culture holds is palatable, admissible, and ethical. In the satisfaction of his hunger the person is governed by tastes which have largely been influenced by culture, by magical, religious, and hygienic rules relating to the nature and preparation of food. Even the amount of food, the order in which and the times at which the person eats it, and the times when he experiences the need to eat are culturally determined.

The Sex Drive

Sex, in the form of sexual intercourse, is the one basic need the satisfaction of which is not essential for the survival of a particular organism, though it is obviously necessary for the reproduction of the group. Because sex is not necessary for the survival of the organism it would appear to have been endowed with a high pressor effect in all animals, and especially males. The high pressor effect assures the impregnation of a sufficient number of females to ensure the survival of the group. The male is capable of fertilizing a large number of females, the female is capable of being fertilized by only one male; thus, while the female can have only one pregnancy at a time the male can during that period produce a large number of pregnancies. The human male is sexually more easily aroused than the female, and sex plays a more dominant role in his life than it does in that of the female.[8] As Tinbergen puts it, "Since the female carries the eggs for some time, often even after fertilization, and since in so many species the female takes a larger share than the male in feeding and protecting the young, she is the more valuable part of the species' capital. Also, one male can fertilize more than one female, an additional reason why individual males are biologically less valuable than females ... and this may be the main reason why courtship is so often the concern of the male."[9]

Because of the great importance of the sexual drive it would seem strange that when the organism becomes seriously disordered the first system to break down functionally should be the sexual. It were as if nature protects the living from the burden of offspring for which they would be incapable of caring properly, and protects the offspring from the effects of inadequate care.

Culturally the expression of the sex drives varies from the greatest freedom to the most rigid and puritanical controls.[10] Virtually every possible expression of the sex drive has been culturally influenced by human beings, from variations in the understanding of the meaning of sex, so that in some cultures, and not infrequently in the most "enlightened," some persons have had produced in them a virtual ignorance of the very existence of sex or its significance,[11] while the techniques of lovemaking, under the influence of the sex drive, may differ as the poles apart in different cultures. The techniques of intercourse, for example, customary among some peoples may be completely unknown to others, while what may be taken to be the most obvious and universal forms of sex behavior in some cultures may, in fact be strictly limited to that culture.

Sex is hedged around by some prohibitions in all societies, as in laws concerning incest, abstinences at various times, vows of chastity, celibacy, and so on, but the manner of the expression of these forms of behavior, as in lovemaking, wooing, sexual attraction, and conjugation, differs greatly in different cultures. Similarly, the responses made to fatigue, somnolence, thirst, and restlessness, bladder and colon pressure, and the states of pain and fear are all culturally modified.

CULTURE, LIFE, AND DEATH

The basic physiological urges become culturally and environmentally modified; and it is the satisfaction of these modified urges —not the purely physiological urges—upon which the survival of the organism and of the group depends. The importance of this formulation of the facts cannot be too strongly emphasized. The purely physiological urges may be satisfied and yet if the culturally conditioned aspects of one or another of those urges is not satisfied both the individual and eventually the group may break down and even perish. Culture is man's device for increasing the ease and rendering more gratifying the means of satisfying his basic needs. When, for any reason, this particular form of gratification is lost the organism is, as it were, shocked, and presents the appearance of a depression of vital energy which, falling below a certain minimal level, may result in death. The depopulation of many parts of Melanesia[12] and of aboriginal Australia,[13] following the advent of the white man is believed to be due to such a cause. Indeed, there now exists good evidence which indicates that the fertility of populations as of persons can be much influenced by their psychic state.[14]

The phenomenon of "voodoo" death in a healthy adult who believes himself to have been the victim of fatal black magic or of the doom which results from the breaking of some taboo, is a good example of the effect of a fatal depression of vital energy following upon the loss of the sense of gratification in the responses made to the psychic states. Such cases have been examined by Cannon, and his suggestion is that in such instances death is due to shocking emotional stress—to obvious or repressed terror and its depressing effects upon the body as a whole, through excessive activity of the sympatheticoadrenal system. This latter system breaks down, the circulation is affected, the red blood corpuscles separate from the serum and begin to clump, semipermeable membranes become permeable and the serum passes through them to drown the tissues which have already been depleted in their oxygen supply owing to the clumping of the red blood corpuscles. There is thus a failure of the circulation with a consequent failure of vital organs to receive a sufficient supply of oxygen to maintain their functions.[15] The actual physiological changes in the organs of animals exposed to anxiety and alarm-producing conditions have been independently described by Selye, by Weininger, and by Wolff.[16]

Needs and Neurosis

The evidence suggests that a neurosis, in any culture, is a result of the failure of the ego to receive adequate satisfaction of the psychic components of its needs, whether basic or derived. When the child suffers need-deprivation, a disturbance in the state of dynamic equilibrium which exists between his needs is produced. Disharmony is generated. Tensions are maintained which should have been reduced and the organism's steady states are thrown out of balance.[17]

Since the motive forces of the organism's behavior draw their energy from this reservoir of needs, should a blocking of energy intake occur the organism will suffer from disturbed tension or need states. Anxiety will increase, and satisfaction will be sought in some other way. Since, furthermore, it is during childhood[18] that the person usually suffers his severest privations, it is probable that most, even all, neuroses have their origins in the privations and disordered responses made to them by the child during the first six years of his life. The child does not know that it is physiologically relaxing to react to frustration as directly as the situation will allow.[19] Indeed, adults in our culture very rarely learn this.

Man is an open energy system constantly receiving, exchanging, and transforming energy within the larger whole, society, of which he is a part. The social or cultural process is an energy system and social man is an interacting part of that system. In such a system man derives the greater part of his zest for living from his life in society. When he feels that there is no longer any place for him in society, when everyone "cuts him dead," and acts as if he were non-existent, an apathy, a depression is likely to overtake him which will result in some pathological state. As Murray has pointed out, zest is highly correlated with pleasure and activity, apathy with un-pleasure and inactivity.[20] These are simply two different states of energy. Society supplies the energy by means of which the person maintains his psychophysical equilibrium, and the form in which this energy is made available and secured is culturally determined. In the course of culturalization the person becomes habituated to receiving his energy in certain forms and his satisfactions consist in the transformation of those energies to his own uses, to the uses of his organism, the satisfaction of his needs. Any substantial variation in the form in which that energy is supplied may render it no longer acceptable to the person, and though he may attempt to utilize it, it will be in an apathetic manner which may cumulatively have a seriously shocking or depressing effect upon him. Hence, it is obvious that satisfaction of physiological urges is not enough; the *form* which those urges have assumed through cultural conditioning must be satisfied if the healthy functioning of the person in his society is to be maintained.

The Culturalization of Needs

Persons who are made to eat food to which they are unaccustomed and which they would not voluntarily eat not only feel unsatisfied after such meals but may even experience a greater or lesser degree of nausea following them. Under such conditions the response to the hunger need is not their own, not that to which they have become habituated; no satisfaction follows and there is no restoration of the organism to equilibrium. Materials for the production of energy have been taken in, but under such unfavorable conditions they may never even get a chance to be partially transformed into energy—they may be vomited. If they do pass through the gastrointestinal tract they may be only partially digested and the amount of energy thus made available will, to varying degrees, be less than usual. Physicochemically some of this energy may be utilized to meet the demands of the physiological urge, but those demands cannot be fully met because the energy has not been properly channeled to it. The deprivation thus suffered and the presence of some energy which has not been properly canalized is a situation which readily leads to more or less serious maladjustment. The surplus energy must find some outlet, and this it may do in a variety of ways. It is in such conditions of disequilibrium that psychosomatic and psychoneurotic disorders frequently have their origin.[21]

Precisely similar states of disequilibrium may result from the inadequacy of the responses made to any of the other needs. Unless, for example, the received canons of sexual attractiveness are satisfied, the partners to a sexual act may obtain little or no gratification from it. In such persons the sex need will not have been satisfied, and among married people may lead not infrequently to a functional sterility with actual failure of ejaculation or even to impotence on the part of the male. The standards of sexual attractiveness are for the most part culturally determined. Lack of sexual attractiveness generally fails to evoke any sexual response. It is not the sexual object but the sexually *attractive* object which evokes the proper response.

This point is fundamental, that it is not the condition but the *culturally* transmuted condition which must do the satisfying: the cultural condition or type of condition to which one has become habituated. Culture has conditioned the form of the urges and the proper responses to them, and the satisfactions are secured in terms of cultural values. But culture is not a response to a specific need but to the integral satisfaction of a series of needs, and no institution can be functionally related to one basic or cultural need alone. Culture is not a molecular, but a molar phenomenon.

DERIVED NEEDS

Our next task will be to trace in some detail how these basic needs become socialized. We have now briefly to consider those secondary or more purely cultural needs which arise out of the integral processes of cultural response to the satisfaction of the basic needs. Since these needs are derived from this process they may be called *socially emergent needs* or, following Malinowski, the *derived needs,* cultural needs or cultural imperatives. It is possible that all derived needs are ultimately based on the satisfaction of the basic needs.

Man must cooperate with other men in an economic relation; he must care for and educate the young; and he must implement the means of enforcement in all such activities.

These cultural imperatives and their responses have been synoptically formulated by Malinowski as shown in Table 5.

It is easy to see how these imperatives and responses grow out of the satisfaction of such a basic need, for example, as sex.

The sexual act leads eventually to the birth of a child. The help-

TABLE 5. DERIVED NEEDS

Imperatives	Responses
1. The cultural apparatus of implements and consumers' goods must be produced, used, maintained, and replaced by new production.	1. Economics
2. Human behavior, as regards its technical, customary, legal, or moral prescription must be codified, regulated in action and sanction.	2. Social Control
3. The human material by which every institution is maintained must be renewed, formed, drilled, and provided with full knowledge of tribal tradition.	3. Education
4. Authority within each institution must be defined, equipped with powers, and endowed with means of forceful execution of its orders.	4. Political Organization

lessness of the child necessitates the expenditure of a great deal of time and energy devoted solely to its care. The men and women who have organized in a permanent sexual relationship will have to organize further to provide the infant with special comforts and protection. Domestic activities will have to be put on a new basis, the infant will have to be fed, cleaned, his wants attended to, and he will have to be trained. In this process specialized tasks fall to the lot of each parent, and they share somewhat different kinds of authority. The arrival of the child entails the development of a new relationship with the members of neighboring families and the social (legal) recognition of the new bonds which have been established between the parents and the child. In turn, recognition must be established of the new bonds which have been created by the parents with the group, for the parents now have become responsible to the group for the proper education of the child.

These new obligatory relationships will inevitably arise in all human societies and will, of course, involve the whole series of basic and derived needs.

The economic, social control, educational, and political responses, the responses arising out of the satisfaction of the basic and derived needs, in turn give rise to all or almost all of those cultural responses which we know.

Again, following Malinowski, some of these cultural responses may be stated in the following scheme:

1. Patterns of communication: gestures, language, writing, etc.
2. Material traits:
   a. Food habits and food getting;
   b. Personal care and dress;
   c. Shelter;
   d. Utensils, tools, etc.;
   e. Weapons;
   f. Occupations and industries;
   g. Transportation and travel.
3. Exchange of goods and services: barter, trade, commerce.
4. Forms of property: real and personal.
5. Sex and family patterns:
   a. Marriage and divorce;
   b. Methods of reckoning relationship;
   c. Guardianship;
   d. Inheritance.
6. Societal controls:
   a. Mores;
   b. Public opinion.
7. Government:
   a. Political forms;
   b. Judicial and legal procedures.
8. Religious and magical practices.
9. Mythology and philosophy.
10. Science.
11. Art: carving, painting, drawing, dancing, music, literature, etc.
12. Recreational interests: sports, games, etc.

In the process of socialization the person acquires a knowledge, sufficient for his purposes, of most of these cultural responses. No person, however, with the possible exception of some who live in the simplest societies, ever acquires a knowledge of the whole of his culture. The individual is fitted for participation in his culture as a person and not simply designed to become a mere repository of it. The member of a culture is so equipped that he can, under favorable conditions, become an innovator and thus a modifier of his culture.[22]

If culture enlarges the scope of man's potentialities, it also limits or constrains their development. As Bidney points out, man's self-consciousness "enables him, individually and collectively, to reverse himself and to attempt to reform his ways in accordance with rational requirements. Since culture is the gift of human freedom, man is able to determine, within limits, the direction which the cultural process should take in the light of his experience and aspirations."[23]

Acquired Needs

Any want, any object abstract or concrete, upon which the person sets value can become a need. Anything to which a person becomes habituated can become a need—bridge, tennis, tobacco, alcohol, philosophizing, poetry, a faith in the substance of things to come, reading, writing, in short, almost anything of which one can think. Some of these needs may have an indirect connection with the satisfaction of basic needs, some may not. It may be that most, if not all, needs, no matter how artificial their form, could be shown to have some relationship to the satisfaction of basic needs. Bridge, to take a crass example, like all games is an activity which satisfies the tension of restlessness, a basic need. So far as emotional nonvital basic needs are concerned the game brings the player into association with other persons, it affords him an opportunity to satisfy his need for expression and the desire to obtain social recognition. In such games the desire to excel in competition with others may become the dominant motivation of a person. He may play to satisfy his need to win or excel. He may not even be interested in the normal rivalry of the game or in the persons with whom he plays. Analysis of such a person's behavior, however, will usually reveal the fact that his competitive drive rests upon something much more profound than the simple desire to win. The re-creation of an infantile general state of tension and its relief may be the underlying motivation of which he is unconscious, as is the case with many gamblers.[24] Dostoyevsky's gambling, for example, affords a good illustration of this.[25]

The element of tension in competition may or may not be itself satisfying. Relief or the promise of relief from that tension certainly is.

NEEDS AND TENSION REDUCTION OR INCREASE

Thus far the satisfaction of needs has been discussed in terms of tension-reduction or a return to equilibrium. Such tension-reduction is, indeed, necessary for the survival of the organism. But the organism may obtain satisfaction from the maintenance or increase of tension. The tensions of sex, bowel, and bladder are among the commonest examples of this fact. The tensions of dangerous sports, circus-thrills and the like, of creative work, and speculation constitute further examples of the satisfaction derived from tension. But in all these instances it should be quite obvious that were the tension to be greatly prolonged it would become decidedly unpleasant, adequate or complete satisfaction being possible only when relief from tension is the end effect.

Competition as tension has its satisfying effects, and in the sense of outdoing others is rewarding in terms both of socially approved achievement and the security of one's ego. Competition is an acquired, not an inborn, drive. It will to a large extent depend upon whether the values of his culture are oriented toward cooperation or competition whether the person will develop competitive traits or not.[26] As an ego-value or means of maximizing one's ego competition is to some extent seen in all human cultures, whether men compete to cooperate or conflict with one another. Competition is, however, certainly not a basic need of any kind. Those who claim that competition in man is an inborn drive have not thus far produced any evidence in the least adequate to support their claim.

But to return to the consideration of wants—any wants—as needs.

Whether or not such acquired needs are traceable to the indirect satisfaction of basic needs, it seems clear that such needs are not necessary, in the sense of being necessary for the survival of the person or necessary to the maintenance of his mental health. In this sense, for example, tobacco may be a need, and it may be felt as a necessity, but it never becomes a necessary necessity. It becomes, as Jowett put it years ago, an unnecessary necessity. Survival and mental health are in no way dependent upon the need for tobacco. The satisfaction of such a need may be completely and abruptly terminated with, on the whole, nothing but benefit accruing to the person. In point of fact, smoking in the cultures of the West is a rather complex form of behavior which is largely indulged because it psychically serves the function of specific tension reduction. "Be nonchalant—light a Murad," was an advertising slogan of some years ago which gave explicit recognition to the function of the cigarette as a tension disguiser in certain social situations. Physiologically tobacco increases tension. It is the behavior associated with smoking which reduces tension during the smoking process. In most situations the person who is smoking is at an advantage over the person who is not.

Alcohol, on the other hand, is both physiologically and psychically a tension reducer—in fact, the best sedative known to medicine. Poetry and philosophizing are capable of performing the same function for persons who have acquired such needs, just as religion or radio may for others.

As everyone knows, acquired needs, unnecessary necessities, may become drives as strongly motivated as the most pressing of the basic drives, even though from the standpoint of biological survival they are quite unnecessary.

The number of man's acquired or psychic needs is very great, and varies in different cultures. It would be impossible to list those needs here.

Linton names three of what he considers to be man's most outstanding psychic needs. These are: (1) the need for emotional response from other individuals; (2) the need for security; and (3) the need for novelty of experience.[27] It is probable that the need for emotional response and the need for security are really one and the same thing, and that both spring from the dependency need for love. With respect to novelty of experience a doubt may be expressed as to the universality or strength of this need. Somehow there always seems to be a plentiful supply of conservatively minded (psychosclerotic) persons who object to novelty in any shape or form. Novelty undoubtedly constitutes a need for many persons, but how frequently it is distributed in any population is a question.

The use of the term "psychic" to describe acquired or emotional nonvital basic needs as distinguished from vital basic needs may, perhaps, be questioned on the ground that the basic needs are themselves largely psychic, even though in their elementary forms they rest on physiological foundations. It has already been pointed out that the basic needs are largely experienced as psychic or culturalized needs, and it is clear that as the person grows the psychic content and ramifications of his basic needs become progressively more complex. The derived needs, as we have already seen, emerge out of the social satisfaction of the basic needs.

NEEDS DEFINED

Since all needs possess a high psychic content it would be less confusing to use distinct terms or phrases to distinguish the various large classes of needs from one another. The following definitions are, therefore, suggested.

VITAL BASIC NEED: *Any biological urge or need of the organism which must be satisfied if the individual or the group is to survive.* Examples are the need for oxygen, food, liquid, activity, rest, sleep, bowel and bladder emptying, escape from danger, avoidance of pain, and conjugation.

EMOTIONAL (NONVITAL) BASIC NEED: *Any biological urge or need which is not necessary for the physical survival of the organism, but which must be satisfied if the organism is to develop and maintain adequate mental health.* A satisfactory short definition of mental health is the ability to love and the ability to work (Freud). Examples are the need to be loved, the need to love, the need to be with others, communication, and tactile and kinesthetic stimulation.

DERIVED OR SOCIALLY EMERGENT NEED: *Any need which arises out of the process of satisfying basic needs, which is not necessary for the physical survival of the organism, and which is not biologically, though it may under certain conditions become socially, necessary for the maintenance of mental health.* Examples are the need for proper clothes, grooming, shelter, the development of skills or the acquisition of knowledge, creative work, etiquette, and religion.

ACQUIRED NEED: *Any need which does not arise directly out of the process of satisfying basic needs, which is not necessary for the physical survival of the organism, but which grows out of the person's relation to the derived or socially emergent needs, and is not usually necessary for the maintenance of mental health.*

The acquired needs are, as it were, superimpositions upon the derived needs. The need for shelter, for example, is a derived need, but the desire to decorate one's house in a particular style is an acquired need. The desire to live in a hut, an apartment, or a house is a derived need, but wanting to put a piano in it is an acquired need. The desire to play the piano or listen to someone playing it may indirectly satisfy some basic need, vital or emotional, but it is not a necessary satisfaction. The desire is posterior to a certain kind of organization of derived needs.

Acquired needs are individual, personal, idiosyncratic needs—idiosyncratic in that acquired needs may differ from person to person within the same culture, whereas the derived needs are usually the same for all persons in all cultures, no matter how their form may differ. In the same culture some persons need tobacco, others do not; and so it is for all acquired needs.

Satisfaction of needs makes for health and cooperativeness; frustration of needs for dis-order or dis-ease and hostility, whether the needs be basic, derived, or acquired.[28]

Maslow has distinguished between "lower" and "higher" needs, and has pointed out that the organism itself dictates hierarchies of values. He points out that the basic needs arrange themselves in a fairly definite hierarchy on the basis of the principle of relative potency. For example, the need for safety is stronger than the need for love, because the former dominates the organism when both needs are frustrated. The physiological needs are stronger than the safety needs which are stronger than the love needs, which are stronger than the esteem needs, which are stronger than the idiosyncratic needs for self-actualization.[29] Higher needs are of later evolutionary and ontogenetic development, but they are no less natural than the lower needs. They are, however, less imperative for sheer survival, less urgent subjectively, their gratification produces more desirable subjective results; a higher value is placed upon them than upon "lower" needs, and their gratification has more desirable health, civic, and social consequences, leading to stronger and truer individualism—that is, the individualism which goes with loving mankind most and being most developed indiosyncratically. As Hadley Cantril puts it, our independence increases with our interdependence.[30]

Lower needs are more localized, more tangible, and more limited than higher needs. As Maslow puts it, "Hunger and thirst are 'much more obviously bodily than is love, which in turn is more so than respect. In addition, lower need satisfiers are much more tangible or observable than are higher need satisfactions. Furthermore, they are more limited in the sense that a smaller quantity of gratifiers is needed to still the need. Only so much food can be eaten, but love, respect, and cognitive satisfactions are almost unlimited."[31] It is essentially because of their development of higher needs that human beings are human. No creature wanting these needs is human. Through their needs human beings create cultures. As Maslow says, culture is not only created for human needs but by them. The difficulty is, however, that the more complex culture becomes the more removed do our cultural responses become from the understanding of the needs they were originally designed to satisfy. In these respects human beings have culturally often achieved the ultimate limits of confusion—as, for example, in the meeting of aggression with aggression, the removal of babies from their mothers after birth, training in competitiveness, and the like. The higher needs, being as weakly expressive as they are, call for a much more sensitive understanding than most cultures, especially of the western world, have yet bestowed upon them.

NEEDS AND VALUES

Organismal Values

Whatever we experience as a need is valued by us; therefore needs provide the origins of our first values, whether the needs be basic, derived, or acquired, whether they have a strong or a weak pressor effect. Thus it comes about that certain values are biologically based, founded on the basic needs, and it is the organism's conscious experience and judgment of these needs which constitutes their value. As far as the organism is concerned no value is attached to anything unless the organism experiences it as a need and places a value on that need by striving to satisfy it and being satisfied as a consequence of an adequate response. Value does not exist without choice. The basic needs constitute the organism's biologically determined system of choices concerning the nature of the satisfactions it must secure if it is to survive and develop in health. It is more than doubtful whether there is at first any cognitive evaluation of the need; but certainly the organism exhibits, from the first, great interest in the satisfaction of its needs. The organism behaves in striving to attain satisfaction of its needs as if it "considered" such satisfaction desirable. But it is perhaps the unconscious autonomic responses—the "wisdom of the body"—that produce the appearance of evaluation or consideration, without there being, in fact, any active thinking involved.

Needs exist in order to accomplish the purposes of the organism, and the purposes of the organism may be briefly described as the actualization of its potentialities. The organism performs the valuing of responses to its needs in terms of the requirements of those needs. Responses or experiences in relation to the organism's needs are not needed because they are valued, but valued because they are needed. It is only when we develop acquired needs that we begin to need things because we value them.

The human organism at birth is equipped with a biologically determined value system which, on the whole, automatically enables it to choose and to demand what is good for it and to reject what is bad. Needs are biologically incorporated *organismal values* which cause the organism to discriminate and choose certain types of satisfaction in preference to others. It is when the organism is able to think about and evaluate the types and forms of satisfaction of its needs that one may speak of *personal values* as contrasted with organismal values.

It is the orientation and directiveness of the biological needs of the human organism, that is to say, its organismal values, which determine the tendency of the personal values of the person in society, and hence, the tendency of the fundamental social values. In many human societies these tendencies have been greatly obscured by the distortion and overlaying, as it were, of social institutions which run counter to these tendencies.

The basic needs are the primary biological values, and our thinking about those needs are but secondary valuations which may or may not add sharper definition and understanding to our conceptions of them. If the basic needs constitute our primary biological values then the latter are as natural events as are the former. In this way value is brought into the realm of fact. The intrinsic requirements of the organism are its basic needs, and these are its basic psychophysical biological values. Whatever the organism values is a value for it. If some philosophers have distinguished the process of attaching value to an object as distinct from the intrinsic value of the object itself, we may readily agree, but we need not fall into the error of thinking that while the latter is a fact the former is not. Value judgments may differ in the specific materials with which they have to do, but as Dewey points out, one must deny "that as judgments, or in respect to methods of inquiry, test, and verification, value-judgments have any peculiar or unique features."[32] And as Julian Huxley has put it, "It is not true that the nature of things is irrelevant to the interests of man, for the interests of man turn out to be part of the nature of things. Nor is it true that science cannot be concerned with values. Science is a method of inquiry which can be applied in all kinds of fields. In any particular field, it has to deal with the subject matter it finds there. In biology it can do something toward explaining the origins of conscious evolution. But as soon as it is applied to man, it finds values among its data; you cannot either understand or control human affairs without taking them into account. For a science of man, the problem is not whether or not to have anything to do with values, but how to devise satisfactory methods of studying them and discovering how they work."[33]

Basic needs are physiologically given or innate "judgments," as it were, statements of the intrinsic requirednesses or necessities of the organism.[34] These are the organismic values. Many of the person's social values will be built upon and developed out of the organismic values under the stimulation of the social environment. This is not to say that all social values are based on organismic values—they may well be, however indirectly—but this is a matter upon which more research is required.[35] Since the basic needs or organismic values minister to the health and survival of the organism, they can *never* be "wrong," whereas the social needs or values can be and often are wrong because they are so frequently based on erroneous interpretations as to what is "good" and what is "evil" for man. The organismic values are innate givens, the social values are derived or emergent evaluations or socially created needs. There are biogenic and social values.

The Basic Test of Value

The basic test of a value is the extent to which it contributes to the survival of the organism as a healthy and harmonically functioning interdependent whole. Health is the state of being organismically sound: that is, sound according to the requirements of the organism. Health is *the* organismic value, the summation of all the organism's values.[36] A soundly functioning organism is something which has a real existence and whose critical requirements can be investigated. When we can state these criteria of health we shall be describing the organismic values. Insofar as organismic health is concerned— bodily "and" mental health—we can determine by experience, by scientific techniques, what conditions make for health and what make for illness. And we can then say that the conditions which make for health are desirable while those which make for illness or malfunctioning are undesirable. The fact is that by so doing we are simply recognizing the intrinsic requirements, that is, the organismic values, of the organism. In science the test of a value which is not arbitrary is its truth. The criteria of organismic health provide such a test.

An organismic value is a property of the organism which has an existence altogether apart from the process of being valued. This being so it becomes possible to identify and describe values as natural events. It has been said that "what is right is what is right for man's nature." The "rights" of man's nature are the "rights" demanded by his basic needs. The rights demanded by man's basic needs are certain kinds of organismal states which can be produced and developed only by certain kinds of satisfactions, for needs exist not simply to be satisfied but also to provide the bases for the growth and development of the organism. The process of satisfaction is the means by which the organism is stimulated to develop; so that the "rights" of man's nature are the satisfactions which his needs require. A need is a term for the particular requirements of the organism. It is of the utmost importance to note that the need determines the nature of the satisfaction it demands. It is the need, so to speak, which sets the value, the criteria of requiredness, and does the valuing. For such basic needs only certain kinds of experiences, within certain limits, can act as satisfactions. Experience is evaluated by the needs as either satisfying or unsatisfying, with all the gradations between. As Maslow states it, "The requiredness of basic needs differentiates them from all other need gratifiers. The organism itself, out of its own nature, points to an intrinsic range of satisfiers for which no substitute is possible as is the case, for instance, with habitual needs."[37]

If we could know what the criteria of requiredness of the basic needs were, we should be able to say how human beings should be satisfied if they are to develop in full organismic health. It has been said that biological facts have nothing to do with human values, with what *ought* to be. The answer to that assertion is: if it can be shown that there exist certain biological facts, biological functions of the organism, which are constant, and which if treated in one way lead to malfunctioning of the organism, to sickness, and to disoperative behavior, and treated in another way lead to well-being, mental health (the ability to love and the ability to work), and to cooperative behavior, then it could be stated that the biological functions of the organism determine the nature of the values of the world in which it must live, for the words *should* and *must* are here equivalent if the organism is to survive creatively as such. Insofar as we fail to recognize this fact we are in danger of overlooking the only scientific means by which we can discover how we should live.

Professor L. O. Kattsoff, who has independently arrived at similar conclusions, puts it this way:

> If a value is that toward which the individual directs his behavior, and positive values are those goals which are conducive to the health of the individual, then we have a meaningful and effective basis for the "ought." A positive value is one which ought to be encouraged or aimed at, its authority deriving from its relation to the health of the individual. The sanction for violating such a value is ill health—a punishment guaranteed in the sense that it will inevitably follow. So we can declare that an individual *ought* to strive for that which is conducive to his health, though he may or may not do so. If he does not, we then can say that he is doing what he ought not to do.
>
> The concept of the "ought," like the concept of value . . . has its basis in the very structure of the organism. It is, therefore, an absolute basis for any ethics or for any theory of values.[38]

The Context of Value

The context of functioning of our most fundamental values is to be looked for in the structure of the organism's basic needs. Here is to be found the natural calculus of biological values, the values by which men must live if they are to develop in health and survive in creative harmony. The objectivity of these values must be recognized, and they must be studied, for the biological values are the natural systems which indicate the direction in which the organism should travel. At a higher level, the level of socially derived values, values constitute the compasses by which men attempt to steer their course in the world of experience. The organism recognizes certain ends as desirable, and because this is the case we can successfully inquire into the objective constituents of its value system. Its preferences are not arbitrary but are conditioned by its organic requirements. When we examine the objective constituents of value we discover that the need determines the character of the satisfaction, and that satisfactions are satisfactory only to the extent to which they meet the requirements of the need. Furthermore, we find that these biological values are universal, that is to say, all men are born with them, with definite needs for definite satisfactions, which are biologically much the same for all men everywhere. When we speak of needs we imply also satisfactions of a particular need-determined kind; for this reason we should, perhaps, speak of need-satisfactions rather than simply of needs.

Basic Needs as Evaluators

Hart writes, "No thing or event has value as a whole, with all its qualities. It has value only partially. To evaluate an object means to reflect upon its properties in terms of the sustenance and enhancement of our life. What an event does, what consequences follow from its occurrence, these comprise our knowledge of its value. Neither motives nor deeds are good or bad in isolation. Their value depends upon the whole context of events, antecedent and subsequent."[39] Biologically the basic needs may be regarded as evaluators, evaluators which are capable of telling us what the organism requires vastly more efficiently than anything else can do. We must therefore study the consequences to the organism which follow upon certain types of satisfactions offered to it, and upon the basis of the consequences to it determine what constitutes the best satisfactions for the particular need and for the organism as a whole. These needs and their specific satisfactions are biological organismic "goods" and therefore must be considered to be social goods. The healthy society must be so constituted as to make readily available the specific satisfactions which the organism requires in order to develop its potentialities to the full. When fully understood recognition of the "goodness" of human basic needs is inevitable, as is the inevitable abandonment of such erroneous notions as "instinctual drives" which are directed toward destructiveness, hostility, and death. As Maslow points out, from the "bad animal" interpretation of man's "instincts" the misconception followed that civilization and all its institutions are but so many bad-animality-restraining forces.[40] In addition to bearing the physical stigmata of his physiological origins within him, it is often said that man also bears the stigmata of his psychological origins within him, and that these are represented by his "instinctual drives." The only way in which such assertions can be answered is by a thorough study of the nature of human drives under different environmental conditions. Such studies have yet to be conducted, but such evidence as we have at the present time unequivocally and unexceptionally points in the opposite direction, namely, that man's innate drives are all oriented in the direction of goodness, and that "badness" is largely the effect of "bad" environmental conditions. The evidence of psychiatry suggests that what the psychiatrist does for the person whose basic drives have been frustrated and disordered, whose neurosis is an expression in part at least of that disorder, is to relieve him of the factors of deformation and frustration, and to restore him to the ability to act in terms of his undeformed and unfrustrated drives more in keeping with their original nature. When, in the ordinary course of living, we have learned to pay attention to the basic needs of the organism in terms of its requirements the labors of psychiatrists will be reduced to a minimum.

As Braatøy has pointed out, "the most basic rule in personal psychotherapy [is] to detect as best one can the essential needs of the patient and let those needs set the rules."[41]

A psychiatrist, Sol W. Ginsburg, has written that "Values represent our orientation to society and our attitude to human welfare. *In the last analysis, adjustment is a name for the process of living up to a set of values.*"[42] The orientation of the *biological* organism *Homo sapiens* to life is as a reinforcer of satisfactions in terms of love.

In the concept of love we have the scientific criterion by which we can measure the satisfaction or nonsatisfaction of human needs—or what is the same thing, human values.

It has been said that "In an age in which science and rationality are all important, many people are unwilling to accept values simply on the basis of faith or precedent. The lack of any other accepted basis for value judgments may thus result in personal disorientation or social disorganization. This has been one of the major effects of an increasing use of the scientific method."[43] It is to be hoped that such an analysis as we have here attempted may contribute toward the more satisfactory evaluation of values in a scientific manner. The view may be expressed, contrary to Margenau, that ethical codes *can* be extracted from the facts revealed by science. "There is a lack of continuity somewhere as one passes from science, which is a descriptive, explanatory description, to ethics, which is normative. Something else must be introduced."[44]

What must be introduced, of course, is the process of extraction. The scientific facts never speak for themselves, but when we ask them the right questions they are likely to give us the right answers. The question we have to ask of the world of fact in order to secure an answer for the world of value of human beings is: What is it that contributes toward human health and welfare? We must always remember that we have become human because we are the valuing creatures of this earth, because of our ability to transmute facts into values and values into facts. "Goodness" and "right" are constituted by whatever contributes to human welfare, and human welfare consists in the capacity to love others and to be loved by them. As we shall see in the following pages, this is but a short way of saying that goodness consists in realizing one's potentialities for behaving in such a manner as always to confer survival benefits in a creatively enlarging manner upon all our fellow human beings, born and unborn.

8 DEPENDENCY, INTERDE- PENDENCY, AND LOVE

Nothing in the world is single,
All things by a law divine
In one another's being mingle—
Why not I with thine?
—PERCY BYSSHE SHELLEY

THE NATURE AND MEANING OF DEPENDENCY

The fundamentally social nature of all living things has its origin in the physiological relationship between parent and offspring which is embraced in the reproductive relationship. In the mammals the maternal and uterine (unborn) organisms are for a time bound together in an interacting association, the uterine organism being entirely *dependent* upon the maternal organism for its sustenance, for the satisfaction of its needs. This process of dependency, as far as we can tell, proceeds largely but by no means entirely, upon a vegetative level.[1] At birth the dependent relationship simply becomes a more externally active process on the part both of the newborn and the maternal organism or its substitute. The dependency of the newborn is a continuation of the dependency of the fetus, a dependency which has its origin in the once inseparable connection between the organism and that other organism out of which it grew.

It is unnecessary to resort to explanations which go beyond what the evidence at present allows, to account for the feeling of dependency and the need for love. Whether a newborn has a feeling of dependency which is sharp and clear-cut, we do not know. It has hungers, needs, and these give rise to or are the states of disturbance

161

or tension in the organism. Such unsteady states, together with the more or less generalized awareness on the part of the organism that it will, following certain motor acts, be restored to a steady state, constitute the conditions necessary for a feeling of dependency. It may legitimately be doubted whether the newborn experiences feelings in terms of anything more than urges, satisfaction, and dissatisfaction. It may also be doubted whether there exists any *distinct* feeling of dependency. It is possible, however, that there exists a generalized, diffused tonal state of the organism which is described most nearly by the word *dependency*. But it must be some time before this diffuse tonal state assumes a more definite form. There is some evidence that this diffuse state never assumes a definite form in the absence of stimulations received from socializing agents. To be dependent means to rely upon some other person or persons for the satisfaction of one's needs. The consciousness of a distinct feeling of dependence cannot be developed in the absence of factors which produce a growing awareness in the infant that practically all his satisfactions are obtained through the responses made to his basic needs by other persons. Such an awareness is, as it were, a precipitate of recurring experiences of cravings which have eventually been satisfied by others, save for whose intervention those cravings would never have been satisfied.

The child is born in dependency, and it also learns that it is dependent. The whole of its social training, however anarchic it may be, teaches it to maintain something of that dependency. Interdependency is the social state. Nondependent individuality is the nonsocial state.

There is good reason to believe that the feeling of helplessness which the child is supposed to experience after birth is a reality, even though it may not be experienced as such, with any sharp definition, for some weeks or even months after birth, just as its feelings of dependency may, during this early period, be of a diffuse and generalized nature. It would seem that the increasing need for love represents the growth and development of a condition originating in the stimulation of the impulses of the diffuse dependency state, impulses which are developed by those who help to give more articulated form to the dependent state by satisfying the child's needs. To have one's needs satisfied is to be loved and at one and the same time to learn to love.

The newborn's appreciation of the stimuli of the external world is already at a significantly developed level. While it has been argued that for the first two weeks or so of his life the newborn is not truly awake, except possibly for brief intervals, in the sense of having a percipient consciousness (a consciousness capable of endowing sensations with meanings, of turning sensations into perceptions), the evidence is now clear that neonates can be conditioned within the first week of life,[2] and there is good evidence of learning in relation to the feeding situation within the first month.[3] There is also good evidence that the fetus is capable of being conditioned *in utero*.[4] In brief, it may be true that the periods of overt activity of the neonate are but blurred half-conscious states, a fuzzy primordium of what will later develop as consciousness; nevertheless it is quite clear that the newborn is capable of learning and registering what it has learned, even though what it has learned may not appear to be overtly enduring or stable. The fact is that an experience has been registered within the dimensions of the mind.

THE REGISTRY OF EXPERIENCE

In the responses of the fetus to stimuli of various kinds, and in the peculiar behavioral syndrome of premature babies, we have fair evidence of the registry of experience within the organism. The prematurity syndrome furnishes proof of the fact that the environment is capable of exercising a substantial and constant influence upon the character of the developing personality, when the organism is exposed to that environment at an early developmental age. Whether or not the influence is constant, the point is that the organism is seriously affected by the environment at a premature age, so far as its future behavioral development is concerned. Is it not, therefore, likely that the stimuli to which the fetus responds *in utero* also write their permanent record, which subsequently influences the development of behavior, into the nervous system? And may not such experiences, as Greenacre and Shirley have independently suggested, contribute toward a predisposition to anxiety?[5]

It has, however, been argued that the incomplete development of the central nervous system and its connections with the sense organs, together with the insufficient amount of oxygen circulating in the brain, serve to maintain the fetus during birth in a state which effectively protects it against such shocks as some psychoanalysts postulate. During the birth process the amount of oxygen which reaches the brain is negligible, so that even were the brain well developed it would fail to record, it is urged, even if it could appreciate, the experience of birth.

To these objections reply may be made that the organism is certainly capable of registering the experience of birth if, as we know it to be, it is capable of responding to the stimuli of the birth process. The registry may have no sharply delimited conscious psychic content, although such evidence as we today possess indicates that the physiological changes induced by birth leave their impress upon the nervous system. But whether these changes may be regarded as traumatic cannot with any certainty be said at this time. The indications are that they can.[6]

The so-called "pleasures" and feeling of "security" of intrauterine existence, the relation of these to the security-seeking patterns of later life, the "anxiety" state originally produced by the "birth trauma," and the relation of the latter to various phobias are no longer in the category of bright speculations to be relegated to the department of unsubstantiated hypotheses. These concepts now occupy the status of good hypotheses which have received appreciable support from different sources, but which require further investigation and verification before they can be accepted as facts.

The reference to phobias recalls the fact that Freud has himself criticized Rank's explanation of child phobias (e.g., fear of small animals as they vanish into or emerge from holes), as based on a birth impression on the ground "that it rests on a presupposition that the infant has definite sense impressions, especially those of a visual nature" at birth, adding "it is not credible that the child at birth has anything beyond tactile and general sensibility." The newborn, it would seem, has a great deal more than that, but however that may be it is seriously to be doubted whether more than a small fraction of children have the least fear of small animals entering or emerging from holes. Infantile anxiety typically "occurs when the child is left alone *in a dark room* (usually the bedroom at bed-time)." According to Rank, "This situation reminds the child, who still is close to the experience of the primal trauma, of the womb situation—with the important difference that the child is now consciously separated from the mother, whose womb is only 'symbolically' replaced by the dark room or warm bed."[7] Freud pointed out, and Rank agreed, that the anxiety disappears as soon as the child becomes conscious of the existence (nearness) of the loved person (contact, voice, etc.).[8] "Every pleasure," Rank asserts, "has as its final aim the re-establishment of the intrauterine primal pleasure."[9] In other words, the person seeks to re-establish the state of pleasure which was his *before he was* separated from the mother. Freud, we think, missed the point when he objected that most children feared the dark. Of course they did, during the nineteenth century. Modern children are much less frequently affected by such fears. With the development of more enlightened means of handling children's bedtime, and the elimination of the horrifying bedtime stories which so often turned the dark into a nightmare, modern children tend to find the dark objectionable only because it puts a period to their day. When children fear the dark it is highly probably the case that they have been taught to fear it.

The fact is that all healthy children enjoy a certain amount of solitude and of darkness, and certainly every healthy person requires some of both. However, to many persons darkness means separation, loss of contact, insecurity, and privation of love; solitude usually having the same meaning for them. Such persons do not enjoy being alone in the dark for any length of time. To them solitude is rarely welcome, while darkness is welcome only as a condition of sleep. To the insecure darkness is anxiety-producing, while light is safe.

On the other hand, to the secure darkness is relaxing while light is adventuresome and stimulating.

In discussing the transition between prenatal and postnatal life several matters of much interest and importance have been touched upon which would bear further discussion here. The first of these is the concept of dependency, its relation to the development of love and the social development of the person. While these matters might be more properly dealt with later, it will be profitable to say a few words at this point. It will in a sense provide a summary of our discussion and direction for the road along which we are yet to travel.

Dependency, Love, and the Development of the Person

Dependency may be defined as the relation of the organism to the conditions which support it. The state of dependency during intrauterine life is largely physiological. There is some evidence that the fetus probably has a sort of generalized awareness of that dependency. With birth the state of dependency is continued in a physiologically altered form for some two or three weeks, and there is an increasing growth in awareness during this period. During the neonatal period the organism is dominantly engaged in the process of adjusting itself to a new environment. Before the fourth week of life is over the infant makes its first personal-social responses in the form of tactually perceptible postural adjustment when taken up, and of a selective regard for the face. It pays attention to sound and to moving objects, and it has differential cries for discomfort, pain, and hunger. Its subsequent development is one of differentiation, enlargement of consciousness and the development in it of a greater specificity of its potentialities.[10] In all this it is assisted by the maturation of its nervous system and the stimulation it receives from those who care for it.

The Cooperative Benefits of Interdependency and Dependency at Birth

The interdependency and dependency naturally implicit in the cooperative relationship between infant and mother at birth are profoundly more significant than has hitherto been realized. During the last few years it has been discovered that immediately after birth the greatest physiological and psychological benefits are conferred upon the mother by the infant and by the mother upon the infant *if the cooperative relationship is permitted to follow its natural course*. In our trained incapacity we have become accustomed to handling the childbirth situation by separating mother and infant, thus deliberately interrupting the biological benefits which they would otherwise normally confer upon one another.[11] Throughout the whole mammalian group there is not a single example to be found in which the young are separated from the mother at birth, and yet this is what we as civilized members of the western world have been doing for a long time. Things were a great deal better before women started going to hospitals to have their babies. Today, more than 85 per cent of American women have their babies in hospitals. Today, also, there is good reason to believe that the advantages of having the baby at home far exceed any to be gained, except in the relatively few abnormal cases, from having the baby in the hospital. The belief that it is more dangerous to have the baby at home than it is in the hospital is contrary to the truth. For example, during the period from January 1952 to July 1954 the records of the Chicago Maternity Center show that home deliveries amounted to more than 8,339 without the death of a single mother. Of some 300 pathological cases requiring hospitalization, three proved fatal. This is a far better record than the average hospital can show.[12] In America we are inclined to forget that in the rest of the civilized world most deliveries are performed by midwives and take place in the home. The advent of "rooming-in," where the maternity arrangements in the hospital are such as to keep mother and baby in the same room, constitutes the beginning recognition of the importance of not separating mother and child. Under less "civilized" conditions the baby's first cry seems to act as a signal to the mother that the child needs to be nursed at the breast. As already stated, immediate nursing at the breast results in changes in the mother which have the most beneficial effects upon her. In the first place, within a few minutes of the commencement of nursing the uterus begins to contract and to return to its normal size and state, while without immediate nursing the uterus practically never returns to normal size. In the second place the hemorrhage which is associated with delivery of the baby is reduced to a minimum as a consequence of the contracted uterus induced by the nursing and probably by accompanying psychological factors.[13] Third, afterpains are either reduced to a minimum or entirely unfelt. The baby, in turn, receives stimulations through contact with the mother's body which serve the important function of further activating its gastrointestinal and genitourinary tracts. Such nursing babies, unlike bottle-fed babies, rarely develop diarrhea or other gastrointestinal disturbances (unless the mother's diet has been high in carbohydrates). Through its sucking the baby receives much needed nourishment and stimulations in the oral and perioral regions, which together with those which it receives from the mother's body activate every sustaining system of the body: the alimentary, the endocrine, nervous, the genitourinary, and particularly the respiratory system. It is important, therefore, here as elsewhere, to remember that what Nature hath brought together no one should ever take it upon themselves to put asunder—unless there exist good reasons for doing so.

The care of the child should begin with caring for the child. The relations between mother and infant during the first few days following birth are of the utmost importance for each of them. The newborn needs the presence of a loving, solicitous voice, the warmth and softness of touch of its mother's body. Bevan-Brown considers the infant's experiences at the breast of fundamental importance for its subsequent healthy mental development. The sucking, tactile, oral, esophageal, and gastric sensations which it experiences are highly significant for its development of a feeling of security. "The infant must be in close association with the mother for the first hours, days, weeks of life, so that whenever he wakes he has the feeling that she is near. Such an association makes the closest possible approximation to his intrauterine security and placental attachment, which has just been broken."[14] If birth is in any way a traumatic experience, then surely what the newborn requires is something a little more calculated to inspire a feeling of being wanted than what it at present so frequently receives. In short, everything possible should be done to reassure the infant that it is among friends, and that although the journey into this world may have been a rough one, it has entered into a secure haven which gives promise of better things to come.

THE IMPORTANCE OF THE MOTHER

The first fulfillment of the infant's drive to receive love from the mother constitutes a fundamental cooperative act. As Alfred Adler has pointed out, "the first act of a new-born child—drinking from the mother's breast—is co-operation, and is as pleasant for the mother as for the child."[15] There is the tactile stimulation about the lips and face, the tongue, the oral cavity, and the liquid and associated stimulations of the gastrointestinal tract. Here, in this act, is the first step in the development of the sense of contact with another person—a pleasure-giving person. One of Adler's students, M. Bevan-Brown, has written a valuable book the main theme of which is the importance of breast-feeding for subsequent mental—and physical—health.[16] Adler comments:

The child's inclination to co-operation is challenged from the very first day. The immense importance of the mother in this respect can be clearly recognized. She stands on the threshold of the development of social feeling. The biological heritage of social feeling is entrusted to her charge. She can strengthen or hinder contact by the help she gives the child in little things, in bathing him, in providing all that a helpless infant is in need of. Her relations with the child, her knowledge, and her aptitude are decisive factors. . . . It may readily be accepted that contact with the mother is of the highest importance for the development of human social feeling. . . . *We probably owe to the maternal sense of contact the largest part of human social feeling, and along with it the essential continuance of human civilization.*[17]

"It is obvious," writes Bevan-Brown, "that a child's mother is, or should be, the first person in the world with whom he associates. She represents the first *personal* relationship, the first *social* relationship, the first *sensuous* relationship . . . it would be reasonable to assume that this relationship, being the first, sets the pattern of all subsequent relationships."[18]

INADEQUATE MOTHERING AND DIS-EASE

Frustration of the drives to receive love from the mother (not necessarily the biological mother, a mother-surrogate will do) at this period not only produces anxiety in the infant, rage and despair, but also a retention of unexpressed hunger for maternal mother love which may then find an outlet through any one of a number of *diseases* and especially through gastrointestinal *dis*-ease.[19] Similarly, if the infant's cries for attention remain unanswered the unsatisfied tensions may express themselves through the bronchial tree in the form of asthma or other respiratory disorders.[20] Kezur and his coworkers, in a study of twenty-five women with peptic ulcers, found that all of them exhibited profound and overt personality disorders. The majority had been rejected by the mother and had turned to the father for support. Ulcer symptoms were precipitated when the supporting figure failed them.[21] Such responses may be regarded as constituting involuntary emergency discharges through the organ-systems involved in the frustration of the need. The energies which should have been discharged outward are now discharged inward.[22] The affection of the organ or organ-systems becomes an affect-equivalent for the original gratification sought by the organism. A large proportion of, if not all, neuroses and psychosomatic disorders may be so explained—their foundations being laid within the first six years of life. In the infant, as in the human being at any age, good health depends upon the adequate satisfaction of basic needs and upon the ability to discharge anger externally when the needs are not satisfied.[23]

"The somatization of tension" is, apparently, a frequent occurrence in children who have undergone severe emotional deprivations. Bettelheim and Sylvester, who have described many such "somatizations" in children, have pointed out that such symptoms may disappear in the course of psychotherapy "without ever having become the specific object of the analytic process. They become unnecessary when the patient grows less anxious with his increasing ability to communicate and therefore acquires more adequate forms of expression."[24] Interestingly enough, as such children undergo reintegration the appearance of new symptoms and their eventual disappearance are seen to represent characteristic steps in the integrative process of their readjustment.

There can be little doubt that the physiological components of the emotional needs of the child must receive the proper stimulations if adequate somatic development is to occur. The subtle alchemy by which love is transmuted in the child into what it most requires for somatic as well as psychic development may, at the moment, be obscure, but that that "alchemical" process occurs there can no longer be the least doubt.

SOCIAL BINDING AND THE FALLACY OF INDIVIDUALITY

The process of caring for the infant consists principally in satisfying its needs. This process represents the commencement of the socialization of the person, the preparation of the person for participation in the social group. To telescope much into a few words, as the child matures and the socializing process continues, with its frustrations as well as its satisfactions, the child becomes more and more firmly bound to the socializing agent, more and more dependent rather than more free, and this social binding continues throughout life. This view of the development of the person cannot be too strongly emphasized. Its implications are of the first order of importance. The conventional view of the person in the socializing process as developing to greater and greater individuality is a seriously misleading one. Of course, every person has a unique personality in the sense that it is never identically like that of any other person, and the differences between personalities are important and tend to become more distinct with age. This is something to be thankful for. But it must be realized that every one of these differences has developed under the influence of socializing factors, and that were it not for the creative action of those socializing factors, those functional-structural differences which characterize each person would not exist.

Every person is socially bound to the group in which he has been socialized. In this sense the "individual" is a myth. From the point of view of the social situation there are no individuals, except as abstracted biological entities or for the quantitative purposes of a census. Even physically and physiologically it is doubtful whether the "individual" has a separate existence in any but an arbitrary sense. Have we not in the term "individual" created separateness where separateness does not exist—where, in fact, relatedness is the true condition? Certainly individualization in man exceeds that which is ever attained by any other animal, but it is an individualization which integratively takes place more fully in relation to the group than in any other living creature. A creature apart from a social group is nothing but an organic being. The member of a human social group is a person, a personality developed under the molding influence of social interstimulation. The person is a set of social interrelationships. As Bogardus has put it, "As a result of intersocial stimulation he moves up from the biological level. The interstimulation that occurs between him and members of the group, not as mere individuals but as persons, explains him more than any other method of approach can do."[25] "It makes no sense," writes Sullivan, "to think of ourselves as 'individual,' 'separate,' capable of anything like definitive description in isolation . . . the notion is just beside the point."[26]

Says Whitehead, "The individual thing is necessarily a modification of its environment, and cannot be understood in disjunction."[27] Both the fallacy of absolute individuals and the excess of individualism, writes Whitehead, are vicious. And as Gutkind puts it, "To think in terms of absolute individuals—absolute individuals are but things—is the outgrowth of our obsession with acquisitive urges. To think in terms of relations is human and paves the way toward the solidarity of mankind."[28] Child writes as follows: "The individual represents primarily a reaction pattern in a protoplasm of a certain constitution and the kind of individual that develops in a particular case depends not only upon the gradient pattern but upon the constitution of the protoplasm in which it occurs. In one kind of protoplasm, for example, the most active region gives rise to a circle of tentacles and a mouth, in another it develops a head, in still another into a growing tip."[29] So, too, the kind of person that develops in a particular case depends not only upon the gradient pattern of his particular inherent potentialities but upon the constitution of the social groups in which his development occurs. The responses which his socializers cause him to make to the stimuli they offer become the habits which form the particular person. The important point to recognize is that the "individual" represents primarily a reaction pattern which makes him a *part* of a whole of which he always remains a part. It is the unhealthy person who regards himself as the whole and everyone and everything else as the part. A person is the product of a field of interactive biological and social forces, and every person constitutes a part of that field all his life.

The so-called "individualist" is no more an individualist than is the soldier under command. Whatever each does he does because he has been subordinated to imperatives which, in each case, are functions of his cultural conditioning. Each acts as he does because he is the end product of certain historically conditioned processes. Each acts as he does not because he is an independent individual, but because he is a dependent person, bound to his social group by ties which cause him to desire to maintain his relationships according to the requirements, in each case, sanctioned and demanded by the group. This does not mean that the person is without free will. Free will the person most certainly has in the sense of being able to achieve ends or purposes. But it is a will that functions largely within the limits and conditions determined by his own past experience within the culture of his own social group. The "spontaneous" conduct of the person is seldom *de novo,* for however seemingly new and original it may appear to be it is usually conduct based on and influenced by models which have been learned in a particular social group. In brief, the person constitutes an interdependent system of social relationships, and it is by abstraction alone that this system may be recognized as a unit.

There is no suggestion intended that the group is superior to the person. The obligation of the group towards the person is to do everything in its power to maximize his potentialities and preserve his integrity as a person. The obligation of the person to the group is to contribute to this development of himself and to that of other persons. In the ultimate analysis the person is not to be conceived as living for the group, or the group solely for the person; each serves the needs of the other. When this has been said it is necessary to add that this reciprocity is best served by the service of the group—and the group consists of socially related persons—to the person. In this way service to the person leads to service to the group. In the profoundest sense of the word, greatness, both for the group and for the person, consists in service.

The Soldier and The Group

The recognition of the importance of this dependence, this precarious dependence, of one person upon another has recently, perhaps, been best illustrated in the findings concerning what used to be called "shell shock" and is today known as combat exhaustion. It has been known to military observers for some time that some combat units suffer fewer psychiatric casualties than others, and this in spite of an equal or a greater degree of battle stress. In the battle situation there is an omnipresent conscious or unconscious fear of death. This fear, it has been discovered, exists in direct proportion to the confidence which the soldier has in his platoon or company, the confidence that his comrades are "all in there together" with him and will support him in his need. During the training period the soldier gains this confidence in the protective functioning of his unit, his group. Colonel Albert J. Glass of the United States Army Medical Corps who reports these findings, writes, "Even the timid soldier comes to feel secure by being in a powerful group and often assumes the aggressive attitude of the organization. . . ."[30] "In brief, the group offers protection against fear to the soldier and provides for his emotional needs, but demands that he give up personal desires and selfish considerations. In its simplest form, group identification is a matter of 'united we stand, divided we fall.' "[31]

Glass points out that "When men fight together and share common tribulations, they become bound by the closest of emotional ties. This affection, which is akin to love, serves to lessen concern for one's own life, thereby decreasing the crippling subjective sensation of fear." The commonness of such an emotional bond has been demonstrated by numerous instances in which soldiers have unhesitatingly performed dangerous and heroic deeds to save their friends, while the close kinship of men forged in battle is responsible for instances in which soldiers prematurely leave the hospital or a rear assignment to rejoin their comrades. Glass concludes, "A member of an adequately led combat unit has an increased resistance to mental breakdown because of the emotional and actual support provided by the group. The failure of such an environmental support is the major cause of combat exhaustion."

To put it plainly: what the soldier must have is the knowledge that he is supported, loved, that he is a recognized and valued part of the group. By virtue of his position the soldier is more precariously dependent upon his fellows than most men are in the normal situations of life. His situation is reminiscent of the maternal-infant dependent relationship, for he is dependent upon his comrades for his very life. What his experience as a soldier so forcefully underscores is that life and love are closely interknit.[32]

Love Described Rather Than Defined

We have spoken much of love but have not yet defined it. This is so because, as has already been pointed out, definitions are meaningful only at the end of an inquiry. However, at this juncture we may not altogether inappropriately tentatively offer a general description of love.

Love may be described as the process of communicating to another that you are "all for" them, that you will support them, not merely that you will accept them, but that you are actively for them. By being "all for" is meant, first, that one is *actively interested* in the well-being of the other, that one is willing to do whatever one can to support him in his needs and further his interests and development *as a human being,* that one is actively interested in him this way not only for his sake but for ours. To love, one must be emotionally involved with the loved one—unemotional love is *not* love, whatever else it may be—and this emotional involvement must be conveyed to the loved one. To love is to be, and to convey the feeling of being, absorbed in another. To love is to confer developmental and survival benefits upon another. Since human beings are so perilously involved with life, love is the assurance, the reassurance, that we convey to them that we are positively for them and that they need have no fear, that they can *depend* upon us, that we will not fail them, and that we are there not only standing by ready to serve, but always will be. The greatest treason that one human being can commit against another is to fail him when he most needs you, and human beings need their fellow men, not merely some of the time but all of the time.

Foote has recently defined love as "that relationship between one person and another which is most conducive to the optimal development of both. The optimal development is to be measured in the growth in competence in interpersonal relations."[33]

Sullivan writes, "When the satisfaction or the security of another person becomes as significant to one as is one's own satisfaction or security, then the state of love exists."[34] Fromm writes, "the essence of love is to 'labor' for something and 'to make something grow.' . . . To love a person productively implies to care and to feel responsible for his life, not only for his physical existence but for the growth and development of all his powers."[35] Love, writes Suttie, seeks *"any state of responsiveness* with others as its goal. Sociability I consider as a need for love. . . ."[36]

THE PERSON, COOPERATION, AND FREEDOM

Leo Loeb has remarked, "In consequence of the more and more intricate interaction between environment and psychical-social individuality, a separation between individuality and environment, especially the social environment, becomes impossible."[37] And that is the truth which must for ever shatter what may be called the biologistic fallacy, the pathetic fallacy which maintains that man is essentially a function of his genes. The biologically exclusive sacredness of the individual is a chimera not only for man but for all other animal groups. The biology of an earlier day may have cried "the individual for itself." To this the twentieth century's greatest physiologist, the late Sir Charles Sherrington, has made the proper reply in one of the outstanding books of our time.

The individual? What are the most successful individuals which Life has to show? The multi-cellular. And what has gone to their making? The multi-cellular organism is in itself a variant from the perennial antagonism of cell and cell. Instead of that eternal antagonism it is a making use of relatedness to bind cell to cell for co-operation. The multi-cellular organism stood for a change, in so far, from conflict between cell and cell to harmony between cell and cell. Its coming was, we know now, pregnant with an immense advance for the whole future of life upon the globe. It was potential of the present success of living forms upon the planet. Implicit in it was for one thing the emergence of recognizable mind. It was among the many-celled organisms that recognizable mind first appeared. It is surely more than mere analogy to liken to those small beginnings of multi-cellular life of millions of years ago the slender beginnings of altruism today. Evolution has constantly dealt with the relation between physical and mental as more than mere analogy. The bond of cohesion now arising instead of being as then one of material contact and interchange between related cell-lives is in its nature mental. It is a projection of the self by sympathy with other life into organismal situations besides its immediate own. It is altruism as passion. It marks, we may think, at the present time the climax of mind.[38]

To bind cell to cell for cooperation by projection of the self in sympathy with other organisms, that is the essence of social life. But no cell is more intricately bound to another than is man to his fellows, to his social group. The binding of the person to his group represents, in fact, a loss of *individual* freedom and a gain in *personal* freedom through increasing identification with the social group—an identification in which the wholeness of the person is increased and preserved only because it is a functioning interactive part of a greater whole, society. In this process the consciousness of self may actually become intensified, the sense of personal identity may become even

more vivid, and one's bondage to one's society more firmly established than ever. "Individuation," as the development of personal
identity, is neither the contrary nor the contradictory of social identification; it *is* social identification.

As Robert Frost has said:

> "Men work together," I told him from the heart,
> "Whether they work together or apart."

This view of the relationship of man to his fellow men in society
does not mean that the social process turns men into automata. Even
in the most totalitarian of states, Nazi Germany and Soviet Russia,
men have not been turned into machines, and however much like
automata they may have appeared and appear, they have been far
from being so, they have still remained human beings, misguided
human beings. And that is the point. It is possible to misguide
human beings, and human beings are constantly in danger of being
so misguided. The danger is such that it would, in fact, be possible
to make at least reasonable facsimiles of automata out of human beings.[39] In virtue of the fact that man is behaviorally so malleable a
creature, he can be molded, within the limits of being human, to
almost any possible behavioral form. Because this is so, because of the
danger of the 'insectification" of mankind, as someone has termed it,
we must make quite certain that there is nothing in our actions or in
our ideas which might lead to the debasement of man. More positively, we must recognize what it is that requires to be done. To
recognize that men are inextricably bound to each other, and that the
will which they have as persons functions strictly within the limits
determined by the pattern of the social group, constitutes reason for
alarm as well as for hope. Alarm, because man is capable of extreme
and fatal confusions, and must therefore be constantly on guard
against these, and hope because he is actually capable of discovering
truths which can teach him to live in fruitful and creative harmony
with himself and his fellow men. This alarm may be recognized as
vigilance, but is more accurately described by the term anxiety. A
certain amount of anxiety accompanies the expression of all needs,

and when these needs are perceived as the total functioning of the organism,[40] they are seen to constitute the one great need: the need to be loved *and* the need to love.

It is necessary to be anxious, to be vigilant concerning one's needs and the manner in which they are to be satisfied. But this does not mean that one has to be constantly worrying about them, any more than one needs to worry about being dry in order to satisfy one's need for water. It does, however, mean that one must be alert to all possible changes in the environment, for the environment is part of ourselves, as we are part of it. Finally, it means that it is imperatively necessary for man to discover the requirements which must be fulfilled if he is to live in harmony with himself and his fellow men—with his total environment. It should always be remembered that separation between the organism and its environment is, again, an arbitrary act.[41]

CULTURE AND NEUROSIS

The individual—the set of interrelated physical and physiological functions—becomes a person with a distinctive identity only through the process of socialization—the process of becoming identified with a social group. Dissociations such as are implied in the phrases "the self in conflict with society," "man against society," imply a false separation of conditions. Society is made up of interacting selves, of men; it is human beings in interaction. The conditions of conflict which arise in human beings do not normally originate from within them, from their organic states, but from those social conditions which fail to satisfy their needs, and exercise a distorting effect upon them. In this sense a neurosis may be produced which is a result of a disorder of some part of his social experience to which the person has been unable to adjust himself.[42] In our society, for example, there are conflicting and mutually irreconcilable institutions which put too great a strain upon the adaptive capacities of most persons—the Christian ethic of love and the business ethic of competition or "free enterprise," for example.[43]

The importance of institutions in determining the content and structure of neuroses is clearly seen in those cases in which the structure of the culture is such as to omit any institutionalization of certain forms of behavior. In such cultures neuroses of certain kinds never occur, whereas in cultures presenting such institutions neurotic forms of behavior with specific reference to these institutions do occur. For example, shamanism and possession are forms of behavior which occur wherever beliefs in the supernatural and the ability of supernatural powers to take possession of certain persons are strongly held. Where such beliefs do not exist or are weakly developed, shamanism does not occur. In medieval Europe when such beliefs were the rule witchcraft and possession were common phenomena. With the decline in the belief in the supernatural, witches and possession have all but disappeared in Europe. In other lands such beliefs have been replaced by counterparts which fit more satisfactorily into the existing cultural structure—such, for example, as the hunting of "communists," anti-semitism, and racism.

The relation between culture and neurosis is significant. On Okinawa, for example, Moloney found out of a population of 400,000 souls that only two persons had become psychiatric casualties after four months of siege and heavy bombardment. He found mental health to be the rule, and was able to determine that the probabilities were high that the extraordinary care and affection which the Okinawans bestow upon their children is related to their mental health as adults.[44] The remarkable mental health of such nonliterate peoples as the Australian aborigines, the Eskimo, the peoples of many coral Pacific atolls, and many American Indian peoples appears to be highly correlated with their permissive child-rearing practices.[45]

Persons, that is to say socialized organisms of the species *Homo sapiens,* come into being only through social interactions. "They are differentiations within the social field of relations. The group, therefore, is genetically prior to personality."[46]

In short, the physiological dependency of the fetus and the newborn becomes, in society, a socially organized dependency, a social dependency in which the interacting person finds the meaning of his life in his relations with other persons and their thoughts and activities. He becomes, as Rank says, a collective being.[47] Unheeded, the socially dependent adult falls into an apathy which may lead to death. As Erich Fromm has put it, "Unless [the person feels that he belongs] somewhere, unless his life has some meaning and direction, he would feel like a particle of dust and be overcome by his individual insignificance. He would not be able to relate himself to any system which would give meaning and direction to his life, he would be filled with doubt and this doubt eventually would paralyze his ability to act—that is, to live."[48]

DEPENDENCY AND CULTURE

John Fiske originally, and many others since, have pointed out that the long period of dependency which is characteristic of the human infant generates social conditions which lead to the peculiar developments of human culture. The importance of this lengthy period of dependence cannot be overemphasized, but the emphasis can and often has been put on the wrong places.[49] Were the anthropoid apes characterized by a period of dependent infancy which was ten times as long as that of man's, they would still not develop anything resembling human culture, since they do not possess the necessary neuropsychic potentialities.[50] The length of the infancy dependency period in the absence of such potentialities has a limited significance for the development of culture. But once granted those potentialities, what we know as human society is inevitable.

This is not to say that if the human infant were so constructed as to be able to learn to walk, think, talk, and care for itself within a few weeks after birth, human culture would not have developed. It would most certainly have done so, and it is equally certain that the human personality would be an appreciably different thing from what it is today in all human beings. But by virtue of such an elimination of the socialization process it is also likely that societies would assume a somewhat atomistic form. However this conjecture may be, the fact is that the prolonged period of infant dependency produces interactive behavior of a kind which within the first two years or so of the child's life determines the primary pattern of his subsequent social development. It is within this period that he learns to love others: the mother who has so consistently, intimately, and lovingly attended to his needs; the father, his brothers and sisters, and whoever else has participated in the process of satisfying his needs. Certain persons become to him the symbols of satisfaction, for they are always the objects which provide him with the means of satisfaction, and the first conditioning which the child undergoes is this: that persons who have fairly consistently been the objects which have provided the infant with the means of satisfying its needs now become satisfying objects in themselves.

The satisfaction of its basic needs becomes indissolubly associated in the infant's mind with persons who have become linked with those satisfactions. The mother is, of course, normally the principal producer of satisfactions and she becomes the first love-object of the child. In this sequence of events, from prenatal to postnatal life, can be seen the determinants, as it were in high relief, of the pattern of life which every person everywhere seeks to secure, namely, a state of dependency in which one's needs are satisfied by persons whom one (therefore) loves. What human beings desire most of all is to have their needs satisfied, security. They also want to feel dependent, either upon some mother-ideal, a deity, other persons, or narcissistically—that is to say, pathologically—upon themselves, but dependent they must feel. Man does not want to be independent, to be free in the sense of functioning independently of the interests of his fellows, freely and detached. This kind of negative independence leads to lonesomeness, isolation, and fear.[51] What human beings want is that positive freedom which follows the pattern of his life as an infant within the family: dependent security, the feeling that one is part of a group, accepted, wanted, loved, and loving; the positive freedom which makes the development of the person emphatically a matter of personal realization; self-actualization, in terms of his membership in the social group in the mutual interest, more or less, of the person and of society; and finally, the opportunity to develop interdependently, not as an "individual" but as a person. As André Gide so well put it, "Man! The most complex of creatures, and for this reason the most dependent of creatures. On everything that has formed you you depend. Do not balk at this apparent slavery . . . a debtor to many, you pay for your advantages by the same number of dependencies. Understand that independence is a form of poverty; that many things claim you, that many also claim kinship with you."[52]

The directiveness and creativeness of the human organism at birth is toward realization in terms of dependency upon other organisms. Everything we know points to this fact.

John Donne (1572-1631) beautifully expressed these ideas in his seventeenth *Devotion*, written in 1624:

> No man is an *Island*, entire of itself; every man is a piece of the *Continent*, a part of the *main;* if a *Clod* be washed away by the *Sea, Europe* is the less, as well as if a *Promontory* were, as well as if a *Manor* of thy *friends* or of *thine own* were; any man's *death* diminishes *me*, because I am involved in Mankind; And therefore never send to know for whom the *bell* tolls; it tolls for thee.[53]

TRANSFERENCE AND DEPENDENCY

The phenomenon of "transference" as observed in the psychoanalytic therapeutic situation, constitutes, as Freud has pointed out, a proof that adults do not overcome their childhood dependency.[54] In the "transference" situation the patient develops emotional relations toward the analyst that are clearly derived from emotions which were originally directed toward the parents. The feelings of dependency upon the parents are transferred to the analyst. The patient becomes deeply attached to his analyst, he falls in love with him, and does everything in his power to maintain the dependent relationship. What he is doing, in fact, is either to continue or to reproduce the early dependency situation of his infancy. It is by making this clear to the patient that the transference is eventually overcome and converted into an instrument for the exploration of the patient's psyche. The reason psychoanalysis can make so little headway with the person who has been unloved is that such a person is often incapable of transference.

Personality and Dependency

A person is not an object in itself, except for census purposes, but a function of activities which he exhibits in interaction with other persons, that is to say, the constituent interacting element of culture. As Harry Stack Sullivan has suggested, personality "is the hypothetical entity that one postulates to account for the doings of people, one with another, and with more or less personified objects."[55] Personality is, in fact, an abstraction, the segmentation of a process at a particular time involving the behavior of a person in relation to others. Whether it is Ego who is doing the segmenting or judging or other persons, the personality is always a function of relations with other persons. The person is a set of interpersonal relationships, and it is during infancy that the pattern which these relationships shall take is largely determined.

Love and Dependency

From the earliest period, during which the infant is primarily concerned with being loved, it learns to love those who love it. This is not the same as to say that the infant is primarily concerned with the satisfaction of its needs, with self-love; the infant does not become aware of its needs unless it is not loved—what it wants is to be maintained in the state of security, stability, or equilibrium in which there is a minimum of need-pressure. Self-love, or as Freud misconceived this stage of development, "Narcissism," is a pathological development resulting from inadequate love by others.[56] When others do not love it the organism attempts to love itself.

The infant inevitably, and to varying degrees where various needs are concerned, becomes aware of its needs, and in this way, perhaps more than in any other, it gradually learns to love those who provide the means of its satisfaction. Without the state of infant dependency human love would not be what it is, and without those affective bonds which tie one human being to another it is more than doubtful whether there could ever have been any future for the human species.

Love is an active *process* with which the infant is born and upon which it improves by learning; it is a process which is developed in dependency, and it is the dependent pattern of love which is maintained throughout the life of the person. We love only those things upon which we are dependent; not, however all things upon which we are dependent. Those which are associated with frustration we hate or dislike, but those which are associated with pleasure, either present, recollected, or anticipated, we love.

It is when human beings begin to think, erroneously, that they can be independent of one another, "social isolationists," that they begin to frustrate and hate each other, that they do violence to all that they are and create much psychological and social havoc. When men learn to understand how dependent they are upon one another, that they are interdependent beings in a great cooperative enterprise, that it is in their nature to be affectionate, cooperative persons, when they understand that being anything else is to be in conflict with themselves and to create divisiveness within society, mankind will be a great deal happier and healthier than it is today. A dynamic science of anthropology, of sociology, of psychiatry, of psychosocial medicine, which is interested in social diagnosis and social planning must become fully cognizant of such facts as these and make use of them.

RELATEDNESS

Man is related to himself only insofar as he is related to others. To love is to relate oneself to others. The infant is born with drives whose urgency is directed toward relating himself to others and having others relate themselves to him. Life is social and man is born to be social, that is, cooperative—an interdependent part of a whole, a working interacting part of a community. Again, I should like to quote Alfred Adler's mature judgment here.

The individual's proper development can only progress if he lives and strives as a part of the whole. The shallow objection of individualistic systems has no meaning as against this view. I could go still further and show how all our functions are calculated to bind the single individual to the community, and not to destroy the fellowship of man with man. The act of seeing means to receive and make fruitful all that falls on the retina. This is not simply a physiological process; it shows that man is part of a whole that gives and takes. In seeing, hearing, and speaking we bind ourselves to one another. Man only sees, hears, and speaks rightly when he is linked to others by his interest in the external world. His reason, his common sense, forms the basis of his control of co-operation, of absolute truth, and aims at eternal rightness. Our aesthetic sense and views—perhaps the strongest powers that impel to great achievements—have an eternal value only when they lead to the well-being of humanity in the direction of the evolutionary stream. All our bodily and mental functions are rightly, normally, and healthily developed in so far as they are imbued with sufficient social feeling and are fitted for co-operation.

When we speak of virtue we mean that a person plays his part; when we speak of vice we mean that he interferes with co-operation. I can, moreover, point out that all that constitutes a failure is so because it obstructs social feeling, whether children, neurotics, criminals, or suicides are in question. In every case it can be seen that a contribution is lacking. No isolated persons are to be found in the whole history of humanity. The evolution of humanity was only possible because mankind was a community. . . .

If the person understood how in evading the demands of evolution he had gone astray, then he would give up his present course and join the general mass of humanity.

All the problems of human life . . . demand capacity for co-operation and preparation for it—the visible sign of social feeling. In this disposition courage and happiness are included, and they are to be found nowhere else.[57]

As Galt has pointed out, the fundamental unit of social motivation and behavior is not the person but the group. The person no more represents the unit of social behavior than the discrete reflex represents the unit of physiological behavior.[58]

THE SELF

In spite of assertions to the contrary it seems indisputably clear that the infant is not born with an ego, with a "self," but that the infant acquires its "self" from other selves, long before it is aware of its own "self." The "self" is learned from other selves, and therefore the type of its own self depends largely, if not entirely, upon the kinds of selves to which the child has been exposed. If it is true that one learns to become a "self," then it is evident that children may learn to become selves in good, bad, and indifferent ways, to name but a few categories. That, indeed, is why children so often resemble their parents, and why the self of the child is a good clue to the covert self of the parent. The overt self worn by the parent may conceal the real covert self. From infancy onwards people can be seen trying on selves likely to be more successful than their own, and sometimes continuing to wear obvious misfits. This is a further evidence of the manner in which the self is acquired.[59]

Beata Rank points out that a fragmented ego is usually acquired from a mother with such an ego. She writes, "When the mother herself is a poorly organized personality, narcissistic and immature, though not infrequently extremely conscientious and eager to become a mother, the child's ego has a very precarious existence. It remains largely undeveloped and hence is not capable of organizing and controlling (libidinal and aggressive) drives. . . ." The ego is fragmented.[60]

Many other investigators have similarly shown that when the mother's ego organization is defective this is almost certainly likely to be reflected in the ego organization of the child. Thus, for example, Spitz found that children whose mothers were characterized by an infantile personality, exhibiting constant rapid shifts in their attitudes, showing hostility alternating with overprotectiveness towards their children literally within minutes, there was severe failure of ego organization. "There was a definite and significant retardation in the social responses and in manipulative ability. Such a retardation is the expression of a diminished capacity of these children to relate themselves to human beings or to manipulate inanimate objects. The resulting clinical picture was a specific one: objectless bodily activity became the children's outstanding occupation."[61]

Similarly Beres and Obers, reporting on a group of adolescents and young adults who had suffered extreme deprivation of maternal love in infancy, state that their findings in every way "confirm the basic concept of the early mother-child relationship in the development of the ego and superego."

Children who have been deprived of the most important factor essential for normal development—that is, continuous and satisfactory contact with a person who can offer the opportunity for satisfactory identification—suffer a distortion of psychic structure. Our cases can be understood in terms of the functioning of an immature ego along with deficient superego development. Normally the ego functions increasingly in accord with the reality principle and less in accord with the pleasure principle. This development requires the ability to tolerate frustrations and postpone gratifications. Our cases, especially in the group of character disorders, manifested a striking weakness of this function. Disturbances of learning, also an ego function, are to be expected and occur with great regularity in these cases. The importance of identification in the learning process is well known. In our patients, difficulty in establishing satisfactory relationships went hand in hand with difficulty in learning. Object relationships, too, are disturbed and consist for the most part of identifications which are transient, superficial and narcissistic in nature.[62]

These investigators found that the damage thus done to ego and superego development was not irreversible, that many of their patients had made some sort of social adjustment.

That the self or ego is not an inborn structure but is created after birth during what has been called "the undifferentiated phase of development" is now coming to be a generally accepted idea.[63]

The awareness of self develops from the merging of the earliest bodily sensations with sensations derived from others. There must be identification with others. Spitz states that the first attempts at identification become visible in the first quarter of the first year, and that these attempts are the same as what has been called "identification with gesture."[64] It seems, however, improbable that identification occurs at so late a stage of development.

According to Jacobson:

The nuclei of the early infantile self-images are our first body-images and sensations. Like the primitive object-images, our concept of the self is at first not a firm unit. It is fused and confused with the object-images and is composed of a constantly changing series of self-images, which reflect mainly the incessant fluctuations of our mental state. With advancing psychosexual and ego development and the maturation of reality testing, a more stable, uniform, and realistic concept of the self and a lasting, firm cathexis of the self-representations will normally be established.[65]

The infant's ego, its self, develops only as the organism comes to recognize and adjust to reality. The infant is clearly not egocentric to begin with. The infant is conditioned to become egocentric by processes of culturalization which produce egocentricity. While the process of socialization, particularly in cultures of the western world, has the effect of binding the person to his social group, that process often has the effect also of rendering the person functionally asocial. The child is trained in what is expected of him and what he may expect of others. But his training, as Galt points out:

. . . is subsequent and parallel to a process in which there is a weaning of the child from the sense of biological continuity and solidarity with his kind, and the establishment within him of a sense of personal identity, motivation and authority which of its nature must be in conflict with the identity and motivation of others of his social group. Expressed differently, the total social behavioral pattern which is the biological heritage of the human infant, as it is of other animal species, is disrupted, and an undue individuation takes place. The individuation, which in the course of time sets up an autonomous individual with private hopes, desires, wishes, gains and losses, of necessity brings about severe conflict when the desires of two or more elements or individuals happen to interfere with one another. The incentives to behavior have inadvertently become tied up with the individual as an arbitrary center of action and motivation rather than with the social group as such a center.[66]

"I" Versus "You"

The workers at the Lifwynn Foundation, under the leadership of the late Trigant Burrow, state, after many years of investigating and analyzing the so-called normal behavior of men in so-called normal communities, that "The normal individual, like the neurotic, was found to be constantly thinking and acting in terms of his individualized self. He has established an image of himself as an isolated unit of behavior with private values, wishes and motivations, and this same image dominates his social interrelations."[67] As Burrow says:

> In a word, the individual neurosis is but an exaggeration of "normality." It is but an expression, in miniature, of the social neurosis. Man is suffering from an organismic dislocation from the environment, from an "I"-complex or "I"-persona. The partitive sovereignty of the separate self. The result is a divisiveness of function, in which dissociation and conflict assume supremacy over the organism's unity and centralization of function. Man's relation to man becomes disordered through the subordination of the human organism to the conditioned artificial affects and prejudices of the "I"-persona. This social mood is divisive to its core, inciting each person to compete with others in the interest of the self. The principle upon which this divisive socially conditioned mood operates is "I"-versus-"You."[68]

In such persons the central principle of creative motivation, the drive to realize the social feeling that is within them, becomes if not blocked then seriously disordered. The personality develops divisively and may become seriously fragmented. At any rate, it largely loses the power to coordinate, to unify, and to operate as a whole. As Adler says, "It is always the want of social feeling, whatever be the name one gives it—living in fellowship, co-operation, humanity, or even the ideal-ego—which causes an insufficient preparation for all the problems of life. In the presence of a problem this imperfect preparation gives rise to the thousandfold forms that express physical and mental inferiority and insecurity."[69]

The muted voices of our inner consciousness strive to tell us what we ought to be, of the life we have failed to live, but could have lived had not something, we know not quite what, skewed the course of our lives. That something is the history of our earliest childhood, the conditioning, the socialization process to which we had been exposed as infants and children. It is that which has made so many of us, in the western world, the partitive, split, disordered, hostile, aggressive, egocentric creatures we have become. We have become slaves of our own egos instead of masters of them. We are out of line with our evolutionary destiny, which is integration and cooperation, *not* disintegration and antagonism. On the personal, communal, national, and international planes, the effects are those of an "I"-persona conditioning: disorder, disease, and disoperation. Burrow says:

It is useless to essay a policy of social and economic cooperation on a non-cooperative basis of motivation. We will achieve a pattern of social cooperation and harmony among individuals and nations only when we have accepted the pattern of internal balance and coordination within the organism of man as a species. As things stand today in this world of division and conflict, the war we have fought will have been fought in vain. It will have been no less vain than the many political and economic wars that have preceded it. Vain too must be the unilateral program of peace that will issue out of it. All our international covenants, all our external diplomatic treaties, all the peace programs yet to be devised must forever remain unavailing if our behaviour dichotomies and antagonisms are ultimately traceable to a functional brain-twist that is internal to the organism of man as a race.[70]

The functional brain-twist is the "I"-persona conditioning of the mind which opposes itself to man's innate drives toward his natural function, which is cooperation.

EDUCATION AND SOCIAL FEELING

We may agree with Adler when he writes as follows:

A careful consideration of individual and collective existence, both past and present, shows us the struggle of mankind for a stronger social feeling. One can scarcely fail to see that humanity is conscious of this problem and is impressed by it. Our present-day burdens are the result of the lack of a thorough social education. It is the pent-up social feeling in us that urges us to reach a higher stage and to rid ourselves of the errors that mark our public life and our own personality. This social feeling exists within us and endeavours to carry out its purpose; it does not seem strong enough to hold its own against all opposing forces. The justified expectation persists that in a far-off age, if mankind is given enough time, the power of social feeling will triumph over all that opposes it. Then it will be as natural to man as breathing. For the present the only alternative is to understand and to teach that this will inevitably happen.[71]

The one point upon which there might be disagreement with Adler is that social feeling will inevitably triumph. On the other hand, if western man continues as disoperatively as he has been doing during the recent past the chances are not inconsiderable that he may destroy himself. It has become *vitally* necessary to learn and teach the facts as we have come to know them, and what it is that requires to be *done;* for to secure the developing "inevitability" of social feeling knowledge of the facts is not enough, they must be implemented by wisdom and the proper action.

Another point Adler seems to have overlooked is that the harmonious cooperative life, in which social feeling does appear to be almost as natural as breathing, has been achieved by several human groups—human beings whom we used to call "savage," "primitive," and now, thanks to the increased understanding of such peoples given us by the anthropologist, "nonliterate peoples."[72] The best known examples of such groups are to be found among the Australian aborigines and the Eskimos.

AGGRESSIVENESS

We of the western world are the inheritors of a trifold tradition concerning the inborn nature of man. This tradition is religious, secular, and scientific. The origins of the religious tradition are buried in the mists of antiquity, but as we know it it has been transmitted to us through the Old and New Testaments, namely, that man is born a rather wild, disorganized, evil, sinful creature. The secular tradition of the last two millennia has in every way confirmed the religious tradition, for the conduct of most human beings during the last two thousand years has in no way challenged that tradition. Finally the scientific teachings of the nineteenth century concerning the nature of nature and the nature of human nature, as influenced by Darwinian theory and subsequently by Freudian theory, has largely served to confirm that tradition.

However, the view that the child is born egocentric, evil, and aggressive, in "sin," though widely held, represents nothing more than the projection upon the child of our own conditioning in egocentricity, in aggression, in evil, and in "sin." The view that the child is born egocentric is not supported by the facts. In the first place, as has already been pointed out, the infant is not born with an ego, it acquires an ego only as a result of the stimulation of other egos. What its own ego will become depends very largely upon the kind of egos which condition it. The fact is that the human infant is born an actively cooperating organism. Charlotte Buhler has pointed out that cooperative behavior among children is more basic than competitive response, finding that the latter type of response in her group of observed children did not make its appearance till about the third year.[73] All observers have found that aggressive responses to the child tend to increase as it grows older.[74] From her great experience Bender finds that far from being inborn, hostility or aggression in the child "is a symptom complex resulting from deprivations which are caused by developmental discrepancies in the total personality structure such that the constructive patterned drives for action in the child find inadequate means of satisfaction and result in amplification or disorganization of the drives into hostile or destructive aggression." "The child" she writes "acts as though there were an inherent awareness of his needs and there is thus the expectation of having them met. A failure in this regard is a deprivation and leads to frustration and a reactive aggressive response."[75]

Indeed, the creativeness of the organism is directed toward maturation in terms of cooperation. Bender calls it "the inherent capacity or drive for normality." And as she says "The emphasis on the inborn or instinctive features of hostility, aggression, death wishes, and the negative emotional experiences represents a one-sided approach which has led our students of child psychology astray."

Maslow writes "I find children, up to the time they are spoiled and flattened out by the culture, nicer, better, more attractive human beings than their elders, even though they are of course more 'primitive' than their elders. The 'taming and transforming' that they undergo seem to hurt rather than help. It was not for nothing that a famous psychologist once defined adults as 'deteriorated children.' " "Could it be possible," Maslow inquires, "that what we need is a little *more* primitiveness and a little *less* taming?"[76]

Similarly, Banham, who during the course of twenty years has studied over 900 children from four weeks to four years of age, concludes that children are born with outgoing affectionate drives, and that "they only become preoccupied with themselves, withdrawn or hostile as a secondary reaction, when rebuffed, smothered with unwanted ministrations, ignored or neglected."[77]

Beata Rank finds that aggression is not correctly conceived of as an unmodifiable innate force of destruction. Aggression she considers to be the human being's adaptation to the surrounding reality, and hence a part of ego-organization. The manner in which the responses are expressed to inner or outer frustration depends primarily upon the structure of the ego—and that is something which is acquired.[78]

With the notion that the child is born to be "disciplined" goes hand in hand the idea that culture exists in order to control and suppress the evil that is within him. Religion, education, penology, psychology, and even psychiatry have been dominated by this point of view. Consider, for example, this typical expression by a psychiatrist of the Jungian school, Dr. M. E. Harding:

> Beneath the decent facade of consciousness with its disciplined, moral order and its good intentions, lurk the crude instinctive forces of life, like monsters of the deep—devouring, begetting, warring endlessly.[79] They are for the most part unseen, yet on their urge and energy life itself depends: without them living beings would be as inert as stones. But were they left to function unchecked, life would lose its meaning, being reduced once more to mere birth and death, as in the teeming world of the primordial swamps. In creating civilization man sought, however unconsciously, to curb these natural forces and to channel some part at least of their energy into forms that would serve a different purpose. For with the coming of consciousness, cultural and psychological values began to compete with the purely biological aims of unconscious functioning.[80]

This is not, it is to be feared, pure phantasy, because Dr. Harding has, in common with many others, inherited these ideas as part of the common tradition of western thought. This tradition is a myth, but we of the western world believe in it as if it were a universally established truth. This myth is part of our traditional but erroneous way of thinking about "Nature" and the animal world. "Nature," according to this tradition, is a jungle pullulating with animals instinctively dedicated to the task of devouring each other. Beasts are brutal murderous creatures who can, only occasionally, be tamed for domestic purposes, and we human beings are animals who have inherited a bestial nature which it is the task of culture to overcome and eradicate.[81] Our nearest relatives, the chimpanzee and the gorilla, so the myth goes, are among the most fierce and bestial of the animals. Is not primitive or prehistoric man closely related to the beast, *Pithecanthropus erectus,* and Neanderthal man, for example?

The Myth of the Beast

In a significant sense the tradition of the western world has inverted the true course of man's social evolution. We suffer from the belief that man originated as an aggressive, hostile, belligerent cannibal, a savage monster who dragged his womenfolk about by the hair. As typical of this, the following is an extract from a recent popularly written book on prehistoric man.

One never knew on retiring whether one would actually be there when morning broke. . . . The facts show now that a bitter struggle for supremacy had been going on ever since our old world was created. . . . Man had constructive ideas. He *wanted* things, and if his neighbors had a specially comfortable shelter in which to hide at night, envious thoughts arose and at times he was able to drive them out of the coveted retreat and occupy it himself. . . . How easy it was to sneak up on an enemy in a neighboring clan in the dense jungle and tap him none too gently on his thick skull with a heavy club or a piece of sharp stone.[82]

This is the characteristic popular picture which many writers and some scientists (who should know better) have aided and abetted in building up in the popular imagination. According to our cultural myth progress or social evolution has taken something like the following course: Commencing with bestial savage prehistoric ancestors who were in a more or less continuous state of warfare with one another, we have gradually, slowly, and painfully developed toward civilization and greater and greater cooperation and peace-fulness.

Contrary to this view the evidence indicates that prehistoric man was, on the whole, a more peaceful, cooperative, unwarlike, un-aggressive creature than we are, and that we of the civilized world have gradually become more and more disoperative, more aggressive and hostile, and less and less cooperative where it most matters, that is, in human relations. The meaning we have put into the term "savage" is more correctly applicable to ourselves than to the people to whom we have customarily applied it.[83] They trusted and co-operated with us, we savaged, ravaged, and did our best to ex-terminate them.[84] They trusted and cooperated with us, but we failed them. They had never heard of Christianity or democracy before we descended upon them, but most of them practiced the Sermon on the Mount and the principles of democracy far more successfully than we of the western world have ever done.[85] Just as we have projected our own bestiality upon the "beasts" we have projected our own savagery upon primitive peoples. Thanks to the labors of anthropologists we now know that primitive peoples are not primitive, except insofar as their technological development may be concerned; we know that they are not savages in the commonly misunderstood meaning of that term, and furthermore, we know that they function in a substantially more cooperative manner, for the most part, than we do.

Neither the "beasts," the chimpanzee and gorilla, prehistoric man, nor "primitive" man are the aggressive bestial creatures we have been traditionally taught to believe. In the cultures of the western world we seem to have forgotten not only the ties which link us to our fellow human beings but those also which link us to our fellow creatures of the nonhuman animal world. As Maurice has remarked, "Mankind is in desperate need of learning and under-standing the truths of Life itself, and these he can only learn in and from the ecology to which he belongs. . . . It is but rarely, if at all, that one finds in the life of the wild, avarice, mean jealousy, treachery, and the other deadly sins with which mankind is obsessed. One reason at least for attempting to save the innocent creatures of the wild is that they present a greatly needed example of mutual tolerance."[86]

Chimpanzees and gorillas are among the most peaceful of creatures. They never attack any living creature, are completely vegetarian, and in the "wild" when they encounter a man, they usually exhibit a natural curiosity which having at a distance satisfied they take their departure in peace.[87] Maslow, who has had considerable experience with young chimpanzees and gorillas writes, "I can certainly say that these young animals are friendly, cooperative, mutually helpful, affectionate and even altruistic, as contrasted with lower animals."[88] It is perhaps not altogether an accident that our best and most sympathetic accounts of apes should have been written by women who have brought up these creatures and long been associated with them. From these accounts we can learn how really docile, retiring, and unaggressive these creatures are.[89] Capturing, mistreating, and isolating "wild" animals, then judging them to be ferocious is a common practice, but that does not make such animals necessarily ferocious by nature. We have projected something of our own "ferocity" upon these creatures, not being able to face it in ourselves as easily as we can in the "wild" animals upon whom we have visited it. Certainly, many wild animals *are* ferocious to the animals they prey upon, but not all animals are predators, and the line of animals which led to man does not appear to have been guilty of the sins which have been visited upon it by civilized writers. Our nearest relatives, the great apes, are peaceful unaggressive creatures. Prehistoric man, up to the Late Neolithic, some 10,000 years ago, seems to have been so. From the Neolithic the progress of man seems to have been modified in the opposite direction, mostly in those societies which were affected by the development of the techniques which enabled men to live increasingly more urbanized lives.[90] With the increasing brutalization of the lives of so many human beings in such societies, with its increasing competitiveness, the development of a point of view which despairs of man and asserts his essential evil is not difficult to understand. To many it would appear that a creature capable of so much evil as man must be born evil. And hence, babies are alleged to be born evil. Such inversions and twists of thought are peculiarly numerous among human beings, and this particular one has already proven well-nigh catastrophic for man. Instead of seeing that it is an evil society which makes men evil, we have inverted the process and said that it is evil men who make an evil society.

It is not evil babies who grow up into evil human beings, but an evil society which turns good babies into disordered adults, and it does so on a regimen of frustration. Babies are born good and desirous of continuing to be good. More than a hundred years ago the woman who later became John Stuart Mill's wife and coadjutor, Harriet Taylor, clearly saw and stated these facts in an essay which was not published till 1951.

We believe [she wrote] that a child of good physical organization who were never to hear of evil, would not know from its own nature that evil existed in the mental and moral world. We would place before the minds of children no examples but of good and beautiful, and our strongest effort should be to prevent emulation. The spirit of Emulation in childhood and of competition in manhood are the fruitful sources of selfishness and misery. They are a part of the conformity plan, making each person's idea of goodness a thing of comparison with some received mode of being good and happy.[91]

Now, more than a hundred years later, we can only regret that Harriet Taylor was not spared long enough to persuade Mill to present this point of view at length to the public.

The belief in the inherent naughtiness of the human infant is a myth, the projection of what we have ourselves, in part, become, and with the warp of our accidie, and with imperfect means resulting from a confused conception of our goals we have produced a progressive deterioration of our children—of humanity.

9 LOVE AND THE PRIVATION OF LOVE

I on my part have come to regard the desire to love, to give, and "to be good" or "co-operative" as influencing the appetites from their very first thwartings. —IAN D. SUTTIE*

All men are born good. He who loses his goodness and yet lives is lucky to escape. —CONFUCIUS

LOVE IS RECIPROCAL

The infant soon learns that in order to be satisfied, in order to be loved, he too must love, he must satisfy the requirements of others, he must cooperate. He learns that he must gracefully give up or postpone the satisfaction of certain desires if he is to achieve satisfaction in others, and if he is to retain the love of those whose love he needs. This, too, is at once a recognizable adult pattern of behavior which takes its origin in these early experiences. From the beginning this pattern of behavior provides the most important means by which the socialization of the organism is achieved—first, through love as a feeling of belongingness (security), and second, through love as authority, the authority of the affectionate tie. "I belong to this family, and it is because these people love me that I belong. I like to 'belong,' therefore I must obey them and retain their love so that I may continue to belong." This is what the child resolves for himself though he may never give conscious expression to the thought. The relationships of his family life condition his personal relationships throughout his life. "They are loaded with affection

* Ian D. Suttie, *The Origins of Love and Hate*, New York, Julian Press, 1953, p. 42.

199

and carry the burden of giving to each a *place*—a sense of belonging, a meaning to the process of arriving and being."[1]

Outside the family, as a "grown-up," the approval (love) of one's fellows is secured by conforming to the standards of the group. This is the family pattern repeated on a less intensive but more extensive scale. To conform means the willingness to forego certain satisfactions in order to obtain others, to suffer a certain amount of deprivation and thwarting of satisfactions as a discipline which may ultimately lead to what are socially esteemed as greater rewards. Conflict, repression, and aggressiveness are the consequences of those experiences both in the family and in the group.

THE PRIVATION OF LOVE

The importance of love in the early social development of the infant cannot be overemphasized. Its significance can best be understood when we consider a disease from which, but half a century ago, more than half the children in their first year of life regularly died.[2] This disease was known as *marasmus,* from the Greek word meaning "wasting away." The disease was also known as infantile atrophy or debility. When studies were undertaken to track down its cause, it was discovered that it was generally babies in the "best" homes and hospitals who were most often its victims, babies who were apparently receiving the best and most careful physical attention, while babies in the poorest homes, with a good mother, despite the lack of hygienic physical conditions, often overcame the physical handicaps and flourished. What was wanting in the sterilized environment of the babies of the first class and was generously supplied in babies of the second class was mother love. This discovery is responsible for the fact that hospitals today endeavor to keep the infant for as short a period as possible. The best place for the infant is with its mother, and if its own mother is not available, with a warm foster mother, for what the infant must have is love. Drs. Ruth and Harry Bakwin, pediatricians of great experience, make the following point:

The effect of residence in a hospital manifests itself by a fairly well-defined clinical picture. A striking feature is the failure to gain properly, despite the ingestion of diets which are entirely adequate for growth in the home. Infants in hospitals sleep less than others and they rarely smile or babble spontaneously. They are listless and apathetic and look unhappy. The appetite is indifferent and food is accepted without enthusiasm. The stools tend to be frequent and, in sharp contrast with infants cared for in the home, it is unusual for 24 hours to pass without an evacuation. Respiratory infections which last only a day or two in the home are prolonged and may persist for weeks and months. Return to the home results in defervescence [disappearance of fever] within a few days and a prompt and striking gain in weight.[3]

MOTHER-LOVE

The emotional deprivation suffered by infants in hospitals may do vastly more damage than the physical condition which brought them there. The infant can suffer no greater loss than the privation of its mother's love, for it would seem that the satisfaction of the generalized feeling of dependency, in itself a basic need, is best accomplished through mother-love. An old Egyptian proverb says that since God could not be everywhere He created mothers. The fact seems to have been more than glimpsed long ago that because the mother is the person usually most profoundly interested in the welfare of her infant it is from her that the infant is most likely to receive the supports and reassurances which love bestows. This is not to say that some other person could not do as much for it. There is every reason to believe that devoted foster mothers or nurses have often successfully taken the place of the actual mother in giving the infant all the love that it required. Normally, however, the infant receives its love from the person best qualified to give it, the mother.

Let us observe what is likely to happen to the infant who is separated from his mother shortly after birth. A typical and early case is one described by Dr. Margaret Ribble.

Little Bob was born in the maternity hospital where the writer was making studies of infants at the time. He was a full-term child and weighed six pounds three ounces at birth. During the two weeks stay in the hospital the baby was breast fed and there was no apparent difficulty with his body functions. The mother, a professional woman, had been reluctant about breast feeding because she wished to take up her work as soon as possible after the baby was born, but she yielded to the kindly encouragement of the hospital nurses, and the feeding was successful. Both mother and child were thriving when they left the hospital.

On returning home the mother found that her husband had suddenly deserted her—the climax of an unhappy and maladjusted marriage relationship. She discovered soon after that her milk did not agree with the baby. As is frequently the case, the deep emotional reaction had affected her milk secretion. The infant refused the breast and began to vomit. Later he was taken to the hospital and the mother did not call to see him. At the end of a month she wrote that she had been seriously ill and asked the hospital to keep the child until further notice.

In spite of medical attention and skillful feeding, this baby remained for two months at practically the same weight. He was in a crowded ward and received very little personal attention. The busy nurses had no time to take him up and work with him as a mother would, by changing his position and making him comfortable at frequent intervals. The habit of finger sucking developed, and gradually the child became what is known as a ruminator, his food coming up and going down with equal ease. At the age of two months he weighed five pounds. The baby at this time was transferred to a small children's hospital, with the idea that this institution might be able to give him more individual care. It became apparent that the mother had abandoned the child altogether.

When seen by the writer, this baby actually looked like a seven months' foetus yet he had also a strange appearance of oldness. His arms and legs were wrinkled and wasted, his head large in proportion to the rest of his body, his chest round and flaring widely at the base over an enormous liver. His breathing was shallow, he was generally inactive, and his skin was cold and flabby. He took large quantities of milk but did not gain weight since most of it went through him with very little assimilation and with copious discharges of mucus from his intestines. The baby showed at this time the pallor which in our study we have found typical of infants who are not mothered, although careful examination of his blood did not indicate a serious degree of anemia. He was subject to severe sweating, particularly during sleep. A thorough study showed no indication of tuberculosis. The child's abdomen was large and protruding, but this proved to be due to lax intestinal muscles and consequent distention with gas and to a greatly enlarged and distended liver, which was actually in proportion to that of the foetus. There was no evidence of organic disease, but growth and development were definitely at a standstill, and it appeared that the child was gradually slipping backward to lower and lower levels of body economy and function.

The routine treatment of this hospital for babies who are not gaining weight is to give them concentrated nursing care. They are held in the nurses' laps for feeding and allowed at least half an hour to take the bottle. From time to time their position in the crib is changed and when possible the nurse carries them about the ward for a few minutes before or after each feeding. This is the closest possible approach to mothering in a busy infants' ward. Medical treatment consists of frequent injections of salt solution under the skin to support the weakened circulation in the surface of the body.

With this treatment the child began to improve slowly. As his physical condition became better, it was possible for our research group to introduce the services of a volunteer "mother" who came to the hospital twice daily in order to give him some of the attention he so greatly needed. What she actually did was to hold him in her lap for a short period before his 10 A.M. and 6 P.M. feedings. She was told that he needed love more than he needed medicine, and she was instructed to stroke the child's head gently and speak or sing softly to him and walk him about. Her daily visits were gradually prolonged until she was spending an hour twice a day, giving the baby this artificial mothering. The result was good. The child remained in the hospital until he was five months of age, at which time he weighed nine pounds. All rumination and diarrhea had stopped, and he had become an alert baby with vigorous muscular activity. His motor coordinations were of course retarded. Although he held up his head well and looked about, focusing his eyes and smiling in response to his familiar nurses, he could not yet grasp his own bottle or turn himself over, as is customary at this age. The finger sucking continued, as is usually the case with babies who have suffered early privation.

In accordance with the new hospital procedure, as soon as the child's life was no longer in danger, he was transferred to a good, supervised foster home in order that he might have still more individual attention. Under this regime, his development proceeded well and gradually he mastered such functions as sitting, creeping, and standing. His speech was slow in developing, however, and he did not walk until after the second year. The general health of this child is now excellent at the end of his third year; also his "I.Q." is high on standard tests, but his emotional life is deeply damaged. With any change in his routine or with a prolonged absence of the foster mother, he goes into a state which is quite similar to a depression. He becomes inactive, eats very little, becomes constipated and extremely pale. When his foster mother goes away, he usually reacts with a loss of body tone and alertness, rather than with a definite protest. His emotional relationship to the foster mother is receptive, like that of a young infant, but he makes little response to her mothering activities except to function better when she is there. He has little capacity to express affection, displays no initiative in seeking it, yet fails to thrive without it. This lack of response makes it difficult for the foster mother to show him the affection which he so deeply needs. Without the constant friendly explanations of the situation from the visiting nurse, she would probably have given up the care of the child.[4]

THE INSTITUTION CHILD

Recent research indicates that to a greater or less extent the history of the emotional development of Little Bob represents the pattern of the history of most mother-separated infants. The history of this unmothered child is by no means extreme, but it does illustrate, rather strikingly, the effects upon the newborn and infant of the absence of those stimulations which are provided by the mother's love. Without those stimulations the psychosomatic effects upon the child are often disastrous. Such a child may be emotionally crippled for life. As adults such children remain fixated at their early dependent infantile level, they demand affection but cannot return it. In this particular field intensive research is now being pursued.[5] What is required are studies which will not only inquire into the personality development of unmothered children, though this is indispensable, but it is also highly desirable to discover the variation in mothering which different mothers have given their children, and to inquire into exactly the amount and quality of mothering the person has received from the mother and how much from nurses and other persons.

Studies are also required on the variations in the kind of mothering the same mother gives her child over the course of the years. A mother may be good for her child for the first year but not for the second, or she may be good for the first two years but not for the next few years, and so on in all possible combinations and permutations. This is a problem which has thus far received no attention.

Studies carried out on children who have spent their infancy in institutions lead to the following conclusion, in the words of one of the earliest investigators in this field:

> [Such infants] undergo an isolation type of experience with resulting isolation type of personality, characterized by unsocial behavior, hostile aggression, lack of patterns for giving and receiving affection, inability to understand and accept limitations, much insecurity in adapting to environment. These children present delays in development and intensification as well as prolongation of behavior manifestations at these levels. At the time of the transfer [to a foster home], the children are at a stage when they can form only partial love attachments; hostility and aggression are at a peak; egocentricity is marked, and they do not recognize the individuality and needs of others. They are unprepared for and unequal to the demands and limitations of a family setting. They are exposed to attention and affection far in excess of anything they have previously known, and react excessively either by extravagant behavior, negativism or both.[6]

The work of Goldfarb originally, as well as that of others since, has demonstrated conclusively that the institutionally reared child is characterized by a personality which is strikingly less differentiated than that of the home-reared child. Such children are markedly more passive and apathetic, as a consequence, presumably, of their highly routinized experience. Motivation and ambition are lacking. Language retardation is severe and persists well into adolescence. Aggressive behavior and instability of emotional response are usual, and deficiencies of inhibition the rule. Such children are restless, aimless in their behavior, unreflective, and lacking in persistence. The impoverished social environment of the institution, the lack of a dynamic and varied social experience, is reflected in the inability of the institutionalized child to develop meaningful reciprocal human relationships. The absence of the loving attention, affection, and stimulation of the family with its human protecting and supporting ties in the experience of such children, leads to a marked insecurity with a resulting hunger for attention and affection. In the younger children attention-seeking behavior is particularly marked, and this is usually combined with hostile, overtly aggressive acts. Eventually, the conflict between the hunger for affection and the inability to respond to normal human relationships is resolved by a more consistent defense of emotional isolation, resulting in apathetic social responses and a pattern of withdrawal from life's tasks.[7]

Such children, while they may improve following adoption into a family, never fully recover from the effects of their early deprivations. It is not difficult to recognize such persons as adults. The basic personality defects are congealed at a level of extreme immaturity. By the age of three years the damage has usually been so effectively done as to affect the institution child for the rest of his life. This does not mean that all institution children are so affected or those that have been cannot substantially recover.[8]

As Goldfarb points out, "Under normal circumstances, early dependency becomes the constructive basis for the development of a growing and secure sense of independence. In other words, independence is a positive and mature adaptation based on a secure grasp of the self in relation to other people. This is to be differentiated from the isolation reaction of the institution group, for the latter reaction represents defensive adaptation to a confused, hazy, and thus fearful grasp of one's relationship to the world of people and things as well as to inadequate methods for meeting reality."[9]

The dependency needs normally satisfied by the mother are in institution children *inadequately* satisfied, and the result is a more or less serious failure of development of the affective life of the person. Such children suffer conspicuously from what David Levy has called "primary affect hunger," which he defines as "a state of privation due primarily to a lack of maternal affection, with a resulting need, as of food in a state of starvation."[10]

It is important to note that *inadequate* satisfaction of the dependency needs, *not* complete deprivation, is sufficient to produce this failure of affective development. It appears that the damage done is related to the degree of privation suffered by the infant. For example, rejected children will show very similar symptoms to institution children. The differences, however, are significant, depending on variables that have been operative or not upon such children.

The deprivation situation is characterized by a marked poverty of affective and social stimulation. In the institution child this is further reinforced by the handicapping barrenness and narrowness of the institution environment. The world of things and of people, of experience, as something lived or undergone is flattened out, and severely limited. The interstimulation of family relationships in all their manifold aspects is lost. And as Goldfarb so well puts it, "The institution child thus establishes no specific identifications and engages in no meaningful reciprocal relationships with the people. The basic motivations to normal maturation and differentiation of personality are absent. Paucity in content and organization of both intellect and feeling follow. The ego structure is primitive and undeveloped . . . Both the 'I' of the inner life, and the 'It' of the outer life, are crippled."[11]

On the other hand, while the rejected child may suffer from a greater or less degree of affective deprivation, the horizon of its experience is usually not nearly as limited as that of the institution child. It is perhaps for this reason that the rejected child does not usually exhibit any defects in abstract thinking as does the institution child. He is more anxious than the latter, more ambitiously purposeful, and possesses a much greater capacity for insight. He therefore usually responds to treatment, whereas the institution child rarely and with much greater difficulty effectively responds.

It is possible that there are some homes in which the rejection of a child has been so extreme as to produce symptoms in it of deprivation identical with those of the institution child. This is an area of social pathology which requires further investigation.

René Spitz has paid particular attention to the child which has been confined to an institution during its first year of life. Infants in two different institutions were simultaneously studied. These institutions were well organized in all physical respects: in housing, asepsis, food, and hygiene. Infants were admitted to both shortly after birth.

The institutions differed in but one factor: in the amount of emotional interchange offered. In the first institution, called "Nursery," the infants were looked after by their own mothers. In the second institution, called "Foundlinghome," the children were raised from the third month by overworked nursing personnel, one nurse caring for from eight to twelve children. The absence or presence of emotional interchange between mother and child formed the one independent variable in the comparison of the two groups.

The response to this variable showed up in many ways, but perhaps most comprehensively in the developmental quotient, which represents a measure of the total development of six sectors of the personality: mastery of perception, of bodily functions, of social relations, of memory and imitation, of manipulative ability, and of intelligence. Toward the end of the first year though the "Foundling home" infants had a developmental quotient of 124 to start with, whereas "Nursery" had a developmental quotient of 101.5, the deprived "Foundlinghome" infants sink to a D.Q. of 72, while the "Nursery" infants rise to 105. By the end of the second year the D.Q. had fallen in the "Foundlinghome" group to the amazing low of 45, corresponding to a mental age of about 10 months. As Spitz remarks:

We have here an impressive example of how the absence of one psychosocial factor, that of emotional interchange with the mother, results in a complete reversal of a developmental trend. . . .
It should be realized that the factor which was present in the first case, but eliminated in the second, is the pivot of all development in the first year. It is the mother-child relation. By choosing this factor as our independent variable we were able to observe its vital importance. While the children in "Nursery" developed into normal healthy toddlers, a two-year observation of "Foundlinghome" showed that the emotionally starved children never learned to speak, to walk, to feed themselves. With one or two exceptions in a total of 91 children, those who survived were human wrecks who behaved either in the manner of agitated or of apathetic idiots.[12]

The mortality rates in the two institutions were striking and significant. During five years of observation involving 239 children who had been institutionalized for one year or more, "Nursery" did not lose a single child through death, whereas in "Foundlinghome" 37 per cent of children died during a two-years observation period. Death, Spitz remarks, is but an extreme consequence of the general physical and psychological decline, which affects children completely starved of emotional interchange.

A large proportion of the children deprived of mother-love show various degrees of depression, in which the main presenting system is a great increase in the exhibition of the emotions of displeasure. Spitz has called this condition "anaclitic depression." In this condition anxiety reactions to the point of panic will occur upon the appearance of a strange person or some ordinary toy. Such children will scream by the hour, often with accompaniments of tears, heavy salivation, severe perspiration, convulsive trembling, dilation of the pupils, and so on.

In 19 children exhibiting the clear-cut symptoms of anaclitic depression the mother had in each case been removed from the child somewhere between the sixth and eighth month for a practically unbroken period of three months, during which the child did not see its mother at all, or saw her at most once a week. The separation had been unavoidable, and before it the mother had had full charge of the infant, and, indeed, had spent more time with it than is usually the case at home. In the course of four to six weeks following the mother's removal each child developed the symptoms described above. No child whose mother was not removed developed these symptoms. When within a period not more than three months after the removal of the mother she was restored to the child, the recovery of all normal faculties was spectacular. Where, as in the "Foundlinghome" children, the mother was not restored no intervention of any kind was effective in bringing these children out of their depression.[13]

The central importance of the mother or of a mother-substitute for the proper psychosomatic development of the child could not be more dramatically emphasized than by Spitz's findings.[14]

Reference has been made to the important findings of Beres and Obers on a group of young adults and adolescents who had experienced extreme deprivation in infancy. Their findings in every way corroborate those of Spitz and other workers, but more importantly they hold out some hope, if not for the complete recovery of such deprived human beings, then at least for the possibility of considerable rehabilitation.

When we survey our cases [the authors write], in the attempt to find any correlations that will permit understanding of the causes of modifications of psychic structure that we noted, we are impressed rather by the individual variations. Changes occur with or without psychotherapy; changes occur early and later in life; in some cases changes take the form of continuous improvement, in others of fluctuation in symptomatology. It becomes obvious that available data do not permit any positive correlations at this time. . . .

The implications for therapy are evident. The therapeutic nihilism which has characterized the approach to these cases is not warranted if we limit the aim of therapy to increasing of ego functioning to the level of social adjustment. The most important single therapeutic factor we believe to be the opportunity for the development of a close stable relationship to an adult person, whether in a placement situation, a casework relationship or in psychotherapy. In this sense, we have been working in the tradition of Aichorn[15] who emphasized the importance of the transference relationship in the treatment of his "wayward youth." The treatment of these cases requires a flexible and a patient approach which must utilize the combined skills of caseworker and psychiatrist. To this extent the therapy of such cases would be very difficult to carry out except with the facilities of a social agency.[16]

Complete recovery is far from being claimed as a possibility for such cases, and while our purpose in this section has been to point out the importance of maternal love for the healthy development of the child, and the extremely damaging effects which follow upon the deprivation of such love, it is important not to leave the reader with a sense of the hopelessness of the lot of such emotionally deprived children. As Beres and Obers point out, there are indications that much can be achieved by and for them. Further therapeutic research in this field is urgently needed.[17]

Holman, in a study of 200 children in England, found that separation from the parents had significantly adverse effects upon the development of the child only when that separation was early and permanent. Temporary separation, either before or after the age of four, was not found to be associated with behavior disturbances, nor was permanent separation which began in the fifth year of life or later. Interestingly enough, Holman found that early separation from the father was no less adverse in its effects than permanent early separation from the mother.[18] Incidentally, Holman found that hostility and ill-treatment from parents had a more damaging effect upon the development of the children than ambivalence.

CRITICAL DEVELOPMENTAL PERIODS

Bevan-Brown has pointed out that "The child does not grow uniformly and homogeneously like a crystal or a carrot, but by stages or phases which succeed one another and which differ from one another."[19] For proper growth and development it is necessary that the potentialities for developing human relationships with which the infant is born be exposed to the organizing influences of another human being. Accumulating evidence indicates that there exist critical developmental periods during which the organism is ready for differential development, within which periods it must receive the proper stimulations if it is to develop adequately. These critical developmental periods may be broadly outlined as follows:

1. The period during which the infant is in process of establishing an explicit cooperative relationship with a clearly defined person—the mother; this is normally achieved by five or six months.

2. The period during which the child needs the mother as an ever-present support and companion; this normally continues to about the end of the third year.

3. The period during which the child is in process of becoming able to maintain a relationship with its mother during her absence. During the fourth and fifth years, under favorable conditions, such

a relationship can be maintained for a few days or even a few weeks; after seven or eight years of age such a relationship can be maintained for longer periods, though not without some strain.

The capacity whereby the child simultaneously develops his own ego and super-ego and the capacity to maintain relationships with removed objects is variously described as identification, internalization, or introjection, since it is according to the pattern set by the parents that the functions of the ego and super-ego are incorporated within the self.

The evidence supports the existence of these three critical developmental periods and we find, indeed, that three somewhat different experiences can produce the lack-love syndrome, as follows:

1. Lack of any opportunity to develop attachment to a mother-figure during the first three years.

2. Maternal deprivation for a period varying for days within the first and second years, and weeks or months during the third and fourth years.

3. Changes from one mother-figure to another during the first four or five years.

With respect to the reality of the critical developmental periods, it is, of course, well known that such critical developmental periods exist in the development of the body, with the principle well established that the earlier the interference with their development the more widespread will the disturbance in growth be. Tissues must reach a certain stage of differentiation before they can respond; later such tissues achieve a certain relative fixity, so that they can yield only a more limited type of response.[20] Recently the concept of critical developmental periods for the development of social behavior and susceptibility to environmental changes has been put to experimental test on dogs and other animals, and confirmed.[21]

What the developing child apparently needs is a stable and continuous development in relation to its mother or mother-surrogate. The stability and continuity must be prolonged, and not too much or too often interrupted. Deprivation leads to isolation and asocial behavior, satisfactions interspersed with deprivations lead to ambivalent and antisocial behavior. The "now-I-love-you, now-I-don't" kind of conduct which characterizes the behavior of many mothers towards their small children produces not dissimilar effects. During the development of his ego and super-ego the child needs a firm hand, as it were, at the helm, otherwise his own steering mechanism remains unorganized. It is the mother who guides him when he is helpless and teaches him gradually how to meet the requirements of his environment, and thus helps construct his ego. It is his mother who gradually teaches the child its obligations to others, and thus builds up his super-ego. If the mother or her substitutes fail in this they produce a person who is likely to be crippled both in his ego and super-ego structure.

 Unless the child has been firmly grounded in the discipline of love and dependency, it is injured in its capacity to develop clear and definite judgments concerning people and things, and its ability to form such judgments as an adult is seriously handicapped. As adults the judgments of such persons tend to remain blurred and vague. Their decisions about the world, people, and things are characterized by doubt, suspicion, uncertainty, misgiving, and unsureness. They vacillate, in short, they see the world through a mist of unshed tears. They are characterized by an inability to enter into the feelings of others because, when they were young, no one adequately entered into theirs.

THE SEPARATED CHILD

Studies on children from birth to 1 year, from 1 year to 17 months, and from 18 months to 24 months of age, and up to 8 years of age, agree in finding that any separation of the young child from its mother is usually a distressing experience to it. Early attachment to the mother or mother-substitute is an emotional need which must be early satisfied if the organism is to develop in a normal manner. If that need is not satisfied the organism can seldom make deep and lasting attachments to other human beings. The organism's capacity to make continuous cooperative relations with others is impaired, and it is of considerable moment to observe that this is the failure which is characteristic of most persons suffering from mental illness.[22]

Work done at the International Children's Centre in Paris and London has revealed that children who have enjoyed normal healthy relationships with their mothers and not been previously separated from them for more than a few hours, when separated from the mother and cared for in an impersonal environment, commonly progress through three phases of emotional response which may be described as the phases of *protest, despair,* and *denial.* These phases are, of course, not distinctly separated from one another but in reality merge the one into the other, so that a child is often for weeks or days in a state of transition from one phase to another.

Protest

In the protest or initial phase, which may last from a few hours to seven or eight days, the child exhibits a strong conscious need of his mother together with the expectation—based on previous experience —that she will respond to his cries. He is acutely anxious and fears that he has lost her, he is confused and frightened by unfamiliar surroundings, and seeks to recapture her by the full exercise of his limited resources. He has no comprehension of his situation, and is out of mind with fright and urgent desire for satisfactions which only his mother can give. He will cry loudly, shake his crib, throw himself about, and look eagerly towards any sight or sound which might prove to be the missing mother. He may seek to cling to a nurse, perhaps the one who admitted him.[23]

Despair

The despair which gradually succeeds protest is characterized by continuing conscious need of the mother coupled with an increasing hopelessness. The active physical movements have diminished and come to an end, and the crying is now monotonous and intermittent. The child is withdrawn and apathetic, makes no demands on the environment, and is in a state of deep mourning. This quiet stage is often erroneously presumed to indicate a diminution of distress.

Denial

Denial is a phase which gradually succeeds despair. In his great need of loving care, comfort, and physical satisfaction, which he cannot provide himself, the little child may push out of his mind the picture of his mother who has (he feels) so cruelly abandoned him. Because the child cannot tolerate such intensity of distress he makes the best of his situation by repressing his feeling for his mother. In addition to the emotional need of his mother he has urgent physical need of food and comfort, and these he will begin to seek wherever he can find them. In the *denial* phase there are two types of response according to whether a substitute mother is available or not:

1. *Denial of the need for mothering by his own mother.* The child's need of loving care and comfort and of physical satisfactions which he cannot provide himself are so great that he is likely to transfer his attachments to anyone who gives him the necessary attention, and adopt her as a substitute mother. As a first step he will have to deal drastically with his feeling for his own mother who has failed to meet his needs, particularly his need of her as a person to love and to be loved by. In a way roughly comparable to that in which an adult may push out of mind the picture of someone who has caused gross offence, the little child may crush the picture of the mother who has (to his feeling) so heartlessly abandoned him. Then he is free to seek satisfaction of his needs in anyone who offers some degree of substitution.

2. *Denial of all need for mothering.* If the child fails to find a human being who will substitute for his mother, or if he undergoes the disheartening experience of becoming attached to a series of people each of whom leaves him and so repeats for him the pain and sense of rejection of the original loss of the mother, he will develop as one who believes that neither mothering nor any contact with human beings has much significance for him.

He will learn by bitter experience that it is folly to become attached to any one nurse, because nurses move on to other wards; thus, after a series of upsets at losing several nurses to whom in turn he had given his trust and warm affection, he will gradually commit himself less and less to succeeding nurses and in time will stop altogether taking the risk of investing love and dependence in anyone. Instead he will become more and more self-centred, transferring his desires and feelings from people on to material things such as sweets, toys, and food. He will no longer show upset when nurses leave. He will also cease showing feeling when his parents come and go on visiting day, and he will unwittingly cause them pain when they realize that although he has little interest in them as particular people he has an eager interest in the presents they bring— an interest which is no greater than the interest he shows in the diversions which anyone else brings into his restricted life. He will appear cheerful and adapted to his unusual situation (a particularly remarkable fact if he has been confined to his cot for several months or years) and apparently easy and unafraid of anyone. But this sociability is very superficial. If the onlooker, or the person to whom this spectacle is deceptively familiar, will pause long enough to assess the child's human relationships in even the simplest terms it will be apparent that he no longer really cares for anyone—and that, in a way which is highly abnormal for a young child, he denies all need for mothering or intimate care.[24]

As Robertson and Bowlby remark, to the child of under two years his mother is the entire world, she is the omnipotent protector, and if the child loses her by death or separation his whole world is shattered, and he experiences an overwhelming sense of loss and an overpowering anger when his imperative need for his mother is not met. The far-reaching harmful effects of such separation upon later personality development are now fairly clear. "The essential nature of these disturbances appears to be an incapacity to make stable, co-operative relationships with other people."[25]

Something of these essential findings had already been grasped by the great American pediatrician H. D. Chapin as early as 1908,[26] the psychologic care of neglected or institution children being positively recommended by him in 1915.[27] In the early 1930's another American pediatrician, J. Brennemann, established a rule in his hospital that every baby should be picked up, carried around, and "mothered" several times a day.[28]

However, as early as the Thirteenth Century we find the following being recorded of the extraordinary Frederick II (1211-1250) by the historian Salimbene:

. . . he wanted to find out what kind of speech and what manner of speech children would have when they grew up if they spoke to no one beforehand. So he bade foster mothers and nurses to suckle the children, to bathe and wash them, but in no way to prattle with them, for he wanted to learn whether they would speak the Hebrew language, which was the oldest, or Greek, or Latin, or Arabic, or perhaps the language of their parents, of whom they had been born. But he laboured in vain because the children all died. For they could not live without the petting and joyful faces and loving words of their foster mothers. And so the songs are called "swaddling songs" which a woman sings while she is rocking the cradle, to put a child to sleep, and without them a child sleeps badly and has no rest.[29]

THE SEPARATION OF PREMATURITY

The abnormally early separation from the maternal uterine environment suffered by premature infants should, according to theory, result in some recognizable deprivation effects during early development and in later life. In the effort to reduce the mortality of premature infants very little attention has been paid to their possible emotional needs. Life in an incubator under temperature and humidity control and the more than doubtful benefits of excessive oxygen[30] is no substitute for the close, tender, loving care of a mother. According to theory, then, prematures should in later life show the effects of their lack-love experience during the first months of their lives. The problem in the prematurely born organism is, however, rendered difficult by a large number of complicating factors. First, there is the factor of prematurity itself. The premature infant varies very little, it often fails to run a temperature or even a leucocytosis (increase of white blood corpuscles) in the presence of infection. It is pretty clear that the premature infant is a very different organism from the neonate. It is quite possible that the premature does not require as much love from the mother as does the neonate; on the other hand, it is equally possible that it requires much more. This is a matter for future research to determine. Second, premature children are likely to engender anxious and overprotective mothers, factors which are likely to have very definite effects upon

the personality of the developing child. The birth process itself probably constitutes a severe experience for the unready premature.
Finally, the rigid schedule upon which premature children are often
put adds complication to an already complicated picture.

In a study of 22 prematures in later life Howard and Worrell have
attempted to throw some much-needed light upon the psychologic
adjustment of the premature. They acknowledge that 22 cases hardly
represent a significant sample for statistical purposes, but they offer
it for such value as it may have, and in this sense their findings
are offered here. With respect to intelligence they found that prematurity as such has neither a beneficial nor a detrimental effect. On
the other hand, so far as personality adjustment is concerned it was
found that over half their cases were significantly unsatisfactory.
"Twelve of the 22 had personalities of the submissive-passive type.
Eight of the 22 showed unusual aggressive tendencies. Other aberrations uncovered were nail-biting, two cases of habit spasm and one
case of chronic masturbation."[31]

Beskow, in a report of 273 prematures of school age, found that
6.5 per cent of them had suffered cerebral hemorrhage, and later had
school difficulty. Fifty per cent presented nervous symptoms.

Hess, in a study of the mental development of 370 prematures,
found that 264 were normal, 68 deviated slightly from normal in an
expected manner for age, 23 were poor, 6 bad, and 9 were extremely
subnormal. Omitting from consideration the 68 prematures who
deviated slightly from normal, there remain 38 who were mentally
retarded, that is, 10.2 per cent. This is a significant figure.[32]

Privation of Love and Organic Consequences

The student who thinks of mind and body as aspects of the functioning of the organism as a whole will not need to be told that not
only are the effects of privation of love in childhood psychological,
but that they are also likely to be physical. In addition to the traits
of the affectionless character which a lack-love infancy produces,
there is some evidence which suggests that social stimulation is
closely related to the development of intelligence in infants. Thus,

Gilliland has found in a study carried out on white and Negro infants six to twelve weeks of age, that the infants reared at home were superior in I.Q. by five points to those raised in an institution. Two other unpublished studies by Gilliland's students on white and Negro infants showed that the I.Q. for Negro infants was as high or slightly higher than for white infants. There is an unsupported theory that Negro infants and children are genetically relatively more mature than white infants and children at these ages. Gilliland suggests that "an even more plausible theory is that, in the typical Negro home with more people living in small quarters, the child receives more social contacts. These contacts, like the effects of home vs. institutional care, result in more social-intellectual development and higher test scores."[33] We have already seen that other observers have noted a failure in the capacity for abstract thought in children who have been inadequately loved.[34]

Disturbances in their affective needs cause regressive and retardative physical changes not only in small infants, but also in children and in adults. Binning and others have shown that, as Fried and Mayer put it, "socio-emotional adjustment plays not merely an important but actually a crucial role among all the factors that determine individual health and physical wellbeing . . . it has become clear that socio-emotional disturbance tends to affect physical growth adversely, and that growth failure so caused is much more frequent and more extensive than is generally recognized."[35] Binning, in a remarkable study on the effects of emotional tensions on the development and growth of 800 Saskatoon (Canadian) children, found "that events in the child's life that caused separation from one or both parents—death, divorce, enlistment of a parent—and a mental environment which gave the child a feeling that normal love and affection were lacking did far more damage to growth than did disease," that such an environment, indeed, "was more serious than all other factors combined." Binning shows that where disease has affected growth "in most cases the reason is the emotional tension arising from the disease and its manner of treatment rather than the disease itself."[36]

Using the Wetzel Grid, Binning demonstrates how, in child after child, emotional disturbances in the home environment reflect themselves in disturbances in the growth pattern of body and mind. Referring to one grid which shows the history of a girl who under unfavorable home conditions developed, at critical periods, first pneumonia, then, shortly after the parents had separated, delinquent behavior, and finally, with indifferent care, became a serious behavior problem, Binning concludes as follows:

[This] grid is by far the most important statistically, whether or not the parents separate. It is also the grid of the child of parents who are "too busy" socially and with business to give the child the time for manifestations of affection the child needs. It is the grid of the child whose parent sloughs his care on to the shoulders of the maid, or the school, or the state. It is the grid of the "spoiled" child. Substitute for delinquency abdominal pain, visual trouble, etc., and it shows too often how medical ailments start. Children need guidance and guidance involves discipline. Not once did we find that discipline administered fairly and with affection harmed growth, even if the family application involved frequent spankings. On the other hand "spoiling" not only seems to *invariably* affect growth but within the growth lag very frequently we see psychosomatic or personality disturbances.[37]

Very similar findings were reported by Durfee and Wolf as long ago as 1933.[38]

Spitz has shown that infants deprived of maternal love suffer severe retardations of growth and development. The physical growth and weight norms are scarcely ever reached in such children, and, says Spitz "It would seem that the developmental imbalance caused by the unfavorable environmental conditions during the children's first year produces a psychosomatic damage that cannot be repaired by normal measures. Whether it can be repaired by therapeutic measures remains to be investigated."[39] Physical development, bodily capacity, as measured by ability to sit, stand, or walk, were all seriously interfered with, as was intellectual capacity, and capacity for social relations.

Talbot and his co-workers, in a study of 51 children who exhibited stunted growth, but in whom no physical abnormalities could be found to account for their dwarfism, found that "the majority were undernourished because of anorexia [loss of appetite] due to either emotional disturbances or mental deficiency or a combination of both, in addition to such factors as parental poverty and ignorance. In the 51 so studied there was a high incidence of rejection by the mother, emotional disturbances and delinquency in mothers, marked poverty at home. Fourteen per cent had severe emotional reactions with chronic grief and anorexia attributable to a broken home brought about by death, divorce and desertion."[40]

Lihn and his co-workers have found that in the infant and childhood histories of adult chronic osteoarthritic patients there was, without exception, the experience, in varying degrees, of being ignored, neglected, or rejected by their overburdened or inconsiderate parents, and often such patients were the victims of early desertion or of the arid emotional conditions of the orphanage.[41]

THE PHYSIOLOGY OF PRIVATION OF LOVE

The retardation in general growth, in bone growth and the other skeletal disturbances in children and in persons who have been unloved may well be due to the inverse relationship which Selye and others have suggested as existing between the hypersecretion of ACTH (adrenocorticotrophic hormone) and the hypersecretion of STH (somatotrophic or growth hormone) from the pituitary under conditions of stress.[42] The skeletal system is but one of the organ-systems of the body which may be affected as a consequence of emotionally stressful experiences. Selye has shown that under conditions of stress the organism tends to be maintained in adaptive balance through the activities of its neurohumoral system. The integrated syndrome of closely interrelated adaptive reactions is termed the General Adaptation Syndrome (or GAS). The three stages of the General Adaptation Syndrome are, the *alarm reaction, resistance,* and *exhaustion.* Whatever the nature of the stressor (the condition producing the stress), whether it be psychological or physical, these stages of GAS maintain their invariable order.

The alarm reaction (AR) is recognized as exhibiting two phases,

(1) *the phase of shock,* characterized by a fall in temperature and blood pressure, depression of the nervous system, decrease in muscular tone, concentration of red blood corpuscles, deranged capillary and cell-membrane permeability, gastrointestinal erosion, loss of appetite, loss of libido, etc.; and (2) *the phase of counter-shock,* characterized by defense phenomena against shock, with reversal of most of the conditions seen in the shock phase. There is enlargement of the adrenal cortex with increased secretion of cortisone and adrenaline, rise in blood pressure, and so on. If the stress is mild tension and excitement are observed, if the stress is intense depression and shock are characteristic.

Resistance is the second stage characterized by disappearance of most of the symptoms, with increased resistance to the evocative stimulus, but greatly reduced adaptability of the nervous system to other stimuli. Libido remains subnormal.

Exhaustion is the third stage characterized by the reappearance of the conditions which had been present during the AR stage as a result of prolonged over-exposure to stimuli to which adaptation had been developed but which (adaptation) can no longer be maintained. "It was found," writes Selye, "that even a perfectly adapted organism cannot indefinitely maintain itself in the stage of resistance. If exposure to abnormal conditions continues, adaptation wears out and many lesions characteristic of the AR . . . reappear as a stage of exhaustion develops and further resistance becomes impossible."[43]

It may be pointed out here that the first phase of the alarm reaction on the physiological side corresponds on the psychological side to the separated child's response of *protest,* and when the separation is prolonged this moves into despair. Selye's *resistance* roughly corresponds to the stage of *denial.* Spitz has drawn attention to the parallels between the General Adaptation Syndrome of Selye and the Emotional Deprivation Syndrome as observed and studied by himself.[44] The parallels are set out in Table 6.

The general physiology of the Emotional Deprivation Syndrome may be summed up in a few words, as follows: Under prolonged stress impulses originating in the brain stimulate the hypothalamus to activity, and this in turn produces secretion of ACTH in the

TABLE 6

General Adaptation Syndrome (Selye)	Emotional Deprivation Syndrome (Spitz)
Tension	Weepiness
Excitement	Demanding attitude
Loss of appetite	Loss of appetite
	Loss of weight
Resistance to evocative stimulus increases	Social sector increases
Adaptability to other agents diminishes	Arrest and regression of D.Q.
	Absence of autoerotic activity
Libido subnormal	
Depression of nervous system	Withdrawal. Insomnia. Decreased motility
Adaptation stops	Regression of D.Q. irreversible
Resistance ceases	Infection liability
Arteriosclerosis of brain vessels	Facial rigidity. Atypical finger movements
Breakdown	Morbidity increases
Death	Spectacular mortality

SOURCE: R. A. Spitz, "Infantile depression and the general adaptation syndrome," in *Depression*, Proceedings Forty Second Annual Meeting American Psychopathological Association, 1953, pp. 93-108.

anterior part of the pituitary gland. This stimulates the adrenal glands to secrete cortisone and adrenaline. The posterior portion of the pituitary gland also secretes vasopressin which acts upon the circulatory system to produce the effects already noted. When the stress is long continued the adaptive mechanism becomes exhausted and the system breaks down.

CRITICAL PERIODS AND DEPENDENCY

Stendler has recently postulated two critical developmental periods during which the dependency drives may suffer serious privations, thus affecting the development of the personality. The first critical period occurs toward the end of the first year of life, when the child begins to test out the mother to see whether he can depend upon her. At this period he especially makes demands upon the mother's proximity, to discover whether he can both depend upon and control her.

The second critical period comes during the two- or three-year-old phase. This is the phase of his development when, in western cultures, the child is required to give up his old ways of doing things and to learn new ones. He must give up the attempts to control his mother, and while accepting his dependence upon her he is also required to become independent, to act on his own initiative, for himself and for others in culturally approved ways.

These two periods are anxious ones for the child because they interfere with the goal responses which the child has customarily made. When, during these periods, excessive demands are made upon the child these may produce excessive anxiety and result in a strengthening of the dependency drive with a consequent development of *over*-dependency.

The timing of disturbances which affect the dependency drive [Stendler suggests] will also be a factor in determining how other aspects of personality will be affected. That is, the dependency drive is so related to other aspects of personality that a disturbance during one of the critical periods will affect other aspects of personality and . . . the effects will differ according to the timing of the disturbance. A disturbance during the first critical period will have a different impact upon personality development than will a disturbance during the second critical period. . . .

Overdependent children produced during the first critical period will be children who have experienced helplessness; who have not been able to control the socializing agent at the time when recognition of the importance of that agent for one's own well-being was dawning. Therefore we can expect such children to be low in ego-strength, with resulting low level of aspiration and low frustration tolerance. Also, such children, while they cling to the socializing agent will tend to see that agent as a punishing figure rather than a helpful one. These things may not be true of overdependent children produced during the second critical period. These children are more likely to be affected in the area of conscience.

They will tend to resolve the anxiety generated by the frustration by overdoing the job of building a punishing voice inside. They will be rigid in their ideas of right and wrong, overconforming in behavior, unduly disturbed by the wrongdoings of other children. They will prefer well-defined structured situations to those which allow for more freedom of choice.[45]

In other words, children who have their dependency needs traumatically disturbed during the first critical period are likely to be affected in the ego aspects of personality development, while those who suffer disturbances of the dependency drives in the second critical period are likely to suffer in the super-ego aspects of personality development.

In the first critical period the child suffers when the parent is *absent,* and it wishes that he were *present.* In the second critical period frustration arises from interference and punishment: the parent or parent-person is *present,* and the child wishes he were *absent.*[46] The latter wish produces intolerable conflict in the child, who hates the parent whom he desires to love because he is punishing, and thus, confused and rendered anxious for fear of separation from the beloved figure, he tends to cling to his dependency more than ever.

MOTHER-LOVE—CONTINUED

The importance of mother-love for the newborn is slowly being recognized by American pediatricians and a few obstetrical divisions in the hospitals.[47] The practice of spending the period of confinement in a hospital rather than at home is of recent origin. In former years most children were born at home and the newborn was kept in a crib by the mother's side where it could be closely watched and tenderly fondled. But today, for example, in a city like New York, more than 90 per cent of all births occur in hospitals, an increase of more than 50 per cent in less than 20 years. It is the custom in most hospitals to separate the baby from the mother immediately after birth. The infant is placed in a crib in a baby-room where it is too frequently handled with efficient indifference by "baby-hardened" nurses. Except for the assortment of sounds issuing from other babies in similar condition, it is left severely alone. After some twenty-four hours when, at last, the baby is brought to his mother's breast for his first attempt at suckling, he is, indeed, "a little stranger." What should have been for both mother and newborn a warm comforting experience is rendered a cold and arid mechanical meeting, during which the mother is often heard to exclaim, "Oh, I'd almost forgotten about the baby." Or "Are you sure its mine? Sure you've taken it out of the right crib?" In every well-conducted maternity division the wrong baby is occasionally given to nurse to the wrong mother. As the Bakwins point out:

> Separation of mother and baby immediately after birth is unnatural and unphysiologic. Among mammals it is the rule that the young remain close to the mother during early life, snuggling and cuddling against her. The mother and her young constitute a biologic unit and to separate the two in the way commonly practiced in American hospitals finds no analogy in the animal world where so much of our knowledge on nutrition and other aspects of physiology has been obtained. How contact with the mother benefits the newborn is not clear but the universality of this behavior in the animal world suggests that it has biologic value. It may, among other things, be a factor in the ability of the mother to nurse.[48]

The Bakwins might have added that not only is it the rule among all mammals for the young to remain close to the mother during early life, but that this is also the rule among all peoples with the exception of a large proportion of those living in the highly civilized communities of the western world.

The home is still, in most cases, the best place in which to have a child. The birth of a new member into the family is an event and an experience in which the whole family should participate, the children as well as the father. With confinement in the hospital the children are separated from their mother, and they frequently feel that this deprivation is the fault of the new baby, and they resent it. In this way hostility develops towards the new member of the family, and permanent injury may be done to the development of good interpersonal relations within the family. The mother also usually suffers as a consequence of this separation from her children. The birth of the child in the home as an event in which all the members of the immediate family participate is calculated to produce a happy acceptance of the new arrival and to contribute in a positive manner to the greater happiness of all concerned.[49]

The love which the newborn receives is not something abstract, but the concrete activity of the mother or whoever it is who does the mothering. It is all those things which the mother does for her child which makes the transition from the uterine state to extra-uterine life as smooth as possible. Ribble suggests that mothering is really a continuance of the closeness of the prenatal state, and the more nearly it imitates certain of the conditions before birth the more successful it is in the first few weeks. It is believed that frequent periods of contact with the mother are good for the newborn because the warmth and the support give him a feeling of reassurance. Babies tend to stop crying when they are picked up and held. Ribble suggests that contact takes the place of physical connection before birth. In addition to all the routine duties of feeding, bathing, and so on, the important manifestations of love in the form of fondling, caressing, rocking, singing and speaking tenderly to the baby are aspects of mothering which have the profoundest significance for the psychosocial development of the child. This, at least, is what by inference we have come to believe from the effects observed in those cases in which mothering has been absent.

CRIPPLING OF THE CAPACITY FOR ABSTRACT THOUGHT

One of the most serious effects of maternal deprivation, upon which all research workers are agreed, is the crippling of the ability for abstract thought or conceptualization. Why deprivation of love should impair the capacity for abstract thought we can at the present time—in the absence of the necessary researches—only conjecture. It would appear that not only does love provide the incentive and conditions for learning, but that the warmth which it conveys somehow stimulates the development of the capacity for abstraction. Bowlby suggests the possibility that the capacity for abstract thought not only underlies ego functioning, but can develop adequately only if ego functioning itself develops favorably. Bowlby writes:

> The failure of ego development in deprived children is perhaps more easily understood when it is considered that it is the mother who in the child's earliest years fulfils the function of his ego and super-ego. The institution children studied by Goldfarb and by Bender had never had this experience, and so never had the opportunity of completing the first phase of development—that of establishing a relationship with a clearly identified mother-figure. All they had had was a succession of ad hoc agents each helping them in some limited way, but none providing continuity in time, which is of the essence of ego functioning. It may well be that these grossly deprived infants, never having been the continuous objects of care of a single human being, had never had the opportunity to learn the processes of abstraction and of the organization of behaviour in time and space. Certainly their grave psychical deformities are clear examples of the principle that injuries inflicted early produce widespread disturbance of growth.
>
> In the institutional setting, moreover, there is less opportunity for the child who has learnt the processes of abstraction and mental organization to exercise them.[50]

A certain amount of the capacity for abstract thought is recovered by the developing person who has suffered some deprivation of love in childhood. The point, however, is that the undeveloped capacity for abstract thought in childhood would seem to interfere with the child's capacity to pick up even those demonstrations of love which are offered it. Dr. Lauretta Bender goes so far as to say that "once the defect [in the capacity to love] is created it cannot be corrected."[51] Goldfarb has stated that he has never seen "even one example of significantly favorable response to treatment by the traditional means of child psychiatry."[52] However, it seems unlikely that any actual tissue damage has been done. What seems more probable is that certain patterns of relationships have failed to become established in that reverberating pool of electrical circuits which serve human beings for a mind, and that the circuits necessary for a fully functioning human being are simply not there. The necessary circuits with which other electrical circuits can establish the relationships which lead to warm human responses have not been developed.

Upon this view, then, we would be dealing with a failure in development rather than with irretrievable and irreversible damage to brain tissue. Such a view affords hope that with the development of more insight into these cases we may be able to develop methods for restoring such persons to a happier condition.

EFFECTS OF SEPARATION AT VARIOUS AGES

A question often asked is whether there are any critical periods during development in which greater damage is done by privation than during others? We do not yet possess sufficient information to be able to answer this question adequately. What, however, can be said is that it would appear that damage can be done to the child by exposing it to deprivation of maternal love for any appreciable period of time during its first eight years. In general the period of privation which is capable of doing damage of a nature severe enough to be recognized by the investigator is about one to four weeks, but it would seem probable that shorter periods of time are capable of doing damage of a substantial nature even though it may not be recognizable by the investigator—unseen psychic scars are not the less real for being unseen. Indeed, the degree of damage done will depend upon a number of factors, such as age and previous maternal care. Burlingham and Freud, for example, have shown that infants between 1½ and 2½ years of age cannot tolerate separation from the mother for more than a day without showing visible regressive effects.[53]

Vulnerability to privation is still serious between the ages of three and five, though much less so than at an earlier age. It should be understood that separation of a few days or a few weeks appears as a much longer period of time to the small child than it does to the adult. "Social time" is of much greater duration for the child than for the adult, and the younger the child the more extended does time appear to it.[54] Hence, maternal privation lasting a few days may, to a three-months-old infant appear longer than a privation of three weeks to a two-year-old. The rule seems to be the younger the child the more likely is the privation to be harmful.

Children between three and five years of age do not live as much in the present as do those of younger ages, and can therefore conceive of a future when their mother will return. They can also more readily understand explanations, and will more easily take to an understanding substitute for the mother. Children between five and eight years of age who have had a happy relationship with their mothers will tolerate separation much better than those who have not. The anxious child will tend to believe that he has been separated from his mother because he has been naughty. Such a belief will lead to further anxiety and to hatred. This may create serious difficulties with the mother upon reunion, and unless the situation is carefully handled, may lead to profound personality disturbances.[55]

DELINQUENCY, CRIMINAL BEHAVIOR, AND SEPARATION FROM THE MOTHER

As a causative factor in delinquency and crime Bowlby has shown that separation from the mother or mother-substitute for long periods or permanently during the first five years of life, plays a highly significant role.

In a study of 44 juvenile thieves Bowlby found that a large proportion exhibited an inability to establish affectionate relationships with other persons, and displayed what he termed the "affectionless character." Fourteen of the 44 delinquents were of this type, and of these, 12 had suffered a prolonged separation from the mother at an early age. These affectionless characters were significantly more delinquent than the other thieves, constituting more than half of the more serious and chronic offenders.

Bowlby points out that strong libidinal and aggressive components were present in the stealing of these juveniles, and that there was a marked failure of super-ego development following the failure in development of the capacity for object-love. He traces this failure primarily to the lack of opportunity for development.[56]

Excessive libidinal and aggressive impulses directed towards the parents are found in one form or another in all cases of functional mental illness. But, Bowlby points out, what characterizes the affectionless character is (1) that he lacks the usual inhibition of these impulses, and (2) that he is unable to establish permanent personal relationships owing to his inability to feel or express love. In other words, while in most neurotics and unstable persons there exists some ability to establish object-relationships, there is an extreme degree of incapacity to do so in affectionless characters. There is a massive inhibition of object-love combined with excessive and relatively uninhibited libidinal and aggressive impulses. Bowlby suggests that the lack of inhibition is the necessary result of a lack of a love-relationship. In short, unless the infant has an opportunity to develop object-love, that is, to recognize and value the mother or mother-substitute as a person from whom love and all its satisfactions are derived, and comes to take pleasure in reciprocating her love, he will never learn to love others. Normally, through the processes of identification,[57] and introjection,[58] there comes to be formed in the child's mind a pattern of feeling and behavior, the super-ego, which is designed to maintain the love-relationship with the object by inhibiting impulses which are inimical to it.

The super-ego [Bowlby says], although often experienced as a foreign body, an agent of the loved object, is in reality the expression both of the need for the object and of love for it, and this remains so despite its frequent use of aggressive measures to attain its ends. Without some measure of object-love the whole structure of the super-ego, whether it operates by violent inhibition or moderate control, could not exist, since both the purpose which it serves and the needs which it expresses would be nonexistent.[59]

If no opportunity is afforded the infant for the development of object-love it will simply fail to develop that mixture of selfish and altruistic behavior which ensues as a result of the normal mother-infant relationship. The unrequited needs of such an infant lead to attempts on its part to gratify its needs in its own way, libidinously[60] and without inhibition, and at a later stage in phantasy. There is a failure to develop an adequate conception of the meaning of reality because there has been a failure in the organization of the experiences of gratification of needs, the pleasure principle,[61] to realization of the reality principle[62] which usually follows as a consequence of normal object-love development, with its normal educative complements of satisfactions and inhibitions. Hence, such children will often steal, preferably from the mother, in order to secure gratifications which have been denied them.

The adequately loved child will gradually learn by the training which he undergoes how to postpone and even renounce some of his needs. In so doing he adjusts to the cultural reality which his mother constitutes for him; he learns to inhibit,[63] to impose upon his ego the restraints of the super-ego based upon the realities of his disciplining and love experiences.

Inconsistencies in the amount of gratification and frustration which the mother gives to the infant may have much the same effect as inadequate satisfaction of the infant's needs. The same privation may be produced by the presence of too many persons attempting to assume the maternal role, as in the case of many families in which interfering grandparents and uncles and aunts live in the same household. Under such conditions the experience of the infant may prove anarchic. In this connection it is well known that unless a dog is trained at the hands of one person but is ordered about by many persons it is liable to grow up lacking attachment to any person and tend to be wild and intractable.

THE MECHANISM OF INJURY IN PRIVATION OF LOVE

The question has been raised as to the nature of the physiological changes which occur in the nervous system of the deprived child. Is the brain of the deprived child in any way affected by its lack-love experiences and its responses to them? Is there any arrest in the growth and development of any part of the neuronal net? Is there, as it were, a "hardening" or consolidation of the type of organization of experience or lack of it, such that it becomes a permanent and unalterable part of the psychophysical nature of the organism?

Bowlby has pointed out that "Children of between 6 months and 3 years who are separated from their mothers often undergo intense emotional experiences of rage and despair and then proceed to organise their social relations on a new pattern; often one in which no particular human being is sought after and loved. It would appear that if this new and psychopathic organisation is permitted to consolidate around the age of three or four years, it tends to become permanent.

"Clearly" Bowlby goes on to say, "this 'setting' of the perceptual and behavioural patterns in the third and fourth years must have as its base important maturational changes in the physiology and anatomy of the brain."[64]

Bowlby's suggestion seems to be that during the critical developmental periods of the first four years unless the organism receives the proper stimulations certain parts of the brain will not grow and develop normally either in structure or in function. There will be maturational changes. "It would be very interesting to know what they are," Bowlby writes. "My own guess would be that the cerebral centres concerned complete their basic patterns of growth at this time, and thenceforward do not change greatly in their general organization. It may be that part of the essential condition for the growth and organization of cerebral centres is the external environment and the sensory stimuli derived from it."

There can be little doubt that every human organism is born with certain potentialities for behavioral development *under the proper stimulation* of certain types of experiencing and responding. Whether these potentialities are localized in "cerebral centres" is, however, open to question. Be that as it may, if we understand Bowlby's "basic patterns of growth" to mean, as he appears to mean, growth within the predetermined inherited potentialities (possibilities) of the organism, then that growth will be completed as a product of those potentialities in interaction with the kind of stimulation those potentialities have received largely from the external environment, and chiefly, if not entirely, from other human beings.

The pattern for growth of these potentialities is a pattern or configuration having a certain general organization and orientation or directiveness. In other words, under the (organismally) normal or expected kinds of stimulations (such as the mother loving the child) the potentialities of the organism will tend to mature in terms of their basic pattern of growth and development. These basic patterns are genotypic, and in interaction with the normal environmental stimuli will develop a normal phenotype; under abnormal or different kinds of stimuli the same genotype is capable of developing a variety of different phenotypes. The genes involved are almost certainly "clocked," that is to say, the rate and time intervals set by the structure of the developing organism itself are factors of quite as great importance for the development of behavior as is "stimulation." These facts hold not only for human beings but also for nonhuman animals. Let us consider some examples from the latter.

Lorenz, Tinbergen, and their co-workers have shown that fish, birds, and the few mammals thus far investigated are born equipped with innate releaser mechanisms (IRM's) which cause the organism to respond to certain simple sign stimuli in a particular manner. Seemingly complex social behavior in these animals is constituted by a relatively few such IRM's. The IRM's do not determine what particular stimuli shall elicit the response, any more than genes determine the characters or traits with which they are connected, but a particular IRM will be activated in a particular manner by a particular class of stimuli. Any object or stimulus within such a class to which the organism is exposed during the appropiate critical developmental period will usually become fixed as the particular stimulus—and no other—which will elicit the particular IRM. This phenomenon is known as *imprinting*. Lorenz has shown that greylag goslings, for example, accept the first living being to whom they are exposed as their mother, and thereafter refuse to accept anyone else as such. Freshly hatched mallards will not respond to the visual stimulus, but will respond to the call-note, and whoever makes the first call-note they will adopt as their mother.[65]

The normal phenotypic expression of the gosling's IRM is toward other geese, but if the "learning" stimuli to which the gosling is exposed during the critical developmental period are derived from other objects of appropiate size, it will thereafter respond only to them. The same is true for mallards with respect to auditory stimuli. The genotype has now become phenotypically conditioned. The object-reaction is now fixed. Such abnormal fixation under ordinary conditions would be extremely rare.

Do IRM's exist in man? At least two IRM's have been attributed to man: the parental response to the baby,[66] and the response by smiling at about the tenth week to anything resembling the human face.[67]

These two responses are social responses in that they are normally elicited by other human beings and require a certain amount of conscious evaluation. It is difficult to see what connection they have with IRM's or imprinting. Walter's criticism is very much to the point here.

Some investigators also believe that they have found the key to a baby's first smile in these impersonal "innate releaser mechanisms." Spitz found that a mask with two eyes and a nose waved slowly to and fro on the end of a broomstick, was enough to elicit the first smile, between the tenth and the twentieth weeks of life, all smiles before that period being attributable to wind. But it is at least a permissible question whether this is "imprint" or association. It would be strange if, in ten weeks, the appearance of a face had not already become associated with smiling fortune in the baby's mind. For the human brain, even at birth, is so highly organised, the electrical rhythms that sweep it are so suggestive of searching mental activity, that it is difficult amidst so much complexity to tell how soon the ape is left behind. The good fairy's gift of learning by association is found in every cradle.[68]

Indeed, there is a considerable difference between the IRM's of animals and those attributed to man. In animals the IRM becomes permanently fixed in relation to the imprinted stimulus; in human beings no such fixations occur in relation to the alleged IRM's. It would, therefore, seem incorrect to suggest, as Bowlby does, that IRM's occur in man. Fixation is a process which only superficially resembles imprinting. Fixation is a term which, in Freud's words, refers to "a conjunction of impulses with impressions and with the objects connected with those impressions. This conjunction has to be effected very early, is very hard to resolve, and has the effect of bringing the development of the instincts concerned to a standstill."[69] This could serve beautifully as a definition of imprinting, except that fixation is not necessarily permanent in human beings where in non-human animals imprinting is.[70]

If there exists anything resembling the phenomenon of imprinting in human beings then it is of a very attenuated nature, and is sufficiently covered by the term *habit*. A child among human beings does not, during any of its critical developmental periods or at any other time, become *fixated* upon any person as its mother, but it does become *habituated* through association to regard a particular person as its mother or mother-substitute. Furthermore, this habituation can be broken and another person can be adopted as the mother. The observations of Burlingham and Anna Freud, among others, abundantly demonstrate this.[71]

Fixation is a pathological process involving an arrest of some part of the libido during the course of its development, with a consequent inhibition of development at an infantile stage. Imprinting is in no way a pathological process, but it is in every respect a normal one.

At the present time it would be best to leave the question open whether the insufficiently analyzed concepts of IRM and imprinting in animals can be applied to man. Further study may reveal that they can, in a modified form, be utilized in the analysis of human nature.

RATE AND FREQUENCY OF LOVE

In animals the gears of the developmental clock are set irreversibly. This is also the case in man with respect to physical development, but *not*—and this is the important difference—with respect to behavior.

There are strong grounds for believing that human beings possess a genotype which determines the nature of the responses that environmental stimuli will elicit. Not only will the responses vary with the nature of the environmental stimuli, but they will also vary according to the *rate* at and the *time* during which the genotype is stimulated.

For example, in embryological development, certain chemical changes must occur between the seventh and ninth weeks if the organism is to develop a normal face. This period is developmentally critical,[72] but the occurrence of the requisite chemical changes is not enough—they must occur at a particular rate.[73] If there is a disturbance in the rate then a cleft palate and harelip may result. Similarly, there is reason to believe that within any period critical for the development of a certain form of behavior the rate at which the proper stimuli are offered to the organism must conform with its genotypic requirements or the responses will fail to develop adequately. For example, during the period in the twenties and thirties when children were being brought up by the pediatrician's clock on a schedule which disregarded the needs of the child, it was possible for a mother to love her child at the scheduled *times*, but in the intervals to give it no love whatever. The damage done to many such children can be explained on the basis of the fact that they did not receive enough love, that is, the *rate* and *frequency* of love which they received was inadequate. Instead of being activated to love by being loved, such children in response to the frustration of their need for love exhibit rage, anxiety, and aggression, and these responses become part of their behavioral organization.

What they do not experience also becomes part of their behavioral organization, and this is at least as important as the rage and despair which these children experience. First, these children undergo a failure of behavioral development owing to the lack of proper social stimuli, and second, the consequent responses of rage and despair take the place of those which would have developed in the form of love and trust.

It is not enough to love children at certain intervals of time; for their proper development during the critical developmental periods they must receive definite quantities of love which must not fall below a certain minimum at any time; this is the *rate* at which love is given. Love must be given at intervals which do not fall below a certain minimum—this is *frequency* (repetition at short intervals). The rate at which love is given is influenced by the frequency with which it is given. If the intervals are too long, then no matter how satisfactory the rate of love may be, the proffered love may fail to produce the proper effects

An explanation that fits the relevant facts as we know them today, as to what happens in the brain of such children is as follows: Electrical circuits of certain kinds are not established in the neuronal net of deprived children because the necessary charges of energy have not been received. Such a child develops a neuronal net which is wanting in certain patterns of electrical circuits. If a child has not been loved it does not have any developed "love" circuits. Hence, when the critical developmental period for their development has passed, incoming changes resonate or reverberate at most against the inadequately developed "love" circuits, and the responses to them are inadequately made. The "know-how" just is not there because it was never developed. The responses, on the other hand, which such children or persons will frequently make to expressions of love are often in terms of the circuits which have been built up in their brains in terms of aggressiveness, rage, and insecurity.

CULTURAL AND CLASS DIFFERENCES

So far as the effects of varying forms of privation upon the personality are concerned the evidence now available for non-literate and other peoples is extremely suggestive.

In societies of the western world there are great variations in the kind and amount of mothering which infants receive. Class differences here play an important role. Among the upper classes the mother tends to shift the burden of "mothering" the infant to a nurse as soon as possible. In Europe, and in the southern United States until very recently, children were almost always brought up by nurses and governesses. In the middle classes the maternal care of the child varied considerably, in some families the children receiving a good deal of attention from the mother during the newborn and infancy periods, in others this task being delegated to a nurse and later to a governess. Among the lower classes universally the mother is the person who gives the child most attention. Such class differences in "mothering" have undoubtedly exercised an important effect in producing class differences in personality. While there now exist a number of studies on national differences in personality there exist relatively few on class and personality.[74]

The upper class Englishman (and Englishwoman) should prove to be good material for the investigation of this problem. Over and beyond the fact that the early training and inhibitions of the Englishman prevent him from ever exhibiting much emotion, there is detectable a certain lack of warmth which, in common with the members of the upper classes of some other nations, may be found to be due to an early lack of mothering. Not all members of the upper classes exhibit this lack of warmth, and many members of the middle and lower classes may show it. This lack of "warmth" in adults often signifies the inability to love other persons, and in such adults one usually looks in vain for that human sympathy with others which one finds in most human beings. There may be something in the idea that the ability of the upper middle and upper class Englishman to rule and govern conquered peoples and to justify that rule, is to some extent due to such lack of sympathetic understanding for others.[75]

The custom among the upper and upper middle classes in England of sending their children away to boarding schools at an early age, of institutionalizing them as it were, outside the warm ambience of the family, deprives these children of the love and affection which is necessary for the healthy development of the personality. This privation of parental love suffered during the tender years of childhood is probably the principal cause of the "coldness," the apparently unemotional character, of the upper class Englishman. On this aspect of the Englishman's character E. M. Forster has an interesting passage.

People talk of the mysterious East, but the West also is mysterious. It has depths that do not reveal themselves at the first gaze. We know what the sea looks like from a distance; it is of one color, and level, and obviously cannot contain such creatures as fish. But if we look into the sea over the edge of a boat, we see a dozen colors, and depth below depth, and fish swimming in them. That sea is the English character— apparently imperturbable and even. The depth and the colors are the English romanticism and the English sensitiveness—we do not expect to find such things, but they exist. And—to continue my metaphor—the fish are the English emotions, which are always trying to get up to the surface, but don't quite know how. For the most part we see them moving far below, distorted and obscure. Now and then they succeed and we exclaim, "Why, the Englishman has emotions! He actually can feel!" And occasionally we see that beautiful creature, the flying fish, which rises out of the water altogether into the air and sunlight. English literature is a flying fish. It is a sample of the life that goes on day after day beneath the surface; it is a proof that beauty and emotion exists in the salt, inhospitable sea.[76]

In contrast with the Englishman's alleged emotional anemia and impervious reticence is the emotional warmth and sensitivity of the French or the Italian. It is significant that the French or Italian family is one in which the members are closely bound to one another in a loving, emotional atmosphere which is different from that encountered among English-speaking peoples. In France and Italy it was generally considered something of a tragedy for a girl to entertain the idea of marrying an Englishman—those "cold fish" apparently incapable of all emotion! The French and the Italians still entertain similar views concerning the English.[77] One cannot help recall here the immortal remark of the anonymous American lady who, in 1843, wrote a devastating reply to Charles Dickens' *American Notes,* "An Englishman in love! Was a monumental statue ever in a fever?"[78]

Insofar as one can speak of "national character," it is a legitimate inquiry to seek to discover to what extent such character structure is determined by the influences and pressures of a particular pattern of socialization through the family. But these are matters which we must reserve for later discussion.

The individual who must receive love and respect but is himself almost incapable of any emotion more closely approximating love than respect, has been, we may suspect, in many instances the victim of a lack-love infancy. This suspicion is abundantly borne out by recent researches on the "authoritarian personality."[79] Adorno and his co-workers conclude that to produce a warm loving personality "All that is really essential is that children be genuinely loved and treated as human individuals."[80]

Illuminating here is a study by David Levy of 21 anti-Nazi Germans, concerning whom he concludes that "in comparison with typical Germans" the anti-Nazis escaped the conventional and rigid family structure of their nation. The anti-Nazis were brought up with more affection and less restraint. "Their world is a broader one, less limited in terms of religious, social, and intellectual boundaries. They have attained a more critical attitude. They are freer from conventional, stereotyped thinking."[81]

Overauthoritative parents are likely to produce developmental failure of the dependency drives, resulting in a rigidified personality who seeks always to be commanded, and feels safe only when he is commanded.

THE OVERPROTECTED CHILD

Yet another cause of developmental failure of normal affective character and of the super-ego is the phenomenon of maternal overprotection. "Smothering" rather than mothering. The over-indulgent mother indulges her child's every wish and protects him from every experience which might deprive him of the pleasure he seeks. He is completely undisciplined. He therefore grows into an egocentric, selfish, demanding, disobedient, impudent, affectively infantilized problem whose social maturation has been seriously impaired. The forms of maternal overprotection and their varying effects upon the child have been thoroughly described by David Levy.[82] Here we may mention the overprotective mother who dominates her child to the point of constricting his development. The dominated, overprotected child becomes shy, withdrawn, submissive, infantile, asocial, and greatly dependent upon the mother.

The *overprotected indulged* children are the victims of an environment rich in love and poor in discipline. The result is an ill-developed super-ego. The *overprotected dominated* children are over-disciplined and therefore not adequately loved. In many of the latter cases the unconscious hostility of the mother to her overprotected child may be very marked, and such children will exhibit all the signs of affect-hunger. But where there is overdiscipline accompanied by some love the super-ego is often developed to the extent of complete submissiveness to and dependence upon the mother. Such a boy is usually described as "too good," a "sissy," very obedient and polite, "ought to have been a girl."

We see, then, how dependent the infant is for its emotional development upon the kind of mothering it has received. And as Spitz and others[83] have shown, this mothering must be given the child especially during the early developmental critical periods of its life if it is to develop as an adequate social being.

The overindulged child looks upon the world as his oyster, and is upset when it doesn't yield to his demands. The overdisciplined child feels that he is inside the shell and is upset at any attempt to extricate him from it. Both wish to keep what they have exactly where it is, for that is how they feel most secure. This form of behavior constitutes an example of a tendency of mental life to maintain at as low a level as possible the quantities of excitation flowing into it or to bring about a minimum of psychic tension. This tendency of mental life has been called the *Nirvana Principle*.

SOCIAL COMPETENCE

In all the examples of failure of one kind or another in the process of mothering, of satisfaction of basic needs, we perceive as the end effect the failure to develop social competence. These deprived and overprotected children are unprepared to meet the problems of life, and their social incompetence only serves to increase their difficulties.

Life is of its nature a test of social competence, and the penalty of social incompetence is rejection.

The failure to develop social competence is due to the privation of love suffered by the infant during the first six to eight years of life. We are thus led to conclude that in order to be successfully social one must have learned to love by having been loved; that, indeed, society is based on love, in fact, *is* but a developed form of love, which is but another way of saying that society or culture represents the evolution of man's attempts to satisfy his needs. Where hatreds exist in any persons within any society we may be sure that they, too, are due to the involvement with love, for hatred is love frustrated. Aggression is but a technique or mode of seeking love.

Love is in its essence, in its beginning and end, *social*. It arises out of the satisfaction of the self-preservative or basic needs of the organism in the primary dependent relationship to the mother, and it demands always the presence of other persons or their substitutes for it to be able to function adequately.

Man's need for society and his need for love are in essence one and the same thing. Ian Suttie, in one of the great books of our time, has suggested that "play, co-operation, competition and culture-interests generally are substitutes for the mutually caressing relationship of child and mother. *By these substitutes we put the whole social environment in the place once occupied by the mother.*"[84]

Social interaction is the extension of mother-child interaction. The ability of the person to interact socially will depend largely upon the character of his early interaction with his mother or mother-substitute.

THE ORGANISM'S INNATE NEED FOR LOVE

The organism is born with an innate need for love, with a need to respond to love, to be good and cooperative. Whatever is opposed to love, to goodness, and to cooperation is disharmonic, unviable, unstable, and malfunctional—evil. Were the infant's needs adequately satisfied he could not help but be good, that is, loving. All of man's natural inclinations are toward the development of goodness, toward the continuance of states of goodness, and the discontinuance of unpleasant states. As Ralph Lillie has pointed out:

A property of the *good* (in the universal or Platonic sense) is that conscious effort tends to be directed toward its continuance, since it is the object of desire; while *evil*, the immediately or ultimately painful, is a feature of reality which conscious effort tends to remove or overcome. The former has thus within itself a property or character which favors its continuance and increase; the latter is inherently unstable.

Scientific analysis shows that stability in all highly diversified or composite systems requires harmonious relations—relations of mutual support or equilibrium—between the different components and activities . . . what should be better known and more widely acted upon is that integration *between* different individuals as seen in the mutually helpful relations of the various units in many human and animal communities—or even between different species of animals and plants—is as much a factor in biological survival and evolution as is conflict. The avoidance of useless conflict, and the subordination of individual interests to the interest of the whole reality which includes the individuals, would thus seem to be rational aims for all conscious beings; and these aims have the further sanction of religion when the whole is conceived in its character as ultimate value or deity.[85]

SECURITY

The biological basis of love consists in the organism's drive to satisfy its basic needs in a manner which causes it to feel secure. Love *is* security—but security alone is not love. Mere satisfaction of basic needs is not enough. Needs must be satisfied in a particular manner, in a manner which is emotionally as well as physically satisfying. Babies as well as adults cannot live by bread alone.

It is worth repeating that the biological basis of love lies in the organism's ever-present need to feel secure. The basis of all social life has its roots in this integral of all the basic needs which is expressed as the need for security, and the only way in which this need can be satisfied is by love.

ETHICS AND HUMAN NATURE

It is a discovery of the greatest possible significance for mankind that the ethical concept of love independently arrived at by almost all existing peoples is no mere creation of man but is grounded in his biological structure as a functioning organism. The implications of this discovery are of the greatest importance, for it means that man's organic potentialities are so organized as to demand but one kind of satisfaction, a satisfaction which ministers to man's need for love, which registers love, which is given in terms of love—a satisfaction which is defined by the one word, *security*—secure in the affections of others and secure in one's affection for them. That is what the human being seeks all his life, and society, culture, and man's institutions, however insufficient some of them may be, all exist to secure that one fundamental satisfaction. The emotional need for love is as definite and compelling as the need for food. The basic needs of man must be satisfied in order that he may function on the organic level. But in order that he may function satisfactorily on the social plane the most fundamental of the basic social needs must be satisfied in an emotionally adequate manner for personal security and equilibrium.

When the needs of the developing social organism are inadequately satisfied, that is, where there have been too many frustrations—thwartings of expected satisfactions—where there has been a significant privation of love, the organism becomes disordered, anxious, tense, fearful, and hostile. This, in fact, is the state in which innumerable human beings in the western world live today.

We know from the observation and study of many peoples—such as the Australian aborigines,[86] the Eskimo,[87] some of the peoples of Melanesia,[88] Micronesia,[89] and Indonesia,[90] the Japanese,[91] Chinese,[92] Burmese,[93] American Indians,[94] and also peoples of western civilization[95]—that the well-integrated, cooperative adult personality is largely a product of a childhood which has enjoyed a maximum of satisfactions and a minimum of frustrations. We also know the obverse to be true, that the disintegrated, noncooperative adult personality is largely a product of a childhood which has suffered a maximum of frustrations and a minimum of satisfactions.

The one thing in the world of which one can never receive or give too much is love. One does not spoil children by giving them too much, but by giving them too little.

On the island of Okinawa, the largest of the Ryukyu chain of islands in the Southwest Pacific, with a population of 450,000 souls, Dr. James Clark Moloney, psychiatrist in the United States Navy, states that he never saw a spoiled, self-centered, fearful child. On the contrary, the children were remarkable for their well-disciplined nature, calm, confidence, and cooperativeness. Dr. Moloney traces these qualities to the excellent mothering which the Okinawan child received.[96] Similar testimony for the children of many other peoples has been given by numerous observers. For example, Mountford, writing of Australian aboriginal children, says:

The wealth of affection that exists between the adults and the children in an aboriginal tribe has to be seen to be believed. There was one baby boy in camp, perhaps nine months old, who was seldom in his mother's arms except for meals. At all other times some man, woman, boy or girl was either carrying him about or playing with him. The older children seemed to go their own sweet way, without hindrance from anyone.

The little folk sat round our fire at all times of the day, yet, in spite of the apparent lack of discipline by the parents, they were not the slightest trouble, any request that we made being obeyed with perfect good humour. There were sweets, sugar and all sorts of dainties in open cupboards, only a few feet from where they used to sit, yet no child touched them.

We grew very fond of these children, and when the time came, we left them with more than a passing regret.[97]

This has uniformly been the experience of all who have known these remarkable people. The fact is that the Okinawan and the Australian child, by being adequately loved, has developed an ego-structure which is cooperative within itself and with others, which is not in conflict with itself, which has learned to love because it has itself been loved. In short, the aboriginal child has received a fundamental training in being related to itself and to other people. And this is achieved in the mother-child relationship.

The biological basis of cooperation, in short, has its origins in the same sources as social behavior, namely, in the process of reproduction. Social, cooperative behavior is the continuation and development of the maternal-offspring relationship; it is therefore as old as life itself, and in spite of recent appearances to the contrary the movement of evolution has, in man, been increasingly directed toward the fuller development of cooperative behavior.[98] Cooperative behavior has great survival value. When social behavior is not cooperative it is diseased behavior. The dominant principle which informs all behavior which is biologically healthy is love. Love, social behavior, cooperation, and security mean very much the same thing. Without love the other three cannot exist. To love thy neighbor as thyself is not simply good text material for Sunday morning sermons, but perfectly sound biology.

Men who do not love one another are sick—sick not from any disease arising within themselves, but from a disease which has been encultured within them by the false values of their societies. Belief in false values, in competition instead of cooperation, in narrow selfish interests instead of altruism, in atomism (especially atom- and hydrogen-bombism) instead of universalism, in the value of things and of money instead of the value of life and of man, represents man turning upon all that is innately good in him.

Man's sense of mutuality and cooperativeness may be suppressed, but so long as man continues to exist it cannot be destroyed, for these are traits which are part of his protoplasm.[99] His combativeness and competitiveness arise from the frustration of his need to cooperate. These are important facts to bear in mind at a time when all the surface evidence seems to point in a contrary direction. The word of the moment may be "fission"—whether with respect to physics or human affairs—but "fusion" comes much closer to reflecting man's natural behavior patterns.

Science points the way to survival and happiness for all mankind through love and cooperation. Do what we will our drives toward goodness and good will are, biologically, as basically determined as are our drives toward breathing. Our highly endowed potentialities for social life have been abused to pervert and deny their nature, and this has led us close to the brink of disaster, a disaster which spells doom, unless we realize what we have done and take the proper steps to undo it before it is too late. For we cannot deny the power of the world forces which we share with all life and which have reached their highest development in our potentialities as human beings, without destroying ourselves.

10 EXPERIENCE, CULTURE, AND PERSONALITY

Man is mind, and the situation of man as man is a mental situation.
—KARL JASPERS*

SECURITY AND LOVE

That love constitutes for the infant an assurance of support, of security, is a fact which has been discussed at some length. Love, for the child, *is* security—emotional security. The need for love arises out of the infantile dependency state, and by being loved the child in its turn learns to love. Love is the first stimulus toward social development, and there is good reason to believe that a lack of love in infancy produces an anxiety-ridden personality. Just as aggression always results from frustration, so insecurity always results from a lack of love. Furthermore, this holds true for the person throughout life, no matter what his previous psychical history. The person who, as an adult, finds himself or believes himself to be unloved, no matter how much he may have been loved at an earlier age, feels isolated and insecure. He may attempt to fall back upon his wealth, his prestige, or his power. A good example of this is provided by the hero of Orson Welles' film *Citizen Kane*. Deprived as a young child of the love of his parents, and brought up in the emotionally arid environments provided by sepulchral-looking steel-vaulted trustees, Kane develops as a power-drunk, essentially lonely person. He surrounds himself with people whose services he attempts to buy, with women whose affection he unsuccessfully tries to win, with stupendous quantities of possessions and enormous estates, but the one thing

* Karl Jaspers, *Man In The Modern Age*, London, Routledge, 1933.

249

which escapes him is love. This he never contrives to secure. Money and power, he finds are no substitutes for love. As he lies upon his bed dying he grasps in his hand a simple toy—a snow-flake globe reminiscent of the day when he was forcibly deprived of his parents' love and protection, and the last word he utters is "Rosebud"—the name of his sled, with which he had been playing on that unforgotten day when he was literally torn from the home to which he was never to return. "Rosebud," the symbol of all he had lost and never been able to recover. Such persons are tragedies to themselves, and when they are in strategic positions, exert a tremendous influence upon their societies, and all too frequently upon the direction of world affairs involving the lives of millions of human beings.[1] This in itself would constitute a good reason for throwing all possible light upon the relationship between love in the socialization of the individual and the functioning personality.

FRUSTRATION

Since nonsatisfaction or inadequate satisfaction constitutes thwarting of expected gratification, that is, *frustration,* it would be well to consider here the effects of frustration upon animals under experimental conditions, as well as upon man.

Hunt has shown that the effects of frustration upon the infant albino rat persist into adulthood. The halves of each of two litters of albino rats were submitted to a controlled feeding schedule of fifteen days beginning at the twenty-fourth day of life. Control animals from all litters were allowed free feeding. After a period of five months, during which both experimental and control animals had been allowed only one feeding a day for five days, the results were very illuminating. The infantile frustrates in the 24-day group hoarded more than two and one-half times as many pellets as their litter-mate controls. The infantile frustrates in the 32-day group hoarded approximately the same number of pellets as their litter-mate controls. It is evident that the effects of frustration did endure into adulthood. Hunt has explained these results by assuming that the hunger aroused in the adult feeding frustration served as a conditioned stimulus. This set off hunger-anxiety in those animals that had suffered sufficiently severe hunger in infancy, so that the total excitation aroused by this adult experience was greater than that in the control animals. Hunt argues that the reason traces failed to endure in the 32-day group was because, being older and better developed, the same feeding schedule that was effective for the 24-day group was sufficiently less severe for them so that it failed to fix the traces of the infantile experience.[2]

Fredericson has reported the results of an experiment devised to test the effects of infantile experience upon adult behavior. The problem was to test the hypothesis that a limited period of competition for food during infancy will result in competitive behavior at a later stage in development, despite the absence of hunger. For this purpose three strains of highly inbred mice were used, the 50 animals involved in the experiment being for each strain virtually identical. The sexes were approximately equally represented. The animals were weaned at 21 days of age, and lived in pairs, males with males and females with females.

The techniques which elicited competition over food consisted of presenting a given pair of hungry mice with a single piece of hard laboratory food. The experimental design consisted of two separate experiments, each with its own litter-mate controls.

The first experimental group was given seven one-a-day trials in competition beginning at 29 days of age. Retested at 72 days of age when they were not hungry these mice were found to compete over food. Their litter-mate controls, that had received no experience in food deprivation or competition over food, tested when not hungry at 72 days did not compete or fight over food.

The second experimental group received only a single experience in competition over food at 33 days of age. This group, when retested at 72 days of age, fought and competed over food. The litter-mate controls, that had never been exposed to competition over food, retested at 72 days did not compete over food when not hungry.

Both control groups competed for food as soon as they were deprived of it, but not when they were not deprived of it; whereas the mice that had experience of competition over food in infancy competed as mature animals even when they were not hungry and it was unnecessary for them to do so. The interesting fact is that but a single experience in infancy over food deprivation and competition was sufficient to determine similar behavior in adult life in those mice. Fredericson concludes that the results of his experiments support theories of personality which emphasize the importance of infantile experience.[3]

In another study Fredericson suggests that the food acts like a conditioned stimulus which elicits competition when the animals are not hungry.[4] This would seem so for the animals do not appear to be in any way frustrated, and there is no other obvious reason why they should compete other than that they were conditioned to do so at the sight of the food in infancy.

Kahn has shown that young mice which are attacked and beaten before the age when they would normally fight are, when placed in situations which would usually stimulate them toward fighting, much more inhibited than are animals which are only defeated as adults.[5] Similar observations have been made by Scott and Marston.[6]

Kahn also found suggestive evidence clearly indicating that mice which had early been isolated from their mothers were somewhat more defensive, strikingly more aggressive, and less investigating than those reared to maturity by the mother.[7]

King and Gurney found that male mice (I) that had been isolated from contact with all animals at 20 days were less aggressive as adults than (M) male rats that had been raised exclusively, after their 20th day, with males, and those that had been raised (F) exclusively with females. Groups M and F were almost equally aggressive, and Group I much less so. Group F tended to be slower to enter into combat than Group M animals. The experimenters suggest that mice raised in groups learn to be aggressive through competitive associations, this learning making them more ready to fight than those raised in isolation. Alternatively they suggest that innate tendencies to aggressiveness may be inhibited in direct proportion to the strangeness of the situation. Animals without early associations being more strange to each other than those with early associations, and are therefore more inhibited in a potential fighting situation.[8]

On the assumption that an adequate amount of sucking represents a definite need which must be fulfilled, Levy took two puppies from a litter of six and put them on controlled bottle feeding. All conditions, with the exception of the time devoted to sucking, were kept as constant as possible for 20 days. One pair of puppies did their sucking from nipples in which the holes were small. This pair was also given supplementary opportunities for sucking; these were the "long-time feeders." The other pair, the "short-time feeders," were fed from nipples with large holes. In test situations the short-time feeders showed a tendency to prolonged sucking of all kinds of objects between meals. These observations led Levy to conclude that thumb-sucking in human infants could be similarly explained by their having had inadequate opportunities to satiate the sucking impulse.[9] Ross, confirming these findings, observed that puppies that had early been deprived of their mother tended to exhibit excessive non-nutritional sucking.[10]

In a similar study on chickens Levy, assuming the existence of a pecking need that would require satisfaction, found that chicks raised on wire mesh which restricted the amount of pecking to a minimum were more restless, had a lower average weight, showed more preening behavior and more pecking at droppings and at the wall than did chicks of the same stock which were raised under similar conditions except that the floor of their pen was earth. The restricted chicks were very much more aggressive than the unrestricted chicks, indulged in more feather picking, and virtually denuded their less aggressive pen-mates.[11] Hymovitch has shown that the early perceptual environment to which rats are exposed is influential in determining their later adult learning.[12]

Even more valuable and more to the point than these studies is the totally unpremeditated series of observations made by Hammett in 1921,[13] entirely without reference to and without any prescient knowledge of such problems as are being discussed here. Reference has already been made to these studies.

While making studies of thyroparathyroidectomized albino rats of the genetically homogeneous Wistar stock, Hammett noted that some of the animals did not die. It had been thought by many observers that such an operation must invariably prove fatal, presumably owing to the action of some toxic substance upon the nerve elements.

Hammett found that the operated rats were actually drawn from two separate groups of rats, and that the greater percentage of survivors came from the "Experimental Colony." In this colony the animals had been petted and gentled, whereas the animals exhibiting the higher mortality rate were drawn from the "Standard" stock, a group whose only human contact was that incident to routine feeding and cage-cleaning. These animals were timid, apprehensive, and high-strung. When picked up they were tense and resistant, and frequently exhibited fear and rage by biting. *"The picture as a whole is one of constant high irritability and neuromuscular tension"* (p. 199).

The behavior of the gentled group was in marked contrast to that of the Standard colony animals. The former had been gentled for five generations. When picked up the gentled animals were relaxed and yielding. They were not easily frightened. "They give a uniform picture of placidity. The threshold of the neuromuscular reactions to potentially disturbing stimuli is almost prohibitively high."

So far as their relations to human beings are concerned it is obvious that the group of rats which had been gentled felt secure in the hands not only of those who fondled them but of all human beings. The laboratory attendant had brought them up under conditions during which they were frequently gently handled, stroked, and had kindly sounds uttered to them, and they responded with fearlessness, friendliness, and a complete lack of neuromuscular tension or irritability. The exact opposite was the case with the ungentled rats, the rats which with reference to their relations with human beings had received no attention from them whatever, except that incident to feeding and cage-cleaning. These animals were frightened and bewildered, anxious and tense in the presence of human beings. This constitutes a very interesting confirmation on lower animals of conditions which we know to exist among children brought up under not dissimilar circumstances.

Let us see what happened when thyroid and parathyroid glands were removed in the 304 animals operated from both groups. Within 48 hours of operation 79 per cent of the irritable rats died, while only 13 per cent of the gentled rats died—a difference of 66 per cent of survivals in favor of the gentled rats. When the parathyroids alone were removed, within 48 hours 76 per cent of the irritable rats died and only 13 per cent of the gentled rats died, a difference of 63 per cent.

Standard Stock rats, placed in the Experimental colony at weaning and gentled, became tame, cooperative and relaxed, and resistant to the effects of parathyroidectomy.

In a second series of experiments[14] Hammett investigated the mortality rate in parathyroidectomized untamed wild Norway rats which had been caged for one or two generations. The wild Norway rat is a very excitable creature. A total of 102 rats was used. Of this number 92, or 90 per cent, died within 48 hours, most of the survivors dying within two or three weeks of the operation.

Hammett concluded that the stability of the nervous system induced in rats by gentling and petting produces in them a marked resistance to the loss of the parathyroid secretion which in excitable rats normally results in death from acute parathyroidectomy in less than 48 hours. Later researches have given us a more detailed understanding of the mechanisms involved (see pp. 221-223).

The animal studies here briefly discussed suggest that the privations and frustrations suffered by the infant organism not only serve to produce a disharmoniously functioning personality, while the satisfaction of basic needs in an adequate manner serves to produce a more equilibrated personality, but also that, as in the case of Hammett's rats, positive evidence is available to the effect that such privations and frustrations produce substantial functional changes in the neurohumoral system which, through the agency of the autonomic system, express themselves in terms of differential viability under conditions in which the organism is exposed to insult or stresses of various sorts. Clinically this type of relationship between personality and viability under conditions of stress has been well known to physicians and surgeons for many years. The outcome of any disease or operation is always more promising in the well-balanced personality than in the anxious patient. The cheerful patient in general does much better than the cheerless one. All this constitutes good evidence that such differences in resistance, recovery rates, and viability, connected as they are with such differences in personality, represent actual differences in the organization of the nervous system. This suggestion is further corroborated by the evidence of psychosurgery. Persons suffering from depressive involutional neuroses, often leading to attempted suicide, who have either blown out their own frontal lobes or had them partially or wholly removed by operative means, often make remarkable recoveries in which more or less complete relief is obtained from the effects of the neurosis.[15]

When in such persons some part at least of the neurologic structures associated with the patterns of mental functioning of the person are destroyed, that pattern of functioning more or less disappears. The fact, however, scarcely needs to be emphasized that the experiences of the infant become a part of its nervous system and to a very large extent determine the pattern of functioning of that nervous system.

Hunt's work was inspired by Money-Kyrle's hypothesis, based on a comparative survey of primitive societies, that "Free feeding and late weaning would seem to promote generosity and optimism. Oral deprivation and early weaning would seem to promote stinginess and greed."[16]

Hunt's experiments on rats brilliantly confirm this suggestion. The probabilities, as we shall see, are high that Hunt's experimental observations may be legitimately generalized for human beings. Levy's experiments on puppies and chicks agree in almost every particular with the observations made on children under similar conditions.

INFANTS

Margaret Ribble has given an account of her observations on 600 infants with reference to early experience and behavior reactions which might be related to later personality disorders.[17] This work is still in progress, but certain results, which have already been briefly discussed in the light of Ribble's findings, will bear elaboration here. Ribble paid particular attention to the anxiety or tensional states of the infant, its metabolic economy, its circulation, the development of awareness, evidences of security and insecurity, respiratory and skin changes, pleasure getting, and the manner in which the tactile and kinesthetic senses participate in the child's primary orientation and development of its sense of reality. Ribble found that all these processes "are related to an innate need for contact with the mother, and that the mother who supplies this contact unstintingly fosters her child's development."

The infant obtains satisfaction for its physiological needs, the need for oxygen, the need to feel, the need to move, the need to suck—all needs quite as strong as the need for food—from the mere act of contact and being held, carried about, and fondled by the mother. Such acts are indispensably necessary if a well-equilibrated child is to develop. After the first week of postnatal life the human voice begins to exercise a peculiarly soothing effect. It is this satisfying effect of the human voice which gradually succeeds in reducing the infant's innate sensitivity to loud noises, as seen, for example, in the "startle reflex." Holding and fondling similarly serves to reduce the fear of falling which is seen in the Moro reflex. In children who have been inadequately mothered these reflexes tend to persist for an abnormally long period of time.

Proper mothering of the infant is a vitally important factor in bringing about a viable nervous integration of the organism, in conserving energy for mental growth, "and in making possible the sublimation of pleasure-getting, or what Freud has called sexual activities, in the interest of socially approved emotional and later intellectual development."

Ribble found that the reactions to inadequate mothering take one of two general forms in babies. They develop a form of negativistic excitement or a form of regressive quiescence.

Negativism

The negativistic reaction is displayed in a refusal to suck, in a more or less complete loss of appetite and an inability to assimilate food. The body muscles are hypertensed, breathing is shallow, and vomiting as well as periods of violent screaming are common. This corresponds to the phase of protest described on pages 214–216.

Regression

The regressive reaction is even more serious than the negativistic. Such infants when put to the breast or bottle make a few sucking movements in response to the stimulus situation, and then quickly fall into a stuporous sleep. The sucking reflex may altogether disappear, and there is a general loss of muscle and skin tone. The evidence indicates that this type of reaction is the result of frustration from too little peripheral stimulation. The organism simply regresses to a fetal state. Ribble believes that such privation interferes with the blood supply to the higher centers, in this way interrupting the developmental processes through which these centers are brought into action.

Treatment calculated to restore general and cerebral circulation, and to stimulate respiratory development, is generally successful enough to lend support to this interpretation. The regressive reaction is identical or at least similar to the disease of infancy already described and formerly known as infantile debility or marasmus. We have seen that this disorder, resulting from inadequate mothering, may result in serious biological as well as psychological damage to the organism.

MOTHERING AND LOVE

The child who has been inadequately mothered, who fails to receive a sufficient amount of love, generally fails to learn to love, and such children generally fail to become satisfactorily socialized. Such a child's personality development frequently follows a definite and predictable course. Both as a child and as an adult he continues to exhibit a marked dependency upon others, he is insecure, he is extremely jealous of his siblings, he is excessively dependent upon others for affection, he has an inordinate desire to be loved, and while he is himself *anxious* to return love, to love others, he finds himself quite incapable of doing so. An additional trait generally present in such persons is a state of anxiety which is a dominating and constant motive underlying much of their behavior. Observations which have been made on persons exhibiting many of these forms of behavior strongly point to the same causes: inadequate mothering during childhood. In some instances it is found that the mother died during the early childhood of the subject, in other instances it is found that the child had been left alone for considerable periods of time and given attention only at feeding time. We have already seen that further observations also strongly suggest that similar disturbances may be produced in a child which has been adequately mothered for several years, and then suddenly deprived of such mothering. The clinical literature affords innumerable examples of such cases.[18]

The feeling of helplessness, of hopelessness, and the depressions and depressive states accompanying such feelings, may in most cases be traced back to failure of expected satisfactions especially in the oral phase of development. Unable to satisfy its own nutritional needs, "to get affection, to be loved, to be taken care of, to get 'supplies'" results in a profound feeling of helplessness. As Edward Bibring points out, "Frequent frustrations of the infant's oral needs may mobilize at first anxiety and anger. If frustration is continued, however, in disregard of the 'signals' produced by the infant, the anger will be replaced by feelings of exhaustion, of helplessness and depression. This early self-experience of the infantile ego's helplessness, of its lack of power to provide the vital supplies, is probably the most frequent factor predisposing to depression."[19]

Whenever we meet with a failure to function as an adequate

human being we may be certain that the cause or causes are to be looked for in the love relationships of the person during the first six years of his life. For our purposes we place great emphasis on the importance of love in the socialization of the person because it is through the means of love that the infant first develops a consciousness of himself in relation to another person—the fundamental social relationship. By being loved the child learns to love. By being loved the organization of potentialities receive the only requisite stimulation which encourages their further development, and self-gratification becomes indissolubly associated with the gratification of another object, with gratification directed towards another object —the mother—and this is the beginning of the process of actively learning to love and cooperate with others.

FREUDIAN AND NEO-FREUDIAN CONCEPTS

Freud's concept of mental life as an interplay of reciprocally urging and checking forces is most useful in enabling us to understand those processes of mental development which are observable in infant and child. Perhaps we may attempt here a brief and tentative unification of the psychoanalytical parameters of the structure of the mind with some of the concepts which have thus far been developed.

The Id and Basic Needs

The most primitive and unconscious source of all the unregulated urges of the person, in which the desire for gratification reigns supreme, is designated by the psychoanalyst as the *id*. The id may be identified with the source from which the basic needs draw their energies.

The Ego and the Culturally Organized Personality

The id or basic drive supplies the energies, and the organization of the id is brought about by the modifications imposed upon it by the external world. This complex of organized drives is the *ego*. The ego is never entirely differentiated from the id. Part of the ego is unconscious and part conscious. The ego may be identified with the culturally organized personality, the civilization of the person.

The Super-Ego and the Value System of the Person

The *super-ego* is an outgrowth and modification of the ego. Its special function in relation to the ego is to rule it. It is essentially the same as conscience. It is to a great extent unconscious, and largely inaccessible to the ego, though in free communication with the id. The super-ego represents the integrated value system of the person.

According to Freud the unsocialized infant directs its libido mainly along one channel, toward its own body (*autoerotism*). Through the stimulation of the mothering process it learns to direct much of its libido toward external love objects (*alloerotism*), while always diverting a part of the libidinal energy in the direction of the self or ego (*narcissism*). Quite obviously, then, failure to receive adequate gratification from external sources will maintain the person in his autoerotic and narcissistic activities. The development from selfish to altruistic behavior is arrested.

On the other hand, the evidence which has become available since Freud's brilliant speculations in this field indicates that the unsocialized infant directs only a part of its libido toward its own body; that, indeed, most of its libido is directed outward toward securing satisfactions for itself, and not inward, as Freud suggests. The evidence indicates, rather, that the inward direction of libido follows only when the infant's attempts to secure satisfaction from outside, from other objects, have been unsuccessful. It is not then a matter of failure to receive adequate gratification from external sources being responsible for the maintenance of autoerotic and narcissistic activities, but it is rather that in the face of such failures the infant turns its libido inward, toward itself, in order to secure those gratifications from and for itself which it failed to receive from external sources. And it is not that development from selfish to altruistic behavior is arrested, but rather that selfish behavior is produced as a result of the failure to cooperate with the infant, as a result of the failure to stimulate it toward altruistic behavior, by being altruistic toward it.

Banham, on completing her study of over 900 children between four weeks and four years of age, concluded as follows:

> There seems little evidence from the observation of infant behavior that "self-love" comes first in the development of human affections. "Other love" is rather the first to appear, and develops along with the child's differentiating percept, and later with his concept of the human being who cares for him. The child is apparently unaware of, and unconcerned about himself. Certainly, he finds objects of interest to explore and sense. At about three months of age he discovers and watches his fingers, he listens to his own babbling and cooing; but his striving, excited affectionate behavior is directed towards another human being, usually mother.[20]

MOTHERING, SOCIALIZATION, AND CULTURE

It cannot be too often repeated that in the dependency relationship of the child to its mother, and later to the father and older persons, is to be seen the primary socializing pattern, a pattern which is variously elaborated throughout one's life. This consists first in the mothering which serves not only to stimulate the development of the infant but also to preserve, by a sympathetic indulgence of its wants, something of the continuity between intrauterine and extrauterine existence. As the infant develops, the indulgence of his wants is gradually changed into a series of regulatory pressures calculated to educate him in the skills and restraints demanded by his social group. This at the same time lays the basis for later attitudes of friendliness, affection, and trust. As Mowrer and Kluckhohn point out, "By withholding the adult cooperation which is so essential to the infant, the parent has constantly at his command a device for increasing the infant's variable, exploratory behavior and for then selectively rewarding (by responding to) those new, more adult-like responses which make their appearance."[21]

In this manner parents make the reward of their love conditional upon the child's making the required response. Such love has been termed *conditional love*.[22] It is because the child is dependent upon others for his satisfactions that he learns to adjust himself to the conditions they set. In studying the processes of socialization we are studying the progressive formation of patterns of behavior in response to social stimuli—the endowing with form of the previously unformed, the organization of the unorganized, the conditioning of certain responses to particular stimuli or patterns of stimuli of social value. Since the stimulus conditions the response, the character of the stimulus must serve as the criterion of the social response. Murphy, Murphy, and Newcomb therefore offer the following definition: "Social responses are those which appear in response to human beings, or to a combination of stimuli in which persons have an important place."[23]

This definition seems unnecessarily to limit the meaning of the social as far as the child is concerned, and also, for that matter, so far as the adult is concerned, particularly in view of the well-known animistic tendencies of the child, that is, the tendency to endow all objects, animate and inanimate, with animate personalized powers, powers which it is possible to commune with and, to some extent, to control. On the other hand, if we take the stimulus as the criterion of the social response, then any stimulus having some social value is capable of evoking a social response. Since the infant shows evidence of regarding almost all things which he experiences in the social situation as objects with which he can interact in a cooperative and mutually satisfying manner, it is not persons alone, in the adult sense of that word, to which he makes social responses, since most objects with which he comes into contact are for the first few years of his life treated as personified objects. The distinction between the animate and the inanimate, between persons and objects, between the absolute value of the immediacy of his own perception and the relativistic value of other people's points of view, are all phenomena of the later childhood socialization process. Furthermore, a vast number of inanimate objects, of artifacts, come to assume more or less considerable social significance, in the sense of eliciting social responses. A crucifix, a flag, a book, a painting, apparel, and a thousand and one other things are all, of themselves, capable of eliciting social behavior principally in terms of socially learned responses to socially significant stimuli. In short, anything which is learned to be a social stimulus to which certain responses must be made is by definition within the energy field of the social, since it is capable of evoking a social or cultural response.

This view of the social has, perhaps, been unduly neglected by many writers on the socialization process, but without a full realization of its significance an important part of that process and its dynamics will be overlooked. The cultural artifacts and the objects of the natural environment in vital association with which the person grows up play a very important role in the socialization of the person. These objects are all endowed with value, and it is necessary to understand that this value originates in basic needs which are culturally satisfied in particular ways according to what is traditionally given in any culture. In that sense the consciousness of the person becomes, as it were, a cultural artifact.[24]

The socialization of the person is largely determined by the operation upon him of cultural processes peculiar to the given society in which the person develops. What a person will think and do socially is a function of the culturalization process to which he has been exposed plus the modifying effects which his own individual constitutional potentialities exert in interaction with that process. We believe, as Frank has put it, that "culture coerces and dominates the individual, through the ideas, conceptions, beliefs and patterns with which he orders and explains his experience, directs his efforts and guides his conduct."[25] This process begins at birth and continues throughout life.

CULTURE AND GENETICS

The question is often raised, and in a period which has seen the doctrine take on so insidious and perfidious a form it is a question more frequently asked than ever before: How can we be certain that culture is not something which is to a large extent determined by conditions which are genetically more dominant than cultural factors? May it not be that biological factors peculiar to each group are really the determining ones in giving its character to any particular culture? In the cunningly devised words of a leading Nazi educator, Alfred Baeumler:

History has shown, and daily shows anew, that man can be trained to be nothing that he is not genuinely, and from the beginning, in the depths of his being; against this law, neither precept, warning, punishment, nor any other environmental influence avails. Realism in the study of man does not lie in attributing evil tendencies to him, but in recognizing that all that man can do emerges in the last resort from himself, from his innate qualities.[26]

This is modestly described as thinking "Copernically" when most others are still thinking "Ptolemaically." Perhaps an unfortunate slip on the part of Herr Baeumler, in view of the fact that Copernicus belonged to an allegedly subhuman "race," for Copernicus was a Pole.

What evidence do we have which significantly bears on such statements? There is, of course, the evidence of America itself where the descendants of immigrants of innumerable nationalities and ethnic groups—English, Scotch, Irish, German, Dutch, French, Italian, Japanese, and others—have become virtually completely identified with American culture.[27] Some groups have not become thoroughly identified with American culture because they have never been permitted to do so, but the influence of the American social environment has been so great that the members of these groups have undergone socialization in a very distinctly more American than foreign manner. The cultural changes which have been wrought in the Japanese and Chinese immigrants into Hawaii have been striking.[28] Culturally, the Hawaiian Japanese and Chinese differ markedly from their Japanese and Chinese ancestors, and this applies to those Hawaiian Japanese and Chinese who have not intermarried.

If any more unequivocally clear cases than this may be called for, they can be readily supplied, thanks to the work of Ackerknecht, who has brought together the data concerning children of white parents abducted by North American Indians during the eighteenth and nineteenth centuries.[29] There are accounts of eight fairly well recorded life histories of such stolen children. All these children were abducted between the ages of four and nine years, with the exception of a girl who was taken in adolescence; all of them forgot their native culture, and even the girl who had been stolen when she was fifteen years of age became "completely" Indianized. In every case these "White Indians" resisted all attempts to persuade them to return to their white relatives and the culture of their birth. As Ackerknecht says, the white Indians seemed to have found "a kind of unity of thought and action and a kind of social cohesion which deeply appealed to them, and which they did not find with the whites, especially not with the pioneers. There is no doubt that this fact largely contributed to their staying with the Indians" (page 34). The remarkable thing about these "White Indians" is that they not only became completely Indianized culturally in the sense of manifesting purely Indian forms of social behavior, but they also developed all the physical powers of resistance said to be peculiar to Indians. Furthermore, most of them lived to be extremely old. Finally, all of them had acquired that facial expression and outward impassability characteristic of the Indians. Concerning four of these "White Indians" it is expressly recorded that having become accustomed to Indian ways they could no longer sleep in a white house or bed.

Such evidence should conclusively disprove the view that culture is something which will express itself in a genetically determined form, emerging from man's "innate qualities," no matter what the environmental influences to which he may be exposed.

11 ISOLATION VERSUS SOCIALIZATION

No man is an Island, entire of itself.
—JOHN DONNE, *Sixteenth Devotion*

IS HUMAN STIMULATION NECESSARY FOR DEVELOPMENT?

What grounds have we for believing that intimate interactive social relations are necessary with another person or persons if the organism is to become socialized? How do we know that a normal individual, left entirely to himself from birth to adult age, would not develop characteristically human forms of behavior?

The answer is that we know with certainty that infants born without the normal sense necessary for the perception of their environments, and without the ability to communicate with others, remain completely unsocialized until some other form of social communication is established with them. The classic cases of the blind deaf-mutes Laura Bridgman and Helen Keller[1] are most illuminating in this connection. Until each of these children had learned the finger alphabet—in other words, communication through the skin— they were virtually completely cut off from interactive social relations with other human beings. They were isolated, and the world in which they lived held little meaning for them; they were almost completely unsocialized. But after the patient efforts of their teachers had succeeded in enabling them to learn the finger alphabet, the world of symbolic communication was opened to them, and development as a social human being proceeded apace. In spite of their blindness and deaf-mutism, the other senses of these children were normal, and from their birth they had been surrounded by other persons, so that it is not true to say that they were completely cut off from all contact with other human beings. The fact is that both children did learn some things from their association with other human beings through the sense of touch, but this was a minimal amount compared to what they learned as soon as they were enabled to communicate efficiently through the symbolic language of the manual alphabet.

Kamala and Amala

Cases more unequivocally clear than these, in spite of a large literature on isolated children, are difficult to cite. The literature has been fully, though not altogether critically, surveyed by Zingg in his book *Wolf-Children and Feral Man*.[2] The occasion for this book was the publication of the diary kept and edited by the late Reverend J. A. L. Singh of the day-by-day history of Kamala and Amala, the so-called "wolf-children" of Midnapore (India). Since this account of the wolf-children in relation to the problem of socialization has been accepted somewhat uncritically by many persons, and has gradually crept into sociology textbooks, it may be useful to examine it here.

Natives and other villagers claimed to have repeatedly seen two children, emerging together with several wolves from an ant-hill which served as the den of these strange companions. According to his own account, while traveling in the company of two Anglo-Indians who witnessed the event, Mr. Singh captured or rescued the two children from the wolves' den at Godamuri, Midnapore, on October 17, 1920. At the time of their rescue it was estimated that the younger child, Amala, was about eighteen months old, while the older one was estimated to be about eight years of age, named Kamala. When taken by the wolves it is assumed that each of the children was about six months of age, and that they had been abducted from different families. Amala died on September 21, 1921. Kamala died on November 14, 1929. Thus, Amala was observed for almost a year, and Kamala for nine years.

When rescued or liberated, it is reported, Kamala and Amala

were unable to stand in the erect position, but habitually progressed on all fours. They ate raw meat and entrails in what is alleged to have been wolf fashion, were without sphincter control, howled like wolves, preferred the society of dogs to that of human beings, and so on. They were entirely without speech and all those other attributes which we have come to regard as specifically human.

Unfortunately, Mr. Singh's account of these children rests on the completely unsupported testimony of one person—Mr. Singh. Affidavits testifying to the good character and truthfulness of Mr. Singh have been issued by his Bishop and the local magistrate, to both of whom he was well known. Four well-known scientists contribute forewords to the book testifying to its genuineness. Notwithstanding such testimonials and any impression of genuineness which Mr. Singh's record may make upon us, one cannot, with all the good will in the world, accept such unconfirmed statements as facts. Verification is a cardinal principle of scientific method, and it is not a principle that can ever be suspended. Whether or not children have ever been reared by animals can only be determined by observation, not necessarily premeditated, carried out under conditions which provide the means of verification. Hundreds of stories and legends have as their theme the rearing of children by animals, and the investigation of these stories constitutes a legitimate and significant activity, but most of the time that activity falls into the realm of folklore rather than fact. Our task must be dispassionately to evaluate the worth of such stories.

There are certain statements in Mr. Singh's account which render the whole work suspect.

Mr. Singh states that two Anglo-Indians witnessed the rescue of the children from the wolves' den, but that one is untraceable and the other dead. Why, during all the years that Mr. Singh was making observations on Kamala, did he make no attempt to obtain statements from these and other men who were alleged to have been present at the rescue? Does one keep such records as Mr. Singh kept merely for the sake of the record? Does one not usually keep such records in order to make the information contained in them available to others? Mr. Singh obviously realized the importance of the subject he was presumably seeking to illuminate; why then did it not occur to him to get the facts of the rescue fully corroborated by his witnesses?

Kamala is presumed to have been kept in the wolves' den for seven and a half years. But wolves do not keep their young for anything like so long a period under normal conditions. Is it likely that they would have departed from the universal practice of wolves in the case of Kamala?

Could a six-month-old child be suckled by a wolf? It is possible, but it is difficult to imagine why a wolf would want to do so troublesome a thing.

Even if the statement were fully corroborated that the children were found together with the wolves in their den, that in itself would not constitute evidence that they were brought there by wolves, nor that they had been suckled and reared by them. Mr. Singh states that Kamala and Amala used to howl regularly almost every night at about ten o'clock, and at one and three o'clock in the morning. The idea that wolves howl at regular hours every night is a widespread folk belief that is not borne out by the observations of such trained scientists as have had an opportunity to study their habits. What was obviously intended as an irrefutable indication of the children's lupine nature serves, rather, to arouse further doubts as to the accuracy of the narrative.

The statement that the children were not observed to sweat probably constitutes yet another example of the influence of folkloristic belief upon Mr. Singh's judgment. The widespread notion that dogs do not sweat except through the tongue is untrue. Dogs have numerous sweat glands on every part of the body.[3] But for the purposes of Mr. Singh's narrative, since dogs and wolves are closely related— and since the wolf-children were alleged to have adopted the habits of wolves—it must follow that wolf-children do not sweat.

The eyes of the children are said to have emitted a blue light at night. "Night glare" is a phenomenon not unknown in human beings, but it is a condition of such rarity that the chances against it ever occurring in two individuals living together are so astronomically high that we are forced to give up all attempt at normal explanation. The necessary extreme myopia or hypermetropia may have been present, but there is no evidence of any such conditions in Mr. Singh's account. I have been unable to find any record of children who were brought up in darkness exhibiting a like phenomenon. It is difficult to conceive of the special structure necessary, the tapetum, developing as a special adaptation to the conditions of life of Amala and Kamala. But what is even more difficult to conceive is the emission of "a peculiar blue glare, like that of a cat or a dog, in the dark" without the presence, as far as one can gather, of any external source of light. This, in fact, is quite impossible, for the light must always be of external origin.

As for the "blue" glare itself, this would appear to be impossible in the case of human beings, for the simple reason that the only possible source of such "glaring" is the fundus (the posterior portion of the base of the eye), and this normally reflects either a dark red, or an orange-yellow color. The blue eye glare of cats and dogs and many other animals is due to the reflective action of particles in the tapetum ("bright carpet"), a specialized layer of cells situated either in the choroid immediately behind the retina or in the retina itself, cells similar to those which in the human iris produce the appearance of the normal blue eye, but which in the latter case have no connection with "night glare." In the offspring of Malayan-Negro crosses it is said that the fundus, through the ophthalmoscope, may appear somewhat bluish, depending upon the presence of certain pigment particles, or even gray, but it is doubtful whether in such cases one could obtain a bluish or grayish glare from the eyes. In those rare instances when "night glare" has been recorded in man, the reflection was dark red or, in the case of glioma of the retina, a yellowish reflection.[4]

There are numerous other difficulties[5] which could similarly be discussed. But let us come to the point. Mr. Singh claimed that Amala and Kamala were reared by wolves. What evidence exists in support of this claim? The answer is: *None.*

Were Amala and Kamala abandoned by their parents? No one knows. Were they congenitally defective in any way? Their unsatisfactory portraits tell us nothing. If these children were not congenitally defective then it would be a reasonable inference to draw that their retardation, or rather nondevelopment as human beings, was due to the fact that during the critical period of their development they were practically isolated from the conditioning influences of human interstimulation.

It was during this conditioning period that, the wish apparently being father to the thought, it is assumed they spent their lives with wolves, living the life of wolves, so that behaviorally they became what they were assumed to have been conditioned by—the socializing influence of wolves.

The evidence, it is to be feared, is not good enough, but taking the matter from the general standpoint of the development of behavior, one thing is certain: Given all the necessary normal potentialities, the human organism does not normally become a person simply by virtue of being born into the species *Homo sapiens;* indeed, he cannot become a person unless he is exposed to the socializing influences of other persons. The attributes of personality are a function of human society, of persons in interaction, of human socializing factors acting upon potentialities capable of being personalized.

The Case of Anna

A valuable account of the effects of extreme social isolation upon the development of a child has been given by Kingsley Davis.[6] This is the case of Anna, a girl who from the age of about eight months until her discovery five years later, on February 4, 1938, had been isolated in a storage room situated on the second floor of a farmhouse some seventeen miles from a small Pennsylvania city. The official who first saw the child reported that "the child was dressed in a dirty shirt and napkin. Her hands, arms and legs were just bones, with skin drawn over them, so frail she couldn't use them. She never had enough nourishment. She never grew normally, and the chair on

which she lay, half reclining and half sitting, was so small the child
had to double her legs partly under her." When removed to the
local county home Anna was in a completely apathetic state, she lay
limp in a supine condition, immobile, expressionless, and indifferent
to everything. She was believed to be deaf and possibly blind, and
she exhibited all the symptoms of chronic malnutrition of the non-
rachitic kind. No sign of organic disease, however, could be discovered apart from the effects of malnutrition.

Her history up to this time from birth was as follows: Anna was
born in a private nurse's home on March 6, 1932. Shortly afterwards
she was taken to a children's home, and for a time she was boarded
with a practical nurse. She was said to have been a perfectly normal,
even beautiful child. Between the age of six and ten months she was
taken back to her mother's home because no financial means could be
found to support her in an outside home. At home she was confined
in one room, where she was fed on a diet consisting solely of milk.
Apart from feeding her the milk the mother paid absolutely no
attention to her. This was her second illegitimate child. Her own
father (the maternal grandfather of the child) wished never to set
eyes on it, and so the mother, a high-grade moron or dull normal,
took this means of keeping it out of the way. Anna's brother ignored
his sister except to mistreat her occasionally.

The bedroom in which Anna was kept reclining on a broken
chair contained a double bed on which mother and son slept. Such
contacts as Anna had with her mother and brother, except for being
fed with milk by the mother, were of a perfunctory or openly antagonistic kind. Toward Anna's fifth birthday her mother began
feeding her some thin oatmeal with a spoon, but Anna never learned
to eat solid food.

In Anna, then, we would seem to have a child who from about
the age of eight months was the victim of extreme social isolation.

Seen over a period of months by Davis, Anna remained virtually
completely unsocialized.

Seen three days after she arrived in the county home (which had
but one nurse for 324 mostly deficient adult patients!) she had be-

come relatively active, was able to sit up when placed in a sitting position, and to move her hands, arms, head, eyes, and mouth quite freely. She had been given a high vitamin diet, massage, and some attention. She turned her head toward a loud-ticking clock when this was held near her, though other attempts to make her notice sounds, such as clapping hands or speaking to her, failed to elicit any response. All her reflexes were normal. In bed she jounced up and down rhythmically—an activity of which she was very fond. It is of interest to note that she very much liked having her hair combed.

She showed no reaction to toys, which she handled in a distracted manner without any element of play. She would frown and scowl in response to no observable stimulus. When physically restrained she exhibited considerable temper, did not cry and smiled only when coaxed. Her subsequent progress was somewhat slower.

Ten days later she was more alert, with greater ability to fix her attention, with more expression, and she handled herself better. Furthermore—and this is important—she had found her tongue in the physical sense. Whereas it had formerly lain inactive at the back of her mouth, she now stuck it out frequently, and with enjoyment. She showed some taste and visual discrimination, and was able to sit up and dangle her feet from the bed. She had learned one social stunt, rubbing foreheads with the nurse. She had not, however, learned to seek attention, to manifest needs, to chew, or to control her elimination.

A month later there was very little visible change except for a slight physical improvement. She laughed when tickled, and the nurse believed that Anna now recognized her. The doctor believed that she was congenitally deficient.

After another month Anna was more energetic, laughed a good deal, and is credited with having made a sound like "da."

A month later she had scarcely made any improvement, and on the performance tests given her by Davis she ranked below the one-year-old child.

Two months later she could walk when supported by making deliberate steps. Her interest in other persons had become more obvious, and her responses more definite and discriminating.

Three months later, on November 11, 1938, when she was removed from the county home, there were a few additional changes. She could barely stand while holding on to something. She obviously liked people, but she was still an unsocialized creature who had learned very little.

During the nine months in the county home she had actually received very little social stimulation; everything had been done for her with minimal encouragement to do everything for herself. She had never been disciplined or rewarded, and most of her care was turned over to adult inmates, many of whom were mentally deficient and scarcely able to speak themselves.

When seen again on December 6, 1938, three weeks after her removal to the foster home, Anna presented her visitors with a surprise—she had begun to learn. She could descend the stairs by sitting successively on each one, she could hold a doughnut and munch it like a normal child, she could hold and drink from a glass, and she could feed herself with a spoon. When one beckoned and called her, she would make an effort to come, smiling and going through excited extra motions.

As Davis suggests, this transformation was most probably due to the fact that in the foster home she was the sole object of one woman's assiduous care. "Her new guardian was using the same common-sense methods by which mothers from time immemorial have socialized their infants—unremitting attention, repetitive correction, and countless small rewards and punishments, mixed always with sympathetic interest and hovering physical presence. These Anna was getting for the first time in her life" (p. 561).

Three months later, March 19, 1939, Davis reports her accomplishments as follows (p. 561):

She was able to walk alone for a few steps without falling; she was responsive to the verbal commands of her foster-mother, seeming to understand in a vague sort of way what the latter wanted her to do; she definitely recognized the social worker who took her weekly to the doctor and who therefore symbolized to her the pleasure of an automobile ride; she expressed by anxious bodily movements her desire to go out for a ride; she seemed unmistakably to seek and to like attention, though she did not sulk when left alone; she was able to push a doll-carriage in front of her and to show some skill in manipulating it. . . . Limitations still remaining, however, were as follows: she said nothing—could not even be taught to say "bye-bye"; she had to be watched to tell when elimination was imminent; she hardly played when alone; she had little curiosity, little initiative; it seemed still impossible to establish any communicative contact with her.

It does not seem accurate to say, as Davis does, that it seemed impossible to establish any communicative contact with Anna. Obviously a number of things had been communicated to her through speech and physical training in the management of various objects and to some extent of herself. She could make more or less adequate responses to certain cues even though she was herself quite unable to speak. Anna herself, after a year of socializing experience maintained a comparatively passive role so far as communication with others was concerned, but that she had participated to a measureable extent in the communicative process can scarcely be doubted.

More than five months later, August 30, 1939—that is to say some eighteen months from the cessation of her period of isolation and the commencement of her exposure to socializing influences—Anna was taken from her foster-home and moved to a small school for defective children. At this time she was a stout girl some twenty pounds overweight for her age, which was seven years and five months. She could walk better and almost run, her toilet habits showed that she understood the whole procedure, and she manifested an obvious comprehension of many verbal instructions.

On November 6, 1930, she is reported as completely unable to speak, simply making gutteral and sucking noises, and wandering aimlessly about, without any ability to concentrate. Examined more than five months later, on April 25, 1940, by the late Professor Francis N. Maxfield, her hearing was found to be entirely normal, vision apparently normal, she was able to climb stairs, her speech was in the "babbling stage," and "promise for developing intelligible speech later seems to be good." On the Merrill-Palmer scale she made a mental score of 19 months. On the Vineland social maturity scale she made a score of 23 months. Professor Maxfield felt that with proper training she would eventually attain a mental level of six or seven years.

On July 1, 1941, the school for retarded children reported that Anna was 46 inches in height and weighed 60 pounds. She could bounce and catch a ball, and conformed to group socialization. Toilet habits were firmly established. Food habits were normal except that she still used a spoon as her sole implement. She could dress herself except for fastening her clothes. Most interesting of all, she had finally begun to develop speech. She was said to be at the two-year level in this respect. She could call attendants by name and could bring one in when asked to do so. She had a few complete sentences to express her wants.

By June 22, 1942, Anna had made slight progress.

[She] could follow directions, string beads, identify a few colors, build with blocks, and differentiate between attractive and unattractive pictures. She had a good sense of rhythm and loved a doll. She talked mainly in phrases but would repeat words and try to carry on a conversation. She was clean about clothing. She habitually washed her hands and brushed her teeth. She would try to help other children. She walked well and could run fairly well, though clumsily. Although easily excited, she had a pleasant disposition.

Unfortunately Anna died of pneumonia in 1943. The school in which she had been placed was a private school for feebleminded children with little to recommend it as a place of training. Davis strongly feels that Anna never received the attention necessary to overcome the initial social isolating handicaps which she suffered.

The question, of course, arises whether Anna was not in fact congenitally defective, and her slow development due to a significant extent to the limiting action of genetic factors. The mother was subnormal. On the Stanford Revision of the Binet-Simon Scale her performance was equivalent to that of an eight-year-old child, her I.Q. being 50, indicating mental deficiency of "middle grade moron type." Anna's father is believed to have been a 74-year-old man of normal mentality.

Congenital or Acquired Deficiency

The fact is that in the present state of our knowledge it is hardly possible to decide whether in such cases we are dealing with a congenital or an acquired deficiency. The quest for certainty in connection with such cases is highly desirable, for they are capable of throwing a great deal of light upon the nature of the interaction between the organic potentialities of the individual and the socializing influences to which he is exposed; hence it is more than ordinarily necessary that in our endeavor to secure such crucial case histories we should be on our guard against unwarranted assumptions and doubtful examples. We must not go beyond the evidence. Most of the accounts of isolated children which we have are unsatisfactory from many points of view.[7] In general the early history of the child is unknown, the genetic status of both parents insofar as their intelligence is concerned is likewise unknown, and the attempts to socialize such children following their removal from the isolating environment have not been systematic or adequate.

Characteristics of Isolated Children

Without discussing all the cases of isolated children which have been reported, a study reveals that they resemble each other in many particulars. For example, such children are unable to speak, though under special training they can acquire some speech. The senses of sight and hearing are functionally undeveloped; there is poor locomotor development, the child is completely nonsocial, and its capacity to become a normal social being is greatly impaired.

Such children by normal standards would be regarded as exhibiting the most pronounced form of amentia—idiocy, with an I.Q. of less than 20 points or two years. But these isolated children display traits in addition to those normally characteristic of congenital idiots which clearly indicate the effects of isolation and not of genetic limitations. These traits are the extreme deficiency of locomotor functions, the inability to walk and to run, as well as more or less functional blindness and deafness. While defective locomotor coordination and defects of sensation are also seen in idiots, it is rarely of this extreme type. Furthermore, whereas congenital idiots can rarely be trained to toilet habits, most isolated children can be so trained. These are important differences, for they suggest that some, at least, of the isolated children were probably not congenital idiots, and that their deficiently developed senses and locomotor abilities were produced by their peculiar conditions of isolation.

Toilet Control

A seemingly unimportant detail such as the ability to learn control of toilet habits indicates that the potentialities involved were present but that in isolation they were never organized in relation to a definite cultural setting. In most idiots the potentialities necessary are wanting owing to the defects of the nervous system. However, some idiots—the high-grade idiots or low-grade imbeciles of the three-year mental age level—can be trained in such habits. The crucial point here is that while all isolated children have been taught to control their elimination, most idiots cannot be so trained. It would be making too great demands upon the law of chance to assume that all the isolated children of whom we have accounts fell into the selected class of high-grade idiots. It would be more reasonable to conclude that in light of their ability to learn toilet habits they were probably not congenital idiots. Additional evidence in support of this conclusion is provided by their extreme locomotor deficiency, a deficiency which they learn to overcome to a considerable extent. This is not usually the case with congenital idiots.[8] If these children were feeble-minded to begin with, then it should have been possible to train them to do considerably more than they were able to achieve. The failure so to train them must be attributed, at least in part, to the effects of the absence of social stimulation at a critical period in the development of the person.[9]

GROWTH POTENTIALITIES OF THE NERVOUS SYSTEM

The work of Coghill and his school has made it abundantly clear that the potentialities for growth in the nervous system continue throughout the life of the person. Nerve cells spring up and grow according to a definite maturative pattern, and this pattern in the nervous system is established in its main outlines before nervous function, excitation, or exercise begins. The cellular potentialities for specific functions are laid down in the nervous system prior to the functional activities which are subsequently observed as behavior. Under the stimulation of the environment such cells begin to function as a dynamic system, dendrites and axons increase in length, they establish relations with adjacent and more remote neurones, and collaterals appear which link separated groups of cells. Experience does not determine these potentialities, but it does determine when and to what extent the potentialities of behavior shall develop into action. In the absence of the excitation of experience we do not know what happens in the nervous system. It is believed that under the influence of different modes of stimulation new specificities of sensitivity are constantly developing through the growth of dendrite terminals, each in relation to the different modes of stimulation. And Coghill suggests that it is such a progressive differentiation of sensitivity, under the stimulus of experience, that essentially constitutes the conditioning process.[10]

The reaction to the environment of the organism through its inherent potentiality for growth must play a part in the conditioning of its behavior. It is probable "that conditioning processes are registered in structural counterparts in the sense that neural mechanisms acquire functional specificity with reference to the experience. In the counterpart of the form of the pattern . . . the specificity of function is fixed by the relations into which the elements grow. In the counterpart of experience, on the other hand, specificity of function is established by interaction of growth and excitation, that is to say, the excitation fixes upon the growing terminals of neurones its own mode of activation." Thus, it seems very likely that the situations of experience "organize themselves into definite structural counterparts through the interaction of growth and excitation."[11]

The cortical cells of the organism begin their function with the beginning of experience "and grow as experience progresses till all the essential behaviour and conditioning processes are registered in them. Every pyramidal cell as a growing unit may be conceived as blending, so to speak, the experience of the individual from the beginning to the end of stimulation and response."[12]

In brief, the behavior of the organism must be considered the result of the growth potentials which determine its specificity plus the effect of experience which stimulates the growth of those potentials and renders possible the actual functioning of those specificities. In the absence of the stimulus of experience the development of functional behavior simply does not occur. Growth of functionally organized patterns of specificities does not take place. Obviously, upon such a theory man is more than the sum of his reflexes, drives, and reactions of all sorts. As Coghill puts it in the concluding words of his book, "Man is, indeed, a mechanism, but he is a mechanism which, within the limitations of life, sensitivity and growth, is creating and operating himself."[13] When, however, the stimulation necessary to operate himself is wanting, as in extreme cases of isolation from the time of infancy, he simply does not learn to do so, so that his physical development is largely and his mental development is completely arrested. Since there has been a minimum of environmental and absolutely no social stimulation, there is nothing but that minimum of environmental stimulation to organize, to fix upon, the growing terminals of the neurons, a minimal stimulation which maintains the organism at a virtually vegetative level. The absence of social stimulation simply results in a nonsocial being, or in neurological terms, in the failure of organization of neuron potentials into specific functioning morphological patterns.

It is possible for a child who has been deprived of the usual kinds of social stimulation from birth to five years to· recover adequate use of its body and sense following intensive training in socialization. Such a case is that of Isabelle. Before turning to the discussion of her case it were well to point out that each case of isolation is itself unique, in that the individual is unique to begin with, the experience of isolation has varied in each case, and there has been considerable variation in the subsequent attempts at socialization. Variability of this kind renders it necessary to proceed with caution when comparing cases. In a well-nourished though thoroughly isolated child, it would be difficult to envisage any real damage to the growth potentialities of the nervous system as the result of an entire absence of social or other environmental stimulation, other than that necessary for the maintenance of life. Nerve cells are not known to atrophy or lose their growth functions with disuse. Assuming, then, for the purpose of argument, that the isolated children of whom we have some knowledge, such as Anna, were normal babies to begin with, how could one account for the apparent damage to their nervous systems, the apparent interference with the growth potentials of the neuronal net?

We have already considered this question with respect to the separated child (see pp. 221–223). Doubtless similar factors are operative in the case of the isolated child, in addition to which chronic malnutrition may so disturb the metabolism of the brain as to do permanent injury to nerve cells and even cause death. The functional blindness of isolated children may have something of a morphological basis in that the nutritional disturbance may reduce the visual purple in the retina of the eyes to a low level.

The Case of Isabelle

Born in Ohio, apparently in April, 1932, Isabelle was discovered in November, 1938. She was then approximately six and a half years old. She was an illegitimate child, and for that reason, she and her mother, a deaf-mute, were secluded from the rest of the mother's family in a dark room where they spent most of their time together. Lack of sunshine and proper nutrition produced extreme rickets. As a result, Isabelle's legs were so bowed that when she stood erect the soles of her shoes came nearly flat together, and she moved about with a skittering gait. When found she resembled a wild animal more than anything else, mute and idiot-like. She was at once diagnosed by a psychologist as genetically inferior. However, a specialist in child speech, Dr. Marie K. Nelson, put her through an intensive and systematic training in speech, and in spite of all prognostications to the contrary succeeded not only in teaching her to speak normally, but to achieve with speech all the usual associated abilities. In two years she covered the stages of learning that normally require six. She did very well at school, participating normally in all school activities.[14]

The case of Isabelle conforms to the type picture of the isolated child with malnutrition, idiocy, and muteness, who, nevertheless under intensive training became a thoroughly normal socialized being. Malnutrition did not do any noticeable damage to the nerve cells of her brain, and her development to perfectly normal social adjustment strongly suggests that she probably received a certain amount of love from her mother during their joint confinement. Unfortunately, no data are available upon this point.

We know from cases such as those of Laura Bridgman and Helen Keller, and from our consideration of the basic needs and their satisfaction, that love can be conveyed to the child by many means other than those of speech. We are told that Isabelle communicated with her mother by means of gestures. Isabelle's sensory disabilities and her nonsocialization were due obviously and entirely to her prolonged isolation. Her ability to recover from its effects was almost certainly due to the fact that she had been adequately loved by her deaf-mute mother.

EXTREME ORGANIC HELPLESSNESS

The great power of love to reach beyond even the most extreme disabilities is illustrated by the following case.

George was born after a prolonged labor of 24 hours, during which he suffered severe cerebral damage. The result was extreme recurring athetosis or fairly complete lack of muscular control, as well as an aimlessness of movements. George could not learn to pronounce more than ten words. He could not stand or walk or balance his head, and could not hold an object even when it was placed in his hands. He was almost postureless and kinesthetically unaware. He did, however, learn to read, to play checkers, to read a clock, and because he received a great amount of loving care he managed to become a cheerful boy with whom other children liked to play. In spite of his handicaps he displayed great morale on many occasions, and before his death from appendicitis at the age of 14, he had made steady progress in social and emotional maturation. In the perception and appreciation of social relations his behavior suggested a considerable approximation to normality.

In spite of severe damage to the parts of the brain concerned with the control of tactile-muscular behavior and the consequent almost total physical disability, this child was nevertheless able to make a considerable social adjustment to the world in which he lived. This, most probably, he was able to achieve because of the great amount of loving attention which he received and which was mediated to him though his senses of vision and hearing, which had developed without any great impairment.[15]

The Case of Patty

As an example of the severe social damage which can be done to a child under anarchic socializing conditions, the case of Patty (here reported for the first time) is illuminating.

In the fall of 1948 Patty, aged three years, was brought to a New York hospital with a fractured elbow. The immediate disappearance of the mother and the child's frightful physical and psychological condition caused the authorities to institute inquiries, from which it transpired that Patty, the oldest of two children by different fathers, had been unbelievably maltreated. The mother, a prostitute, lived with the two children in one room of a four-room apartment occupied by another family. The remainder of the story is best told in the words of the nurse in whose charge Patty was placed on admission to the hospital.[16]

I was on duty the hectic morning that Patty K—— was admitted to the children's Ward of the N—— Hospital. Children were crying, nurses were hurrying to and fro and Patty looked terrified. Most children were frightened when they came to this new and strange place, but the remarkable difference about Patty was that she didn't cry but rather cringed from any person who approached her. Her mother had come to the ward with Patty but left immediately without even saying goodbye to the child.

It didn't take us long to discover that Patty didn't know how to eat. When given her tray of food, she would grab as much as she could hold in one hand (her broken arm had been set and put in a cast) and hide the food under the bedclothes. When she finally learned the food would not be taken from her she ate ravenously, as much as three traysfull per meal and anything given to her between meals. After one week of diligent training she learned to use a spoon and rarely slips from this practice now. Her capacity for food has greatly slackened so that she now eats a normal amount for a three year old.

Our greatest nursing problem with Patty was due to the fact that she was totally incontinent of urine and feces. After she had been with us about two weeks and had come to trust a few chosen people we attempted to toilet-train her. The first time I took her into the bathroom I didn't understand her screaming terror of the toilet. Later we learned she had been "toilet-trained" at home by being locked in the bathroom for two or three hours a day. The rest of the day she spent tied to a chair because she "stole food out of the icebox" according to her mother. At this point I might add that Patty is one of two illegitimate children by the same mother, each with a different father. The mother remains unmarried. After six weeks Patty is toilet trained to the extent that she goes into the bathroom willingly and daily has a bowel movement after breakfast and after lunch but not to the extent that she will tell us when she has to have an excretion. If any of us forget her for a few hours she is likely to have an accident. This is probably due (in part) to the fact that she is just learning to talk.

When Patty came to us she could say just three obscene words and the remainder of her vocabulary consisted of unintelligible mumblings. By this time Patty has learned a number of words and can say a few complete sentences. Her sentences are those frequently spoken by the nurses on the ward, such as "Here comes the Doctor." "Don't touch that," "I'll be right back," or "Stop it, Patty." The best feature is that Patty uses each sentence at the appropriate time.

For a long time we were perplexed as to what we could do about the child's constant denudative actions. Because she could not get the hospital gowns over her cast she just ripped them off. She would tear as many as five or six gowns a day. Finally we decided to buy some bright red overalls and a brightly colored shirt. It worked! She never has torn or taken off these clothes or the many others that have been given to her since. However, if made to stay in bed very long in the morning she invariably attracts attention by tearing off her hospital pajamas.

When Patty was first allowed out of bed to run about the ward her gait suggested propulsion. She would run headlong until she hit the wall or a door. She has overcome this, but her manner is still that of a child who has been so restrained that she runs wild when given freedom.

She has yet to learn how to play. It is a rare occasion for her to sit still as long as five minutes concentrating on one toy.

After eight weeks of a daily tub bath Patty is just now getting over her fear of the water. Plastic toys in the tub have helped us here. The child's mother has admitted that she didn't bathe Patty because "Patty doesn't like water." The numerous abscesses covering the little girl's legs and buttocks when she was brought to the hospital confirmed our guess that she hadn't been washed much.

Patty is beginning to have faith in more people. After the first week she started to come to us nurses of her own volition. Next she progressed to approaching anybody dressed in white, whether it be a lab technician, X-ray aide or nurse. Her greatest fear has been for any or all men, but she is slowly getting over that.

She had no idea of how to show affection. If she liked someone she tagged that person and continually butted them with her head. Now she can hug as well as the next child.

Since Patty has been with us, receiving a great deal of attention and affection, she has become extremely jealous of all the other children. The moment someone picks up a baby to cuddle, Patty is racing around the ward pulling linen from the beds, tearing up books and doing anything else that she knows will attract attention.

There is still a large amount of work to be done with this child and it will take someone with a great deal of patience and time to do it. We are hopeful that the little we have done will not be undone by sending her back to the home she came from, but rather that she can be placed in a good foster home.

Unfortunately it was not possible to follow the subsequent history of Patty.

It is evident that the social damage done to Patty was not as great as it would have been had she been completely isolated. What Patty was suffering from was extreme social neglect coupled with long-continued and massive frustrations, as evidenced by her importunate demands for love and her curiously aggressive behavior.

It is probable that Patty was born with, at least, normal intelligence potentialities. The poverty of the socializing stimuli to which she was exposed was such that she simply failed to develop as a normal social being. In other words, her development as a human being was largely determined and limited by the kind of social stimulation she received. Patty's history, as well as that of all the other isolated or quasi-isolated children cited in this chapter, suggests that the human organism develops as a person to the extent only to which it has received the adequate socially personalizing stimulations; in the absence of such stimulations it fails altogether to develop as a person, and its social competence is nonexistent.

With reference to all children, and with poignant reference to such children as Patty, this chapter may be concluded with the words of Alfred Adler:

The child's inclination to co-operation is challenged from the very first day. The immense importance of the mother in this respect can be clearly recognized. She stands on the threshold of the development of social feeling. The biological heritage of social feeling is entrusted to her charge. She can strengthen or hinder contact by the help she gives the child in little things, in bathing him, in providing all that a helpless infant is in need of. Her relations with the child, her knowledge, and her aptitude are decisive factors. . . . It may be readily accepted that contact with the mother is of the highest importance for the development of human social feeling. . . . *We probably owe to the maternal sense of contact the largest part of human social feeling, and along with it the essential continuance of human civilization.*[17]

12 THE DIRECTION OF HUMAN DEVELOPMENT

In the long run the fate of a civilization depends not only on its political system, its economic structure, or its military might. Perhaps, indeed, all of these ultimately depend in turn upon the faith of the people, upon what we believe and feel about Man; about the possibilities of human nature; about our relation or lack of it to such intangibles as the meaning of morality or the true nature of Value.

—JOSEPH WOOD KRUTCH*

HUMAN NATURE

What is a human being? That is the question this book set out to answer, though the question was phrased differently. We set out by inquiring into the nature of man's original nature and the manner in which that nature is influenced and conditioned to assume a socially functional form.

The kind of answer each person or society returns to the question: "What is a human being?" will largely determine the health of such persons and societies. What human beings and their societies *do* about human beings is determined by the inner attitudes motivating their outer acts.

In this last chapter let us recapitulate our main findings, and endeavor to draw the significant conclusions—conclusions which, in all humility, we hope may help humanity direct its own development toward the attainment of the optimum degree of health and happiness.

*Joseph Wood Krutch, "Speaking of books," *New York Times Book Review,* August 16, 1953, p. 2.

288

The Child Is Born Good

The age-old view that the human being is born "a natural barbarian," "an animal," "not naturally 'good' according to any standards set by civilized society"; that "children are *naturally* hostile," "little anarchists," "aggressive," "braggadocious and cruel,"[1] arises from the misinterpretations of the doctrine of "the Fall" or of "original sin." The reinforcement which these views received from nineteenth-century evolutionary biology and psychoanalytic theory in the first half of the twentieth century almost succeeded in hardening this view of the nature of human nature into something resembling an incontrovertible fact, a Law of Nature. Happily, in recent years, as a consequence of studies influenced both by developments in evolutionary biology and psychoanalytic theory, evidence has become available which indicates that the traditional view of human nature is unsound and, what is worse, capable of being profoundly damaging to human beings and to their societies. For this evidence indicates that human beings are born good—"good" in the sense that there is no evil or hostility in them, but that at birth they are wholly prepared, equipped, to function as creatures who not only want and need to be loved by others but who also want and need to love others. The evidence for these statements has been cited at some length in these pages. Let those who know of any evidence which controverts these statements bring it forth. I do not believe that such evidence exists.

The belief is widely held by many students of human nature that human beings are born neither good nor evil but indifferent; that whether they become good or evil or both depends largely, if not entirely, upon the social conditioning they are made to undergo. This view sounds reasonable enough, but the evidence I believe, when critically examined proves this view to be as unsound as the traditional view alleging the inherent brattishness or hostility of human nature.

The evidence cited in the present book shows that the human organism at birth is a highly organized creature—*not* a disorganized, unready, unprepared, "wild" beast; that the newborn is highly organized to function as an increasingly growing-in-love harmonic bestower-of-benefits-upon-others, whose birthright, as an American philosopher has said, is development. The inner requirements of the infant are such as to cause him to want to be loved and to want to love others, and the basic needs of the infant are structured to function in this manner. The infant expects to have its needs satisfied, and when the infant's needs are satisfied it develops as a loving, cooperative, harmonic human being—that is, as a healthy human being. We have accepted the definition of health, attributed to Freud, as the ability to love and the ability to work. The infant is equipped with the potentialities to develop both capacities. How well a human being will develop his capacities to love and work will depend largely upon the kind of training he will have received during infancy and childhood. The evidence shows, beyond any doubt, that the development of all the organism's potentialities for being human is a matter, reduced to its simplest elements, of certain kinds of stimulation and response: the stimulation of other human beings.

This stimulation, we have learned, must be of a certain kind. It must, in the first place, minister to and satisfy the needs of the infant. In order to minister satisfactorily to the needs of the infant it is desirable to know and understand the nature of those needs. In order to understand the nature of humanity and the direction of development which humanity may in future successfully pursue, it is indispensably necessary to understand the nature of the basic needs of the organism; these needs, whatever changes they may undergo, remain at the core essentially the same throughout life, from birth to death.

The nature of these needs has been discussed, and we have found that needs must be satisfied within reasonably short intervals and with certain frequencies—that it is not enough to "love" an infant three or four or five times a day, but that he must be loved for the greater part of the day—all the day—until he has had those inner securities built up within him which will later render it unnecessary for him to be in any way anxious about those stimulations which at the outset of his postnatal career are so indispensably necessary for his development.

As human beings we are the creators of human beings, and we shall always have the kind of human beings among us that we make. The role of chromosomes and genes should not be underestimated in the making of human beings, but as we have earlier pointed out (pp. 85-86), the expression of the chromosomes and genes is to a certain extent under environmental control, and to the extent that we control the environment we control heredity, for heredity is the expression of the interaction of the genes with environment. We cannot get more out of genes than we put into them or, to phrase this more constructively, we can get more out of genes than would otherwise be possible by providing them with environments in which they may optimally express themselves. Genes determine the limits of development under all environments; environments should therefore be provided which enable the human being to attain his fullest development within those limits.[2]

Heredity, like constitution, is not as earlier generations thought it to be, the equivalent of predestination, but is the expression of that which is biologically given in interaction with that which is environmentally provided. Heredity should mean not Fate, but something about which we can, if we will, do a great deal. We shall not be able to substitute environment for genes, but we should always bear in mind that genes are not determiners of traits but of the responses of the developing organism to the environment. We can, therefore, always do something toward controlling the expression of those responses. It is good to know this, and it should serve to induce an optimistic mood. As E. L. Thorndike has remarked, "To the real work of man—the increase of achievement through improvement of the environment—the influence of heredity offers no barrier."

The making and molding of human beings as human beings is in our power as human beings. Since this is so, the direction of human development, of human evolution, is within our power as human beings—for good or evil. It is necessary, then, that we shall make quite certain that the direction of that development shall be good and neither evil nor confused.

What Is Good?

The evidence we have now considered tells us that "good" is whatever the person does that confers survival benefits upon others in a manner which contributes to their ability to love and to work—in other words, to their ability to do likewise to and for other human beings. Human welfare is whatever contributes to the maintenance and development of human health—the ability to love and the ability to work.

To the extent that any person departs in his behavior from the undeviating practice of his capacity for love and work, to that extent we would have reason to believe that forces inimical to his healthy functioning are at work in him. We should seek to understand those forces and remedy them by providing the person with those conditions of life which will most contribute toward his healthy functioning. It should be one of the functions of education to make human beings understand the nature of human goodness, and what it is that must be done to develop such goodness as has already been developed in one by one's educators. It should be the primary function of all human societies to provide those conditions which shall make it possible for as many human beings as possible to function as good human beings. This constitutes the answer to the question "Education for what?"[3]

What the human organism requires most for its development is a nutriment of love; the source of virtually all health is in the experience of love, especially within the first six years of life. No matter how well the needs of the human organism are physically satisfied, unless the physical satisfying of those needs is accompanied by love, the human organism will not develop satisfactorily, that is to say, it will not develop as an organism that has been so harmonically satisfied that its principal interest lies in satisfying others. After all, this is what most of us want most of all to do all our lives, however confusedly or not we may recognize it: to satisfy others. The tragedy is that so many of us have failed to learn, because we had not been properly taught, how to satisfy others. To be rejected at any age because those who have been responsible for us have failed to teach us how to love others is, perhaps, the most unkind of all the inhumanities which human beings commit against human beings.

The child that is unloved does not develop properly; it may even sicken and die principally as a consequence of insufficient love. Some children manage to survive under the most barren of human conditions—we do not yet know why. Some day we shall study such children and discover the answer, but it would appear that most, if not all, children suffer seriously crippling effects when exposed to an inadequate diet of love. There has here been cited but a fraction of the evidence supporting these statements. The material now available showing the fundamental importance of love for the healthy development of the human being is of considerable proportions.

From all this material it seems now clear that the main principle by which human beings must guide the future course of their development is love. It is, therefore, of the first importance that we be clear as to the meaning of love.

WHAT IS LOVE?

Love is that form of behavior that contributes to the healthy development of both the lover and the loved. By healthy development is meant the increase in the capacity to function as a totally harmonic person who confers creatively enlarging benefits upon all with whom he comes into association. Love, it would seem, is the principal developer of the potentialities for being human, it is the chief stimulus to the development of social competence, and the only quality in the world capable of producing that sense of belongingness and relatedness to the world of humanity that every healthy human being desires and develops.

Love is creative, creative both for the receiver and the giver. Genuine love can never harm or inhibit, it can only benefit and create freedom and order. Love has a firmness and a discipline of its own for which there can be no substitute. No child can ever be spoiled by genuine love, and there are few if any human problems which cannot be most efficiently solved by its application.

We may tentatively set out below the qualities and characteristics of love, upon which most students of the subject seem to be agreed.

The Qualities and Characteristics of Love

1. *Love implies the possession of a feeling of deep involvement in another, and to love another means to communicate that feeling of involvement to them.* Essentially this means that while love begins as a subjective state, it must be activated and made objective, that is, it must be demonstrative if it is to be fully realized. Love is not passive, it is active, it means involvement.

2. *Love is unconditional, it makes no bargains and trades with no one for anything.* It is given freely and without any strings attached. It says, in effect, to the loved one: "I am for you because you are you—and not because you are going to be something I want or expect you to be, but simply because you are you as you now are."

3. *Love is supportive.* It conveys to the loved one that he can depend upon those who love him, that they will always be standing by to give him the support he most needs, with no questions asked, neither condemning nor condoning, but endeavoring sympathetically to understand, that no trust will be misused, that no faith will be broken; that he will never under any circumstances be failed in his needs.

4. *Love is firm.* Love is characterized by a firmness and integrity which not only conveys a feeling of security to the loved one, but serves also as a discipline in that it helps the loved one to respond in kind. But love continues even though we know that the loved one may never respond in kind. The firmness of love conveys to the loved one that both one's "Yea" and one's "Nay" are equally the firm evidence of one's love. The loved one, therefore, comes to incorporate this kind of firmness within himself.

> Let me not to the marriage of true minds
> Admit impediments. Love is not love
> Which alters when it alteration finds,

Or bends with the remover to remove:
O, no! it is an ever-fixèd mark,
That looks on tempests and is never shaken;
It is the star to every wandering bark,
Whose worth's unknown, although his height be taken.
Love's not Time's fool, though rosy lips and cheeks
Within his bending sickle's compass come;
Love alters not with his brief hours and weeks,
But bears it out even to the edge of doom.
    If this be error and upon me prov'd,
    I never writ, nor no man ever lov'd.

So wrote William Shakespeare.

5. *Love is most needed by the human organism from the moment of birth.* Our evidence indicates that love is the birthright of every human being, the birthright which is indispensably necessary for the optimum development of the person. It seems to be clear that the best environment, in which love is most efficiently and satisfactorily provided, is within the warm ambience of the bosom of the family. The pattern of love which the child learns within the family, if he learns it well, he will later extend to all human beings.

6. *Love is reciprocal in its effects, and is as beneficial to the giver as it is to the recipient.* To love another means to love oneself as well as the other; in this sense love is the highest form of selfishness as well as the highest form of unselfishness, the best of all forms of conduct for the development of the self, one's own self and the selves of others.

7. *Love is creative* in that it actively participates in the creative development of the loved one as well as contributing toward the further development of the lover.

8. *Love enlarges the capacities of those who are loved* and of those who love so that they become increasingly more sensitive in probably all areas of their being.

9. *Love continually elicits, by encouragement, the nascent capacities of the loved one.* In the absence of love those capacities will either fail altogether to be elicited or fail of healthy development. For example, the capacity to feel sensitively, to feel warmly toward others,

the capacity to perceive rapidly the changing character of a situation, the capacity to identify with others, the ability to adjust rapidly to rapidly changing conditions, and the like. In all these capacities the person who has been loved is more efficient than the person who has been inadequately loved.

10. *Love is tender,* with a tenderness that abjures every form of insensitivity and every form of violence.

11. *Love is joyful,* it is pleasure-giving, happiness-producing, it is goodness itself. This does not mean that love is necessarily associated with states of ecstasy or gaiety. Love may produce temporary states of nonpleasure or displeasure, as for example, in children and others who are forbidden some immediate satisfaction for their own "good." Prohibitions stemming from love contribute to the development of the capacity for love and mature character.

12. *Love is fearless.* Love has no element of fear in it,[4] and produces no fear in others. Love braves all conditions and situations in a security-producing manner; hence, love tends to reduce fear, allay suspicion, soften all harshness, and produce peacefulness.

13. *Love enables the person to treat life as an art* which the person, as artist, is continually seeking to improve and beautify in all its aspects.

14. *Love as an attitude of mind and as a form of behavior is adaptively the best and most efficient of all adjustive processes in enabling the human being to adapt himself to his environment.*

15. *For the person and for the species love is the form of behavior having the highest survival value.*[5]

Adequate love is necessary for the adequate physical growth and development of the human organism, as well as for its adequate psychical growth and development; and intelligence as well as mental health is furthered by the contributions which love makes to the developing person. In love, in short, we have discovered the touchstone and the compass by which man may guide his own most successful course through the shoals and reefs of this life, instead of being tossed about, as he has in the past, and as he is being at present, in a rudderless boat upon a mysterious and uncompassionate sea.

To live as if to live and love were one is not a new recommendation; what is new is that the meaning of love should have been rediscovered in the twentieth century by scientific means. Every people has its equivalent of the Sermon on the Mount, and our churches have constantly reminded us of the existence of love and enjoined us to practice it. This being so, it may well be asked why it is that we seem so monumentally to have failed to realize such injunctions? Why is it that there have been so many members of churches but so few lovers? Why is it that there are so many Christians but so few followers of Jesus?

The answer, it seems to me, is that we have been miseducated out of the capacity to be lovers of our fellow human beings, and that we have on the other hand been confusedly trained to keep our eye on the main chance. For the most part this has been the secular training of western man. We have tended to live by false values, and to transmit these values to the young. We have tended to make egotists of creatures that are biologically organized to function most efficiently as altruists. The evidence indicates that from birth onward the direction of the human being's drives is toward cooperation, and that healthy development consists principally in the encouragement of the optimum fruition of these drives. If, as in the western world we have largely been doing, we interfere with the development of those drives by opposing to them requirements that are antagonistic toward the development of cooperativeness, these drives tend to become deformed and weakened, while at the same time conflicts are engendered within the psyche which produce great personal and social disoperativeness.

It appears, then, that whatever contributes toward personal and social health and happiness is good and desirable for human beings, and that whatever contributes to the contrary is bad and undesirable for human beings. In short, whatever militates against or is opposed to the development of the tendencies toward cooperation in the person and in the society militates against and is opposed to the healthy development of the person and of the society. In essence this is to say that uncooperativeness or unlovingness is the worst of all the sins which one human being can commit against another.

In this volume we have, I hope, sufficiently explored the meaning and requirements of cooperation to be able to take for granted what it is that human beings must cooperate with. Perhaps it will bear repeating in a phrase: What human beings must cooperate with is the desire of other human beings to be loved—to be cooperated with. One cannot secure love by seeking it, but only by giving it. Having discussed and set out the criteria of love, of loving, there should be no difficulty in understanding what it is that requires to be done: Human beings must be satisfied in their need for love. The direction of human development lies in and through the course of love; all else is secondary to this. The primacy of love is unchallengeable—and unchallengeably clear as the first requirement of human development. All the agencies of socialization should be based upon the understanding of this fact. Since all agencies of socialization are educative, education constitutes the key to the solution of the ills of humanity, and the means by which all the potentialities of the organism for being human may be unlocked. Hence the importance of understanding the meaning of man for education and the meaning of education for man.

Education and Human Relations

In keeping with the general materialization of western man and the high value placed upon techniques, education has progressively degenerated into instruction. It is not unlikely that if, in the western world, we go on as we have been doing in the immediate past, in a generation or two scarcely anyone will remain who understands the difference between education and instruction. Instruction is the process of pumping information into the person, it literally means "to build into"; whereas education means the process of nourishing or rearing a child or young person, in the sense of the Latin word to which it is related, *educere*, to lead forth. We must recognize that today, in the western world, we have far too much instruction and all too little education. We are far too busy filling up the young with what we think they ought to know, to have much time left over for helping them become what they ought to be. There is after all, a difference between *knowing* and *being*—it is better to be more than one seems and to be wise rather than knowledgeable. We pump in the information in the hope that somehow the recipients will know what to do with it or what it is for, and that somehow this procedure will make the beneficiaries of it realize their potentialities. By this means we naively suppose that human beings will learn how to distinguish the good from the bad and to act accordingly, that by this means they will learn how to use their minds and evaluate evidence critically, that by this means they will become better persons and better citizens. Never have we been more mistaken—as the record shows.

In the United States for the year ending in 1953 we find certifiable mental illness to exist in 1 out of every 4 families; we find that a murder was committed every 72 minutes during the day; that during every hour of the day there were 15 crimes of violence —stabbings, shootings, clubbings; that during every hour of the day there were 7 robberies and 26 cars were stolen.[6] What is perhaps worse than all this, if it could be worse, is that 1 out of every 43 children has a police record.[7] Juvenile delinquency, broken homes— 1 out of every 3 marriages ends in divorce or separation[8]—these are all tragic evidences of the failure of education—education primarily in the home and secondarily in the school. This is perhaps not surprising in a land in which of our total national income 5 per cent was expended on alcoholic beverages as compared with approximately 3 per cent spent on education.[9]

EDUCATION—TEACHERS AND PARENTS

We have made a fundamental error in distinguishing what goes on in the training of children in the home from what goes on in the training of the young in the schools. Education begins at birth, and the parents are the first educators, the mother usually being the principal of the parental educators. Because the first half dozen years of the child's life are so critically important for its development there can be little doubt that the parents, and in particular the mother, constitute the most important educators in the life of the person.[10] Hence, if any disinction is to be made between parental and school education it should be in terms of emphasis upon the supreme importance of the first six years of the child's life. This, however, in no way implies that the education of a human being is a discontinuous process, with a first part at home and a second part at school. On the other hand, education must be regarded as a continuous process, and it should be based upon a single and unitary viewpoint as to its nature and purposes in which everyone, parents and teachers, participate *together*.

Education is the process of teaching human beings to live in ways which contribute to the welfare of their fellow human beings. The theoretical background emerging out of the facts we have discussed in this book with respect to the meaning of "welfare" has already been examined at sufficient length. If the analysis of the facts is sound and the theory is likewise sound—as I believe it to be—then it is clear that the most important function of education is to draw out and develop the potentialities of the child for being a loving human being. The evidence suggests that to achieve the status of a loving human being is the most desirable and important that a human being can achieve. To produce loving human beings should be the primary purpose of education, and all else should be secondary to that purpose. Reading, writing, and arithmetic are but skills, techniques, means, which should be designed to assist the loving human being to realize to the optimum his potentialities for getting the most out of life by putting the most into it. Reading, writing and arithmetic are not ends in themselves but secondary means—means to the end of realizing the fullest richest life possible within the limits of the abilities of each human being. Such skills are secondary to the main purpose of living—which is life, a life that is worth living insofar as it realizes its highest form in the developed loving human being.

In our schools we pay lip-service to such an ideal of education, but in practice we teach *subjects,* we no longer teach human beings. Too much of our attention is devoted to problems of discipline, so that for many teachers their task has reduced itself to one of baby-sitting, for the original baby-sitters—the parents—who have failed to sit as they ought to have done. This problem has become so serious in the United States that in many high schools a permanent squad of police has been installed in order that some semblance of discipline shall be maintained! Perhaps these are extreme cases; in any event they are mentioned here in order to underscore, as it were, the kind of disciplinary problems with which the school is faced which under a reasonable system of education would never in the first place have arisen.

A patient, in searching for an explanation for his mental illness, remarked: "My mother's impulses never seemed to correspond to my needs."[11] This probably represents a sound statement of the origin of many mental diseases, and it may be profitably paraphrased in the statement that the impulses of many educators seem rarely to correspond to the needs of the young. This is not difficult to understand when one realizes that what the young want is principally to be stimulated in their need for human development, whereas too many teachers are engaged in filling them up with a number of subjects which to the child appear to be quite unrelated to his most fundamental needs. What is human learning if not the development of the needs for being human?

Almost all children find their lives in school puzzlingly unrelated to their lives at home. This should not be so. School should constitute a continuation and an enlargement of the experience which begins in the home and terminates in the world outside, only to be renewed again in the home and once more reinforced—as it should be—in the school, and so on until one's education is completed . . . if one's education ever is completed. The love which should and often does exist between parents and children—though it is more often found between mother and child—is the model and the pattern of the human relationship which should exist between all human beings. Lest there be misunderstanding as to my meaning, let me say that I mean exactly what these words imply, namely, that human beings should love each other as a mother loves her children, and that this should be possible for males as well as for females . . .

whether they have ever biologically engendered children or not.[12] But whether the male will learn to love as a parent, or in any other capacity, will depend largely upon his mother, for as La Barre points out, "The human male has no instincts, and no anatomy to teach him to love a child as such. If the male learns the pleasures of paternity as opposed to those of procreation, it is the result of the mother's teaching him."[13]

But how is it possible—to take but one instance—it may be asked, and indeed is it desirable, for members of the opposite sex to fall in love with one another, to love each other as a mother loves her child? The answer is that it is both possible and desirable. The love which should and can exist between male and female should consist in a developed form of maternal love in which all the elements of maternal love persist. A man should love a woman with the tenderness, respect, and care for her welfare with which a mother loves her child, but in addition he should be drawn to and love her for her qualities as a whole. Her external attractions, whatever their nature, may initiate the process but they should never constitute the *end* of it.

This is a different conception of love between the sexes from the romantic and prevailing erotic view. Contemporary love between the sexes is mainly sexual, the male being drawn toward the female principally through the stimulus-value of her curvilinear properties, the female, under the influence of selection pressure, generally settling for a male largely on the basis of his market value as a scarcity commodity, providing also he is someone who, with all his faults, one can like or learn to like.

Too many persons in our western cultures confuse a sexual attraction with love. As long as the opposite partner remains physically attractive the psychophysical disturbances the subject feels are equated with love. But such disturbances are no more akin to love than cupidity is to Cupid. Under such environmental conditions when the physical attractiveness ceases "love" also ceases. Such "love" is, of course, not love, but a crass sexuality. Such persons are sexual without being loving, whereas the loving person cannot be sexual without loving.

The essence of love between the sexes is the tender regard, respect, and care for the other person's welfare—and if it is not that, then whatever else it is, it is not love.

For a healthy human being it is possible to be as much interested in another's welfare as a mother is in her child's. There is a tender regard and involvement in such a person's interest in other human beings which has but to be experienced for it to be understood how well some persons have achieved this maternal capacity for love, even of the stranger.[14] It is in the development of this maternally based capacity for love that the future of humanity lies. Until this truth is fully understood and practiced, so far as the direction of human development is concerned almost all other activities will remain in comparison diversionary and stultifying. It must be the task of educators to awaken to this truth, and what it is that requires to be done to realize it.

The school, like the home, must become an experience in the growth and development of one's capacities for becoming a loving human being. But, in addition, the school has to provide the child with the necessary equipment, the technique and skills, with which it can the more satisfactorily realize—creatively realize—its potentialities for contributing to the welfare of its fellow human beings. The best equipment with which the teacher can provide the child is himself—the teacher's own being. A good teacher must mean something to himself if he is to mean anything to his pupils, and he can mean no more to his pupils than he means to himself. Hence, the value of a good teacher is exceeded by nothing, unless it be the value of a good parent. But when we truly understand the meaning of good teaching it is realized that the good parent is essentially a teacher, and that the good teacher is essentially a parent. How much of what is good in us do we not owe both to parents and to teachers? Where parents fail teachers often succeed. In a period when many of those who act as parents are not the biological genitors of their children it has become apparent that the complex feelings of parentage have no necessary connexion with biological parentage, that between persons who are biologically not kin the deepest feelings of kinship can develop.

There are some who have suggested that it would be a desirable thing to abolish social parentage.[15] This is silly. What we need to do is not to abolish social parentage but to deepen and extend our conception of it. Teachers should stand to their children *in loco parentis*. As the child's parents are its domestic parents, so at school the teacher should be to the child its school parents. I am suggesting that we deepen and extend the kinship system, not in terms of classificatory relationships, but in terms of changes in attitudes. All adults, particularly teachers of the young in the schools, should take a parental interest in the welfare of children. Unfortunately, in the past the attitude of the teacher to the child often resembled that of the company sergeant to the newly inducted private. We have seen that when the sergeant behaves as a reassuring parental figure to the men in his charge their mental health and their efficiency under battle conditions are greatly improved. It is not only schoolteachers, but teachers of every kind who have this lesson to learn: To teach well, one must love one's pupil as a mother loves her child. There have been some teachers who have grasped the truth of this principle, and they have unexceptionally been the great teachers; perhaps the greatest of them all was and is Heinrich Pestalozzi (1746–1827). It was Pestalozzi who said that "Love is the sole and everlasting foundation on which our nature can be trained to humaneness." And it was Pestalozzi who wrote: "The good instincts of mankind, in their pure state, are more than gifts of art or chance. Their fundamental qualities lie deeply buried in man's nature. All men feel the need to develop these powers and the paths along which Nature reveals them, must be kept clear and easy of access. To achieve wisdom and tranquility, the processes of human education must be kept simple and of universal application."[16]

It is through love that teachers of every kind, whether they be actual or derived parents, must seek to develop those fundamental qualities and powers, of which Pestalozzi speaks, along the paths which Nature reveals. We need to recall, in the words of Francis Bacon, that Nature in order to be commanded must be obeyed.

If, then, what has been adumbrated in this book as the nature of human nature, the requirements for the development of human nature, is sound it will be understood that learning and being loved are more closely interrelated conditions than has hitherto been clearly understood. This, perhaps, indicates a more intensive statement of the law or reinforcement. To live, to learn, and to love, these are the three great chords of being; to unify them into a harmonic series requires the skill of an artist. Life regarded as a public performance on the violin, during which one must learn the instrument as one goes along,[17] rarely results in anything more than an unhappy fiddler. A human being should be a work of art. He can be turned into a work of art by other human beings who are artists, and thus learn to become an artist himself, an artist who, in turn, works continually to improve himself and help others to improve themselves. Knowing what is to be done, how else can one better achieve what is to be realized than with the tenderness and loving care of a mother?

All of us are to some extent the product of the maternal principle. The next best thing to being a mother is to behave like one. And by behaving like a mother, we of course mean the possession of those attitudes of mind which condition one to behave toward others as a mother does toward her child. Perhaps the English, the Germans, and those Germans of the Orient, the Japanese, are the peoples who have most departed from this ideal, for that there has been a departure is suggested by the fact that many nonliterate peoples such as the Eskimo and the Australian aborigines—to name two of the most primitive—have pretty closely approximated to the realization of this ideal. Not all earlier men may have been cooperative and loving, but that many of them were there can be no reasonable doubt. The Italians[18] and the French[19] are somewhat more influenced, in their human relations, by the maternal principle, but these peoples are far from having learned the lesson completely. Indeed, their recent history indicates a significant deterioration. And yet to the extent that the Italians and the French retain their warmth they are warmer than the

English, the Germans, and the Japanese. It is no accident that these latter peoples make the most efficient soldiers. One of the kindest and most significant things one can say about any people is that they make poor fighters. It is not by fighting that any human problem will ever be solved, any more than any child will ever be improved by spanking, rather than by love and by the understanding which is love.

There burns a pure flame within us; that flame is love. It is the source from which we draw and convey our warmth to others. It is the light which guides us in relation to our fellow men; it is the flame before which we warm the hands of life, and without which we remain cold all our lives. It is the light of the world. The light which it casts enables us clearly and unambiguously, unfalteringly, to see our relation to our fellow men. It is the task of teachers to keep that flame alive, for if they fail to do that, there is a real danger that the light may go out of the world.

Our present educational and social failure to recognize the new bases of human relationships must change if we are to survive —nothing less than that. We must cease doing violence to human nature. By doing violence to human nature we have produced the unique paradox of the creature who, by nature capable of being the most loving and peaceful, has been turned into the most destructively violent on the face of the earth. Our shattered values have made the horrible, devastating threat of an atom-bomb world a reality. Clearly, we need to know at least as much about the maker as about the manufacture of atom-bombs.[20]

Human beings who are torn and distracted by internal insecurities and anxieties, who are conditioned to love their neighbors on Sundays and to compete with them on weekdays, cannot long survive. A nation of such persons must eventually founder on the reefs of its own false values. External defenses can never make up for the lack of internal controls. What needs to be done is to develop internal controls in human beings so that they can withstand external pressures and maintain internal equilibrium. This can never be achieved by doing violence to their nature. It can only be done by strengthening those basic needs with which all human beings are born—not by frustrating them. It is these basic needs that provide us with the basic values which human beings must seek to satisfy and fulfill if they are to live and function in optimum health and happiness.

VALUES, ETHICS, EDUCATION, AND THE GOOD LIFE

A value is the judgment of the quality of an experience.[21] Such value judgments are biologically based in and originally constituted by the basic needs of the organism, and all other needs, secondary, tertiary, quaternary, and so on, are eventually built up upon the functioning of these needs. Values are in essence guides to need-gratifications. The experiences that will gratify my needs create my values, therefore the structure and functioning of my needs determine the range and limits of my values. I must have oxygen to gratify my need for air, but whether that oxygen comes to me in a tent, a house, a factory, a mine, or in a strato-liner, and whether it vary all the way from pure to polluted will depend upon accidental conditions which must neither fall below nor exceed certain limits. Within these limits, which my biological needs determine, I can adapt myself to any atmospheric conditions. And so it is for all other needs. The experiences that will not gratify my needs are negatively valued by me—these, too, are values. My judgment of the quality of these experiences and my acceptance of them or not will largely be determined by my organismal needs—needs which I share with all other human beings.

The supreme value is love, and if we use this as our touchstone of value we cannot possibly go wrong. Man is the evaluating animal, and he evaluates on the basis of his needs. Every human being is born a creature that evaluates all experience in terms of the desire to be loved and the desire to love. We at long last have thus arrived at an understanding that there do exist certain universal values, and that these are born with every human being. "What is right is what is right for human nature." It was Aristotle who declared that the important thing about the nature of man is not what he is born *as,* but what he is born *for.* In order to know what man is born *for* it is indispensably necessary to understand what he is born *as,* and when we understand what he is born *as* we will the better be enabled to assist him to realize what he is born *for.*

Since we now have some understanding of the basic structure of human nature, we are at least in a position to be able to test our theory. The basic needs are not logical inferences but factual phenomena; they *ought* to be satisfied if the organism is to survive or develop, and that *oughtness* is as much a fact and lies as much in the world of *is* as do the basic needs themselves. "Ought" is in this case merely a way of denoting a necessary response— which, again, falls within the world of *is.* As Arnold Brecht has so well put it, "Thus it is a factual statement rather than a logical inference when we say that feeling some specific requiredness as an *ought* is part of our human equipment. This urge, this demand, this *ought,* whatever its value and validity, is a factum, a datum, found in the world of *is.* It would be so even if only a part of mankind felt this *ought* as such. Here is the bridge, or one bridge, between *is* and *ought.*"[22] The nature of the basic needs conditions the oughtness of the responses; what ought to be is what the basic needs determine, and what they determine we are now for the first time able to decipher. In the nature of the basic needs we have the Rosetta Stone which translates for us into the vernacular what the direction of human development ought to be, what, indeed, it must be if the human race is to survive.

But much more than survival is involved. What is involved is the realization of the potentialities for goodness of all human beings everywhere for the greatest good of all humanity—the unbridgeable gap between *ought* and *is,* when we look at what *is* in terms of what we know the basic needs to determine, and at what *ought* to be if human beings are to develop in optimum health and happiness. To realize the good life in the person and behavior of each human being, our evidence indicates that each human being must be adequately loved, that is to say, he must have his needs adequately satisfied for being loved and loving others. Such human beings will create institutions and societies which will be the best that human beings can possibly create and, within whatever limitations those societies operate, they will remain infinitely perfectible. Utopia would not at once descend upon the earth, nor would all human problems immediately be solved. But under such conditions they would become more capable of solution than they have yet ever been.

The reciprocal adaptation which human beings make to one another in terms of love is the basic adaptation, the basic adaptation which binds, reproduces, and preserves the person and the group. This kind of adaptation has been called by Professor Hugh Miller "associative adaptation."[23] The behavior of human beings is either "good" or "bad" to the extent that it is better or worse associatively adapted. "Associative adaptation" is here but another name for love. It is to be noted that it is not said that a person is either "good" or "bad," but that his behavior may be good or bad in virtue of its quality of associative adaptation or love. Our assumption has been throughout that all human beings (with a few possible exceptions) are basically good, but by unfortunate conditioning they are frequently caused to function badly. "Goodness," then, is virtually equatable with "love," and "badness" with a failure of love.

Ethics, then, for us becomes both the art and the science of the reciprocal adaptation of human beings to each other in love in loving attitudes of mind and in loving conduct. There is, of course, nothing new in this view of ethical conduct. What is new is the scientific validation which the discoveries made in recent years concerning the nature of human nature have brought to this view of ethics.[24] Our revised conception of human nature, as set out in the pages of this book, should have the profoundest influence upon religion and ethics, but it should be fairly clear that religion and ethics are basically taught not so much in the churches as in the home and in the school.[25] The churches should continue to develop and consolidate what has been taught in the home and in the school —if what has been there taught is sound and humane. If it is not, it does not seem to me that the church can do much to undo the damage that has been done. The churches should be the preservers not of inflexible orthodoxies but of the truths by which men must live and from which they must never depart—truths, however, which are infinitely perfectible. It is not with the institutionalization of the religious impulse, but with its education, that the church should be concerned, with the development of a religious attitude which embraces a sense of the possibilities of existence and a devotion to the cause of those possibilities. The church must become not merely the repository of the highest ideals of humanity, but an active participant in the educational process of helping human beings realize those ideals.

Christians believe that God is Love. Our inquiry in this book has amounted to the conclusion that Love is God. It is a distinction with a significance, the difference being that while most Christians accept the view that God is Love, and let it go at that, Jesus himself felt also that Love is God, that love of God was essential, but equally essential was the love of man for man. This seems to me to represent the great contribution of Jesus, the development of the seedling Old Testament injunction to love one's neighbor as oneself. Jesus not only sent men to God, but he also sent God to men, by sending men to men. He enjoined men to live a way of life with their fellow men which was the way of love—love for each other. This way of love I would call *philia*, distinguishing it from the Platonic and Old Testament "eros": love in which man seeks God in order to satisfy his spiritual hunger by the possession and enjoyment of the Divine perfection, and from the New Testament love of man for God, *agape*, which implies the whole-hearted surrender to God, placing one's entire faith in Him, and desiring only that His will should be done.[26]

For too many modern Christians *agape* has taken the form of a kind of apple-polishing of the Divine. The concept of love which we have here been developing most closely resembles *philia*, but is not identical with it, for our concept is best called by what it refers to, namely, *maternal love*.

It will fall principally to mothers and teachers to spread this gospel, and toward this end I would strongly urge that the nursery school be made part of the educational system of the land. In nursery school children between two and five years of age would, for a few hours, each day receive the benefits of mother and teacher working together on the complementary task of contributing toward the child's development. The nursery school would represent the principal agency through which the parents could be brought together with the school in the complementary task of developing the potentialities of the child. In nursery school parents, especially the mother, would be encouraged to help teachers and teachers would be encouraged to help parents in the joint enterprise of helping the child. The parents would contribute what the teachers ought to know, and the teachers would contribute what the parents ought to know, for the benefit of the child as well as for the benefit of all concerned. The teaching the child receives at home and the teaching it receives at school must be joined and unified. The teaching of the elementary skills of reading, writing, and arithmetic is important, but not nearly as important as the most important of all the skills— human relations.

A scientific approach to education must begin with the basic assumption that values must in the long run be tested by their capacity to contribute to the happiness and creativeness of human beings living together. If we have found a scientific basis *in fact* for what *should be,* we should at least be willing to give it a try.

Our schools need to be transformed into institutes for the study of the science (theory) and the art (practice) of loving human relations. Children in such schools will continue to be taught the theory and practice of human relations from their earliest years. It is in the nursery, kindergarten, and elementary school that the most fundamental learning will be done, and it is for this reason that we must learn to understand that the most important teachers in the human community, in addition to the parents, are the teachers of the young. College professors on this scheme of values, valuable as they are, are not as important as elementary school teachers. Our society, therefore, needs to undergo a fundamental change in its attitudes toward schoolteachers, to revalue them for what they are worth—as next to the parents the most important members of the community, for teachers are the unacknowledged legislators of the world, the midwives of humanity. We need, therefore, to elevate the status and increase the prestige of the profession of teaching the young, and to reward its votaries in such a manner as to encourage the finest persons among us to dedicate their lives to the high and significant task of helping human beings realize their potentialities.

The teaching of the three "R's" must be secondary and supplementary to the teaching of the primary skill of human relations, for what, indeed, is any instruction worth if it is not integrated into an understanding of man's responsibility to man? Whatever is learned should be learned primarily with reference to its significance for human relations, and always with the emphasis on cooperation, on adaptive association, on love, on shared relationships. Cracker-barrel human relations are not good enough. Children should be taught not how to become submissive echoes of their teachers and their traditions, but how to evaluate humanely, sympathetically, and critically the world in which they are living. They should be taught not only the overt but also the covert values of their society, and they should be taught not only what is right with their society but what is wrong with it, and that it is going to be their responsibility to put things right, and how they may be put right.

In this light education must be conceived to be the drawing out of the best that is within the person by making available to him all the encouragements and supports and stimulations which he requires, to enable him to become a loving, cooperative, non-conflictful person, who is not only aware of what is right with the world but is also equipped with the knowledge, the desire, and the wisdom necessary to bring it nearer that ideal of what it should and can be . . . a person who will not be a competitor, but a cooperator, a person for whom altruism will be a passion and selfishness a disorder; a person wise enough to know that

> He who would love his fellow men
> Must not expect too much of them . . .

a person who will want to improve the world as he finds it, and not accept things as they are; a person who will not risk wrecking the social machinery by exceeding the speed-limit of rational inquiry; who will not abolish anything, but merely render it necessary to discontinue it, dispelling fear by supplying facts and knowledge; who will recognize the strange necessity of beauty; who will have a sense of personal responsibility for decency and justice; who will never offer up the smoke of incense before an empty shrine, nor pretend to a creed he does not believe; a person, in short, who having had a loving order made within himself will make loving order in the world—

> be to other souls
> The cup of strength in some great agony,
> Enkindle generous ardour, feed pure love
> Beget the smiles that have no cruelty—
> Be the sweet presence of a good diffused,
> And in diffusion more intense.
> —GEORGE ELIOT

SURVIVAL AND FULFILLMENT

Humanity today stands on the threshold of a possible new dispensation—the self-dispensing fulfillment of its evolutionary destiny. Until recent times humanity has been engaged in a struggle for existence, for survival. This struggle has for large masses of humanity been progressively decreased. The population of the world increases at an accelerating rate, a fact which since the days of Malthus has constituted cause for alarm to many students of humanity. Whether uncontrolled increase of population in the world or in any community is or is not desirable the fact of increase bears abundant testimony to the ability of large and increasingly large numbers of human beings to survive.[27]

The problem of physical survival has largely been solved. On the other hand, for the larger number of human beings the problem of psychological survival has not been solved. In the United States alone one out of every eighteen persons will spend some time in a mental hospital.[28] By psychological survival is meant survival, or better, fulfillment of one's potentialities for being a happy, creative, and cooperative human being. Julian Huxley has referred to this subject in the following words:

Human life *is* a struggle—against frustration, ignorance, suffering, evil, the maddening inertia of things in general; but it is also a struggle *for* something, and for something which our experience tells us can be achieved in some measure, even if we personally find ourselves debarred from any measure that seems just or reasonable. And fulfillment seems to describe better than any other single word the positive side of human development and human evolution—the realization of inherent capacities by the individual and of new possibilities by the race; the satisfaction of needs, spiritual as well as material; the emergence of new qualities of experience to be enjoyed; the building of personalities. But it cannot be achieved without struggle, not merely struggle with external obstacles, but with the enemies within our own selves.[29]

The realization of inherent capacities by the person and of new possibilities by the race—that is what is meant by fulfillment. If human beings are enabled to fulfill themselves they will encounter no enemies within themselves. At the present time the greatest obstacle in the path of human progress is not the atom or hydrogen bomb or any other external obstacle, but in the disordered selves of human beings. The self of a human being is the means through which he sees and evaluates the world. An imperfect means applied to the achievement of confused goals is not the best of auguries for a happy dénouement. A self that is organized to function in terms of love is different in its effects from one that is disorganized to function on the dual basis of some sort of relation to society in which there is, first, a religion in some way concerned with the doctrine of love, and second, a secular tradition which offers high rewards to the successful competitor. Man requires no supernatural sanctions for love. Love is a fact of nature, and it is the most important of all the facts about human nature. Love is and should be the most natural of religions for human beings. The person who has been brought up to be a loving human being will not be able to see the world in anything but loving terms. Violence will be as foreign to his nature as it is at present common to the acquired nature of most men of contemporary western civilizations. To most persons, conditioned as they are in the western world today, love and violence are not only not incompatible but are perfectly reconcilable forms of conduct, whereas in fact violence is not only contrary to man's basic nature but inimical to it.[30]

Man's self is the means of whatever ends he achieves, and the ends he seeks to achieve are largely determined by the nature of the self that has been built into him. Hence the pressing necessity of realizing that healthy human development and survival depends upon our ability to help human beings fulfill their potentialities and thus develop selves that are as much in harmony with their basic inner necessities as they are in harmony with those of all other healthy human beings. No man ever achieves his real self until he is his best self. We know something of the nature of those necessities, and we have good reason to believe that if we would but act upon that knowledge we will have taken the most important step in the right direction toward the fulfillment of humanity's promises.

Human nature is good. It is our present *human nurture* that is bad. We need to conform human nurture to the requirements of human nature. Our nurture must be based on basic human nature. Human beings and nations of human beings will solve their problems only when they have learned this lesson and applied it to themselves.

> Truth is within ourselves; it takes no rise
> From outward things, whate'er you may believe:
> There is an inmost centre in us all,
> Where truth abides in fulness; and around,
> Wall within wall, the gross flesh hems it in,
> Perfect and true perception—which is truth;
> A baffling and perverting carnal mesh
> Which blinds it, and makes error: and, *"to know"*
> Rather consists in opening out a way
> Whence the imprison'd splendour may dart forth,
> Than in effecting entry for the light
> Supposed to be without.   —BROWNING, *Paracelsus*

Appendix A   LEARNING THEORY

We learn looking backward. We live looking forward.—ANON.

The need for love . . . provides the incentives and conditions for *learning* by experience and for accumulating knowledge from generation to generation and so of building up an immortal tradition.   —IAN SUTTIE.*

The method is the message.   —ANON.

We have been inquiring into the relationship between the manner in which the child is reared, and those mental configurations or habits which are formed in childhood and continue as a basic part of the motivational system of the person. The person, as a social being, may be regarded as a more or less stable system of adjustive habits capable of self-regulation and of change. These habits are mostly acquired by *learning* from other human beings. It may be of value, therefore, for the better understanding of the manner in which the organism becomes socialized to inquire into the elements of the learning process.

Most theories of learning are unavoidably oversimplified,[1] and this is true of the account of human social learning which will follow. We do not yet know enough about the physiology and psychology of learning to be able to give a thorough account of it, which is why the title of this appendix emphasizes theory. Much of the experimental work on learning has been done on rats (psychological rodentology), and some on monkeys, but we must always remember that culture is not a maze, nor human behavior comparable to that of a rat moving in a maze.[2] We shall miss our cue if we extrapolate from the findings on rats and monkeys to the conditions prevailing among human beings, and yet we should be in error were we altogether to neglect the findings of the rat psychologists, for in the absence of similar experimental knowledge for human beings we can, with caution, usefully consider these findings insofar as they may eventually lead to a better understanding of the learning process in man. It cannot, however, be too strongly emphasized that learning theory insofar as it relates to man is at the present time

* Ian Suttie, *The Origins of Love and Hate*, New York, Julian Press, 1943, p. 20.

317

in a somewhat primitive state. There are some who believe that learning theory constitutes nothing more than an elaborate system for labeling the obvious after the fact, having no analytic value whatever, nor in any way adding to our understanding of personality and culture.[3] While this may be true of the application of learning theory to socialization by some investigators, and while there may be a good deal of truth in this point of view generally, it is necessary to make a start at some point with a theory of learning, however inadequate, if we desire to attain some understanding of the manner in which the human being learns his culture. Labels may ultimately prove to be helpful in the analytic process involved in thinking more clearly about the nature of learning.

THE SPONTANEITY FACTOR

Before proceeding with the exposition of learning theory it is necessary to make certain preliminary limiting statements. The first of these requires special emphasis because in the concentration on learning theory it may be neglected. This is the fact that there is some reason to believe that not all behavior is an expression of what is learned. When, for example, a person is confronted with a novel situation that lies outside the competence of his learned responses, his behavior may function upon an almost if not entirely purely, organic level. Fear, anger, curiosity, the flight reactions of embarrassment in a social situation are familiar forms of such behavior. In such circumstances the behavior exhibited may be wholly or almost wholly in terms of unlearned responses. Such responses have been attributed by Moreno to a *spontaneity factor*.

. . . there is within the range of individual expression an independent area *between* heredity and environment, influenced but not determined by hereditary (genes) and social forces (tele). The *s* (spontaneity) factor would have in this area its topographical location. It is an area of relative freedom and independence from biological and social determinants, an area in which new combinatory acts and permutations, choices and decisions are formed, and from which human inventiveness and creativity emerges.[4]

Even when socially learned responses are made to novel situations it is probable that they are integrated in a matrix of unlearned responses. Indeed, this of necessity characterizes the greater part of the learning process of the infant. The distinction between *situation* and *response* so far as the infant is concerned is artificial. The situation is the response and the response is the situation for the infant, and it is in this relational situation-response world that he makes his unlearned attempts at behavior spontaneously.[5] From this relational universe he gradually learns by successful selection to make the most adequate responses to situations which become slowly but surely more differentiated for him, but until they are differentiated they are novel situations, and spontaneity is defined as the adequate response to a novel situation. It is these selective acts which the Morenos regard as creative. "He may create," they write, "as an individual actually very little—most of his acts resembling those of his peers, but the logic of the child in feeling creatively is justified by the *mode* of his experience, its status nascendi, rather than by the originality of his experience."[6]

Spontaneity, as conceived by the Morenos, is the inherent tendency of the person to experience as his own state a freedom or autonomy of action which is quite independent of any external influence, and free from any internal influence which he cannot control. Whether or not the spontaneity factor is a genuine or important element to be considered in the analysis of the learning process future research may reveal. It is a factor to be borne in mind. Meanwhile, it appears probable that many of the emotional relationships of the person to the environment are the outcome of integrative processes which are only indirectly related to the learning process.

SOCIAL LEARNING

All social learning takes place under social conditions, in social situations; therefore the proper evaluation of any learned act cannot be made in terms of learning principles alone. The social conditions, the immediate social situation, in which the learning occurred must also be known. Psychology describes the principles of learning, the social sciences describe the conditions. Those who are interested in understanding human behavior must acquaint themselves with both, and—as we have to some extent already seen—with something more: an understanding of the biological or organic bases of human behavior and the varying organization which these undergo in differing cultures. With an equipment based on such foundations there is more than a promise that the sciences of behavior will develop predictive powers which in the not too distant future will place them in the forefront of the applied sciences.[7]

By behavior is to be understood any act of a living organism. By social behavior is to be understood the acts of the organism which have been learned in the interactive process with other persons, the interactive process involving not only other persons but also things. The organism learns from experience, and learning is the profit which accrues from experience. Indeed, learning may be defined as the alteration in behavior that results from experience.[8] Purely organic behavior in a human social group is of minimal survival value. Derived needs in particular require derived responses, and these must be socially learned. What, then, is learning reduced to its simplest terms? In its simplest terms *learning is*

the process by which a stimulus becomes connected with a response.
Upon analysis learning is seen to assume two principal forms, as the
strengthening of one out of a number of more or less distinct responses
to a need, and the formation of new receptor-effector connections. The
first is typical of simple selective learning, and the second of conditioned-
reflex learning. A mixed form of learning also occurs in which new
receptor-effector connections are set up at the same time that selective
learning is taking place.

SELECTIVE LEARNING

Learning which of a number of random responses to a need will best
satisfy the need is the process of *selective learning*.

CONDITIONING

Learning by conditioning means to set up new receptor-effector connections rather than to strengthen connections already strong enough in
combination to evoke overt responses. For example, meat (the unconditioned stimulus) is presented to a dog; this is followed by salivation
in the dog (the unconditioned response) while at the same time a buzzer
(the conditioned stimulus) is sounded. After a number of such experiences the dog is exposed to the sound of the buzzer alone, to which it
then responds by salivation (the conditioned response). A new receptor-
effector connection has been established. The necessity of selecting one
response from the varied responses normally evoked is eliminated. Such
conditioning frequently occurs during the selective learning process in
which the response comes to be made to any one of a number of stimuli
associated with the original stimulus situation.

In all these processes the organism itself establishes or acquires automatically adaptive receptor-effector connections. Such acquisition is *learning*.[9]

SIMPLE CONDITIONING
First Trial

Unconditioned stimulus ⟶ Unconditioned response
   (Meat)   (Salivation)
Neutral stimulus ⟶ Unconditioned response
   (Buzzing)   (Turning head or no response)

Later Trials

Conditioned stimulus ⟶ Conditioned response
   (Buzzing)   (Salivation)

Following Hull, the substance of the elementary learning process seems to be this: Stimulus energies produce a condition of need in a setting of receptor discharges. This combination of conditions activates numerous vaguely adaptive response potentials mediated by the unlearned receptor-effector organization of the organism. The relative strengths of these various response potentials vary from instant to instant (oscillation factor). The resulting spontaneous variability of the momentary unlearned behavior reaction potentials produces the randomness and variability of the unlearned behavior evoked under given conditions. Should one of these random responses, or a sequence of them, result in the reduction of a need dominant at the time, there follows as an indirect effect what is known as *reinforcement*. This is an important principle common to all forms of learning. This primary reinforcement consists, first, in a strengthening of the particular receptor-effector connections which originally mediated the reaction, and second, in a tendency for all receptor discharges occurring at about the same time to acquire new connections with the effectors mediating the given response.

The first effect is known as primitive trial-and-error learning; the second is known as conditioned-reflex learning. In most adaptive situations both processes occur concurrently. Hull points out that "very likely they are at bottom the same process, differing only in the accidental circumstance that the first begins with an appreciable strength, whereas the second sets out from zero. As a result, when the same need again arises in this or a similar situation, the stimuli will activate the same effectors more certainly, more promptly, and more vigorously than on the first occasion."[10]

Reinforcement

In the more complexly developed organism, and particularly in man, there are numerous situations in which learning occurs with no associated primary need reduction. Under such conditions analysis reveals that the reinforcing agent is a situation or event involving a stimulus aggregate or complex which has been closely and consistently associated with the need reduction. Such a situation or event is called a *secondary reinforcing agent,* and the strengthening of the receptor-effector connections which results from its action is known as *secondary reinforcement.*

The organization within the nervous system brought about by a particular reinforcement is called a *habit.*

For our purposes "the law of reinforcement" is best stated by Thorndike, who called it the *law of effect.*

Of several responses made to the same situation, those which are accompanied or closely followed by satisfaction to the animal will, other things being equal, be more firmly connected with the situation, so that when it recurs, they will be more likely to recur; those which are accompanied or closely followed by discomfort to the animal, other things being equal, will have their connection with that situation weakened, so that, when it recurs they will be less likely to occur. The greater the satisfaction or discomfort, the greater the strengthening or weakening of the bond.[11]

There have been many restatements of the "law of reinforcement," but it should in justice be pointed out that the credit for possibly its first and most succinct statement belongs to Shakespeare when, in *The Taming of the Shrew,* he makes Tranio say:

> No profit growes, where is no pleasure ta'en:
> In brief, sir, study what you most affect.

The "affect" or "effect" is the reinforcing agent, the degree of satisfaction, the "pleasure ta'en," the degree of complacency or of tension reduction, and in some cases increase in tension. In short, it is some form of what may perhaps best be described as *reward* which reinforces the connection between the originating stimulus and the adaptively most satisfactory response. Furthermore, under such rewarding conditions an increment of learning takes place, and when the stimulus is again repeated the same response is more likely to occur. This is another way of stating the law of effect, and this form of the law may be spoken of as *the law of reinforcement.* When a stimulus or drive is followed by an unsuccessful response, a response which produces no reward, any existing bond between the stimulus-energy and the response is weakened and in time finally suffers extinction so that the unrewarded response fails to occur on subsequent occasions.

LEARNING AND CULTURE

The whole of human history can be described as a learning process, as a gradual—in large part—improvement in adjustment.[12] If we are to understand something of the nature of this adjustment it is of fundamental importance that we make these simple principles of learning our own, for they are of some significance for an understanding of the relation of learning to the development of culture and its maintenance. From the bare-bones point of view of learning theory a person is an organism that exhibits behavior which is constantly being reinforced, and the same may be said of culture—the behavior of social groups is a function of interacting persons in stimulus-response or motivation-reward situations. Thus, when we describe the learned behavior of a person, what we are really doing is to describe some segment of the cultural habits or learned ways of doing things peculiar to the group in which he has been socialized. In this sense a description of a culture is the description of the behavior of the persons comprising it.

It is with the process of the acquisition of learned cultural habits that we are primarily concerned in considering the social development of the individual, with the strengthening of cultural habits in persons by rewards or their weakening by the lack of them. With the description of this process we shall continue presently. Meanwhile let us proceed with our discussion of learning theory.[13]

THE PROCESS OF SOCIAL LEARNING

In order to learn, four conditions must obtain. One must: (1) want something or be motivated; (2) do something or act; (3) notice something during the act; and (4) get something or gain satisfaction. In this series of events we have a statement of the four essential elements of learning, more briefly described by the terms *drive, response, cue,* and *reward* or *reinforcement.*

The *drive* is but another word for urge or need, and is usefully retained as a synonym because it emphasizes the motivational aspect of needs, just as "urge" emphasizes the aspect of tension. The term *drive* suggests activity leading to purposeful behavior. The drive, need, or urge is the motivation which stimulates the organism to act, and one could equally well use the term *motive* to describe this condition or aggregate of conditions. It is important to understand that by *drive* we mean not only the basic drives, but also the derived or socially emergent drives, and also the fact that any impulse, no matter in what way it arises, is capable of acting as a drive. Allport calls this the principle of *the functional autonomy of motives.* Allport regards "adult motives as infinitely varied, and as self-sustaining, contemporary systems, growing out of antecedent systems, but functionally independent of them."[14] It remains, however, an open question whether the satisfaction, however indirect, of some basic needs does not lie at the bottom of every autonomous act.

The *response* consists of purposeful acts calculated to bring about a reduction in the intensity of the drive. The response is what the organism does in relation to the drive. The response may be recognized as consisting of two series of acts: (1), the act immediately preceding the reward (the act closest in time to the reward), is the *goal response,* the response most strongly reinforced, and (2), *instrumental acts,* the acts leading up to the goal response. The instrumental acts are also strengthened increasingly in the order of their temporal relation to the reward, a fact which is subsumed in the concept of *the gradient of reward or reinforcement.*

The *cue* is a stimulus which is originally perceived during the response, and which, becoming associated with successful response, frequently provides the originating stimulus for the response. Cues may be provided by stimuli originating from outside the organism (exteroceptive stimuli), or by stimuli from within the organism (proprioceptive stimuli), or the combination of both. Cues are those stimuli which serve as guides in the performance of a response. They give direction and orientation to the response, they act as indicators. They indicate to the organism when, where, and how to respond. The drive motivates the response, the cue guides or directs the response along the appropriate channels. When the dominant character of a stimulus is its intensity it may be spoken of as a drive; when it functions primarily as a guide it may be referred to as a cue. The ability to notice a cue can be learned as a response. This is called learning to pay attention.

The *reward* is the reduction in the intensity of the drive. It is the event which satisfies the need. The reward signifies that the proper *adjustment* has been made by the organism, that the proper biologically or socially adaptive acts have been performed.

These four elements of learning apply to derived or acquired needs as well as to basic needs. Striving to attain social goals is satisfied by achieving them.

Social learning theory, reduced to its simplest terms, is for the most part the study of the circumstances in which cues become connected with responses. Such studies are conducted in a multidimensional matrix sandwiched in between need and reward situations. In fact all, or almost all, behavior is calculated to mediate between these two situations—those in which impulses are aroused and those in which they are satisfied. In the satisfaction of his basic and later his derived or acquired needs the person learns to make the proper responses to the cues originally accompanying them. A great number of cues are provided directly to the growing person by his culture as the conditions which must be followed by certain acts if the person is to achieve and earn the approbation of the group. The formula here is universal and follows the simple pattern of our learning process. The desire for social approbation or the avoidance of social disapprobation is the drive to which a response is made in the presence of cues provided by the situation, and the attainment of the goal, the reward of social approbation or the avoidance of social disapprobation, is secured and the intensity of the drive is satisfactorily reduced. This may be illustrated from a common experience of everyday life.

Arriving in the morning at his place of work Mr. Smith always greets his fellow workers with a hearty "Good morning." Why does he utter these words of greeting? They may have become automatic with him, and amount to no more than a formula completely devoid of affective content, in spite of the overt heartiness. Whether this be so or not, Mr. Smith had to learn how and when to use those particular words, either under conditions in which it was repeatedly explained to him, or by observation and imitation, or more usually by all three means: that it makes others feel happy—however slightly—to be greeted, that one feels happier for having done so and being greeted in return; that it is a mark of friendliness, a form of politeness which helps to make "the wheels of social intercourse go round more smoothly." A greeting is, of course, a form of social recognition. In urban areas Mr. Smith will have learned to greet in this way only those persons whom he knows, the rest he will pass by in silence. In rural areas he may greet everyone, even perfect strangers. In urban areas it is good form to behave in the first way and not customary to behave in the second way, while in some rural areas it is usual to behave in the second way and not customary to restrict one's greetings merely to persons whom one knows. Such urban-rural differences in behavior are due to many conditions, and are learned primarily through training or socialization. It might be well to remind ourselves here that fundamentally learning or training and socialization are closely intertwined with one another if they are not one and the same thing.

Mr. Smith has acquired the habit of saying "Good morning," that is to say, under certain conditions he utters certain sounds and does things with the muscles of expression of his face, the latter almost unconsciously. Why does Mr. Smith behave in this manner? The answer can most economically be given in one word: Security. He wishes to remain secure, to be undisturbed, not to be disapproved by his group, but to be approved, recognized. He is aware that in order to maintain the approval of his group he must not offend by failing to do those things which are socially required of him. In the morning he greets others because he feels an urge to do so, and having virtuously performed this social rite he may proceed upon the more or less even tenor of his way. In this type of behavior virtue is indeed its own reward. The reduction in the intensity of the urge is achieved by the utterance of the formula which is the proper response to the particular situation, and eliciting or not a greeting in return. The behavior may be broken down as follows:

Drive: Social obligation: The traditional way of behaving;
Cue: Under certain conditions: The learned conditions;
Response: To greet another person: The learned response;
Reward: And thus, with the consciousness of having made the socially approved response in the socially obligatory manner, reduce the intensity of the drive.

Under other conditions it will not be enough for Mr. Smith to make the greeting in order to secure reduction in drive. His greeting under such other conditions will have to be returned, and the returned greeting will then constitute the greater part if not the whole of his reward. Failure to receive the reward will be disturbing to him.

All social behavior, with few exceptions, can be analyzed in this elementary manner, and the ability to do so renders possible a more efficient understanding of the manner in which the individual becomes socialized.

Reward and Habit

Responses tend not to be repeated unless they are rewarded. In fact repetition of a response gives rise to fatigue, an urge to which the proper adjustive response is rest. Rest is incompatible with the repetition of an unrewarded response, and a conflict situation arises in which the restoration of energy, the reward of the response to the fatigue drive, inhibits these unrewarded responses. This is the pattern by which rewards attached to urges are, in social situations or conflict situations, made to compete with each other, and new habits antagonistic to old ones set up. The new habit must be stronger in virtue of the greater strength of its reward if the old one is to be inhibited and superseded. The old habit or response is not, however, dissolved into nothingness; it is merely superseded, inhibited, and weakened.

Learning and Inhibition

The likelihood that a given need will elicit a given response that can be *increased* is the type of behavior that is called *learning*. The likelihood that a given need will elicit a given response that can be *decreased* is called *inhibition*.

Inhibition, of course, forms a large part of the process of learning to become a social being, and the elements of the learning process already described apply with equal force to the analysis of inhibition as to learning. When, for example, a child desists from making the responses which it has been informed are extremely undesirable and has perhaps been severely punished for having made those responses, the cessation of such behavior is not due so much to the reprimand or the spanking, but rather to the fact that the child has become aware that the reward for not making such responses is greater than the reward for making them. This is the usually claimed rationale behind punishment. One more illustration: A child "fears" to enter a certain room because the reward for not entering it is greater than that for entering it. On the same principle some persons who actually fear to enter a certain room will nonetheless force themselves to do so in order to secure the reward of the excitement achieved by doing so and the anticipated relief which will accrue following the experience. Such behavior is well accounted for in terms of the principle of reward.

Stimulus Generalization

There are several other principles of learning which may be considered here. The first of these is the principle of *stimulus generalization*. The response involved in the original learning becomes connected, by associative reinforcement, with a considerable zone of stimuli other than, but adjacent to, the stimulus conventionally involved in the original learning: this is stimulus generalization. In fact, every energy impinging upon the organism's receptors, whether they be apperceptive or anatomical, in the zone of stimuli to which it is exposed is, under certain circumstances, capable of evoking the same response. Such stimuli are said to be functionally equivalent. This spreading of the results of learning to other stimuli is called *primary stimulus generalization*. The fact that many stimuli alike possess the potentiality of evoking the same response constitutes *primary stimulus equivalence*.[15]

It is not necessary for such stimuli to be present during learning. They need only be similar to or resemble the original stimulus to which the particular response was made. This fact renders possible the transfer of what is learned in one situation to other similar situations. Every situation falls into a class or pattern of situations, and since no two stimulus situations are ever exactly alike the person, willy-nilly, learns to respond to patterns of cues rather than to a specific cue, at least in social life. When, for example, a child learns that a given form of behavior yields rewards in his relations with his siblings, he is likely to try this behavior with other children, that is, he generalizes or transfers habits which have been learned in one situation to other more or less similar situations. The same principle of generalization applies to responses.

Response Generalization

Just as there is a degree of equivalence among stimuli so there is a degree of equivalence among responses. Thus, a stimulus which has come to be connected with a particular response may, under certain circumstances, elicit a different response without prior training. This is known as *response generalization*. The different response will, in some respects at least, resemble the original response, and will be equivalent to it. In other words, to bring about the reward different responses may be tried in the same situation. A child desiring food may make various muscular efforts to secure it on one occasion, upon another he will make gurgling sounds, on still another he will utter novel sounds expressing his desire, or he may cry, or perform any number of similar acts. In this way he learns that any one of a number of a certain class of acts will bring about the desired result.

Discrimination

On the other hand, the child also learns that many generalized responses are not rewarded, that particular stimuli call for specific responses, that discrimination of stimuli and of response is necessary. He learns to respond selectively by the discrimination of stimuli and the making of the properly differentiated response. Thus, the child in attempting to behave with other children as it does with its siblings may be severely rebuffed, and he learns that the same responses cannot be made to all persons. To the properly discriminated stimuli he learns to make the properly discriminated responses. In other words, by the reward of the response to one pattern of cues and the non-reward or punishment of the response to a somewhat different pattern of cues a *discrimination* is gradually established. The process of discrimination is the means by which the specificity of the cue-response connection is secured. In this manner, also, the child comes to learn the importance of cues and to be on the watch for them. By this means he learns to adapt his responses to a single drive in a multiplicity of different ways depending upon the differential cues associated with the drive. The cue, indeed, may be called the *adaptive stimulus,* since it enables the organism to make the correct discrimination which will lead to the most appropriate response.

The Gradient of Reward or Reinforcement

Immediate rewards are more effective than remote ones. When a number of different responses are made to a cue and the last of these responses is followed by reward, the connection between the last response and the cue will be strengthened the most, while the connection with each of the preceding responses will be strengthened by a progressively smaller amount. Where a series of responses are made to a cue or series of cues the connections more remote from the reward are strengthened less than those closer to the reward. That is to say, the effects of reward increase in a gradient, the closer the connections are to a reward the more they are strengthened. This is the principle of the *gradient of reward or reinforcement*. This principle accounts for the increased tendency to respond the nearer the goal is approached, simply because the connections between the cue and the goal-response have been most strengthened. The gradient of reward has the tendency to cause the subject to choose the shortest of alternative responses to a goal and to eliminate unnecessary responses from a sequence.

The effects of reward are not restricted to the particular cue-response sequence which is associated with the goal-response; they also strengthen the other cue-response connections leading up to the goal-response. There thus often exists a hierarchy of responses in which there is a graduated spread of reward in general determined by degree of proximate relation to the goal-response. The spread of the effects of reward has the function of strengthening the connections to responses which comprise the first steps of the sequence leading to reward. This function can be greatly reinforced if certain stimuli involved in the sequence acquire a sub-goal, or secondary rewarding value, by repeated association with the primary reward.

ANTICIPATORY RESPONSE

Wherever possible responses near the stage of reward tend to occur before their original time in the response series, they tend to become anticipatory. Unnecessary or useless acts in the response sequence tend to be crowded out. Anticipatory responses enable the organism to adapt itself to a situation even before the actual drive has come into play, and by generalization even in the absence of the original cue eliciting the goal-response. For example:

A child touches a hot radiator. The pain elicits an avoidance response, and the escape from pain rewards this response. Since the sight and muscular feel of the hand approaching the radiator are similar in certain respects to the sight and muscular feel of the hand touching the radiator, the strongly rewarded response of withdrawal will be expected to generalize from the latter situation to the former. After one or more trials, the child will reach out his hand toward the radiator and then withdraw it before touching the radiator. The withdrawal response will become anticipatory; it will occur before that of actually touching the radiator. This is obviously adaptive, since it enables the child to avoid getting burns.[16]

The tendency for responses to occur in a sequence does not necessarily depend upon the subject's insight into the adaptive value of the process.

ANTICIPATORY RESPONSE AND CONDITIONING

The mechanism of anticipatory response is clearly related to that of the conditioned reflex or response, the response made to a cue strongly associated with the original cue response. Mowrer and Kluckhohn have, however, correctly objected to the practice of many writers who equate conditioning and all learning on the ground that clarity is best served if the term *conditioning* is "restricted to that special sphere of learning in which an incidental stimulus becomes so strongly connected, by associative reinforcement, with a 'right' or 'goal' response that this stimulus can alone elicit the response," and they propose to make clear what they believe to be the essential difference by adding the words, *"in the absence of the original motive.* Such stimuli" they add "may be referred to as *signals,* in contradistinction to *cues.* Both, however, are properly called *signs,* to indicate that they both gain their significance, or *meaning,* from the same process, namely, associative reinforcement."[17]

Mowrer and Kluckhohn's definition of conditioning may be accepted with the proviso that it applies equally well to the processes of ordinary learning reinforcement, that at most, the conditioned reflex is, as Hull says, a special case of ordinary learning reinforcement. A distinction may certainly be made, but this does not apply to fundamentally different principles or laws, but only to the differences in the conditions under which the same principles or laws operate. Whereas selective learning involves the differential strengthening of one from a number of more or less distinct responses to a need, conditioned-reflex learning involves the formation of receptor-effector connections *de novo* in respect to one conspicuous act. The difference, if it is a difference, is that in selective learning such a conspicuous act may constitute one of a whole series of acts, and which one shall become the conspicuous conditioned response will depend upon the particular conditions prevailing in a given need situation. Since so much particularly of the emotional life of the person is developed by a process of elaboration of conditioned emotional responses we would do well to pay further attention to the nature of the conditioning process here.

While the goal-response and the cue which has directed the drive is reinforced most strongly there are, at the same time, other cues whose connections with the goal-response are also reinforced. The former is a primary and the latter a secondary or associative reinforcement. Under almost all conditions the original cue may elicit the secondary response. The primary response is the unconditioned response, the secondary response is the conditioned response, and as we have seen it may also be called the anticipatory response. Furthermore, the conditioned response is capable of being made equally well in the absence or the presence of the original cue or need situation. The importance, however, of the conditioned response lies in the fact that it is capable of being made in the absence of the original cue or motive (drive). This fact has the most important implications for the understanding of the social development of the person and of the group, for by its means the development of sign and symbolic behavior becomes possible, the development of a highly complex means of communication-language, the development of abstract thought, and the power to transmit and acquire the complex equipment necessary for social life. Spelt has shown that conditioned responses are capable of being developed in the fetus,[18] and Wenger has shown that the newborn is capable of conditioned responses.[19] In the case of the fetus the conditioned responses are to a buzzer originally associated with a loud noise, in the case of the newborn the response is with lid closure to the conditioned stimulus of a vibrator applied to the sole of the foot originally associated with an unconditioned flash of light. Thus, from the moment of birth, and possibly even before, the human organism is capable of learning, and by a pattern which the conditioned response almost perfectly illustrates. It is desirable, therefore, that the conditioning process be fully understood.

In the simplest form of conditioning the organism responds to a stimulus while another stimulus is also presented; for example, a light is flashed and the eyelids close, at the same time the sole of the foot is stroked; later the stroking of the sole of the foot leads directly to response.

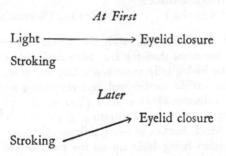

At First

Light ——————→ Eyelid closure

Stroking

Later

————→ Eyelid closure

Stroking

A child frightened by the loud sound made by the fall of a window shade, responded thereafter to the sight of a window shade with fear, though she appears to have originally responded to the sound of a falling window shade. She was freed of this fear by simple reconditioning. In pleasant circumstances over the course of several afternoons, with a reasonable supply of candy at hand, it was gradually demonstrated to her that quite a variety of amusing games could be played with a well-trained window shade. In other words, her conditioned response to the window shade was reconditioned. Under more rewarding conditions the child learned to respond to the window shade with interest rather than fear. The connection between pleasure and window shade was now stronger than the connection between fear and shade, so that the latter connection became weakened and finally extinguished.

At First

(Unconditioned
stimulus) Loud noise ⟶ Fear (Unconditioned response)

(Conditioned
stimulus) Window shade ⟶ Turning (Unconditioned response)

Later

(Conditioned stimulus)
Window shade ⟶ Fear (Conditioned response)

Under Reconditioning the following processes occur:

(Conditioned stimulus)
Window shade ⟶ Fear (Conditioned response)
(Reconditioned stimulus) ⟶ Reward (Reconditioned response)

The reward now associated with the window shade becomes biologically more dominant than the fear associated with it; there is a reinforcement of the biologically more rewarding response, and in time an extinction of the earlier conditioned, less rewarding response. This has been called the principle of *dominance* (Razran; Murphy, Murphy, and Newcomb), but is clearly an illustration of the principle of reward or reinforcement. Much human learning follows this pattern of a new cue-response connection being built up on the basis of old cues with new responses, or old responses with new cues. In terms of everyday language, old habits are sloughed off and new ones formed.

Conditioning and reconditioning are processes constantly proceeding during the socialization of the child. Cues which once served to produce a particular response come to produce another response, and the same responses come to be made to different cues. Responses are made to signs which stand for significant conditions or situations, though the condition or situation is not present to the senses. We respond to things even though the actual thing is no longer there, that is, we respond to the sign of the thing as if we were responding to the actual thing of which it is a sign. All human beings are well stocked with such tendencies to respond, and in daily life we draw upon these to make the necessary adjustments called forth by the signs which impinge upon us.

The ability to delay and regulate one's responses, the capacity to live, as it were, in the future, and to plan responses to stimuli not present to sense are frequently exhibited aspects of conditioning in daily life. Delayed reaction experiences illustrate the manner in which these processes work. A person whose behavior is motivated by a particular stimulus will generally continue to respond to anything which is capable of acting as the sign of that stimulus after the original stimulus has disappeared. Thus, the presence of a light may be noted in connection with a goal, and though the light which is a considerable distance away is extinguished the goal is nevertheless reached without difficulty by keeping the position where the light was in mind. This represents the pattern of much human behavoir.

Second and higher order conditioning, in which a conditioned response may be built upon the foundation of another, and a third and a fourth upon these, very probably plays an important part in socially learned behavior. It is generally found that the secondary or higher order stimuli have the effect of attenuating or extinguishing the connection between the lower order stimuli and the response. This finding has the most important significance for learning theory, since it is obvious that, first, it can be utilized in a practical way for the attenuation or extinction of habit, and second in explaining the acquisition of new habits. Second and higher order conditioning are specific forms of reconditioning.

In the process of social development the individual becomes conditioned to complicated patterns of stimuli rather than to purely discrete stimuli. A significant item of such a pattern may, by generalization, evoke the response called for by the pattern; a part stands for the whole. This is a type of learned behavior which is most common to social man.

An immense amount of conditioning takes place during the social development of the person without his being aware of it. Music, for example, which has been heard during meals is usually rated more highly than when it is heard unaccompanied by an enjoyable meal.

SUBLIMINAL CONDITIONING

One may make all sorts of responses in certain situations and yet be unable to give any good reason for making them. Murphy, Murphy, and Newcomb refer to negative conditioning of this sort where words which were regularly followed by electric shocks later aroused withdrawing movements and also inner disturbances shown by the galvanic skin reflex.

Although the subject may not remember that the word was followed by shock, the word produces the inner disturbance. (Indeed, the disturbance is *greater* in those instances in which the subject's memory fails him. There is here something like the blocking or repression to which psychoanalysts have called attention.) One has learned at the visceral level what he has not learned on the verbal level. Social learning of this sort may be of great importance in the tension-fear-prejudice situation, though its nature never becomes clear to the learner.[20]

Rationalizations will be offered to explain these responses while the true causes remain hidden from the person himself. The same mechanism is at work in the posthypnotic state with respect to posthypnotic suggestions.[21] And, indeed, much that transpires in the psychotherapeutic situation falls into the class of subliminal as well as liminal conditioning.[22]

Subliminal stimuli or stimuli which do not enter consciousness at all may become conditioned and modify social behavior. Murphy, Murphy, and Newcomb give an account of a reaction-time experiment, in which the subject was asked to lift his hand from the telegraph key the moment a light was shown. With practice the subject reduced his reaction time to 0.2 second.

But the experimenter inserted in the external ear a tiny cylinder containing a wire which could be made to hum as soon as the switch was thrown. The experimenter made sure in all cases that the humming was truly subliminal. No subject could tell when it started or stopped. In the next series of reaction-time experiments the switch was thrown a small fraction of a second before the stimulus light was flashed. The result, after practice with the method, was a reduction of the apparent reaction time in some cases to less than 100 one-thousandths of a second. The subject had been conditioned to the subliminal sound of the humming in the cylinder.[23]

Subliminal cues play a considerable role in conditioning, and there is some evidence that this type of conditioning is operative from the moment of birth and probably even before. In Chapter VIII (p. 163) we saw that the fetus at the thirty-first week will respond with vigorous movement to the sound of a doorbell buzzer when this is placed over the fetal head, these responses increasing in vigor as the fetus nears term. The fetal heartbeat will increase in rate when a vibrating tuning fork is placed on the mother's abdomen. Similar increases in fetal heart rate have been recorded after loud sharp noises have occurred near the mother. As early as the fifth month the fetus may hiccough. The fetus may suck its thumb or fingers, it swallows, excretes urine, and sometimes passes stool. It is quite possible that in respect of some of these forms of behavior the fetus is capable of being conditioned. Reference has already several times been made to Spelt's conditioning of a fetus to sound. It has also been suggested that such conditioning may play an important role in the subsequent personal development of the person. May it not be that occupational differences in pregnant women, through the externally originating stimuli to which they expose the fetus, cause certain responses to be made by the fetus which influence the later development of the person? Greenacre, as we saw in Chapter V (p. 92) suggests that fetal responses to unpleasant stimuli may even give rise, on the organic level, to a predisposition to anxiety which might prove an important determinant in producing the severity of any neurosis.

These are at the present time nothing but suggestions. We must await the findings of future research on fetal and infant behavior along these lines before we can come to any definite conclusions.

The newborn would certainly appear to respond to stimuli of a subtle nature, as is witnessed by the fact that it is soon able to perceive the difference between being wanted and not being wanted. The stimuli which enable the newborn to perceive this difference would, at the adult level, be described as of a subliminal nature, but it appears certain that such "subliminal" stimuli are in some way sharply discriminated by the newborn, even though they may not be cognitively evaluated— they certainly are organismically evaluated. We have seen that the newborn is capable of being conditioned to such stimuli.

In the course of his development the person learns to make considerable use of such subliminal cues, and the strong tendency of adults to judge other persons or situations by "instinct" or "intuition" is in large measure based on such subliminal conditioning.

> I do not like thee Doctor Fell,
> The reason why I cannot tell.
> But this I know, and know full well,
> I do not like thee, Doctor Fell.

This venerable quatrain may now, at long last, be explained as the expression of an attitude which was subliminally conditioned.

As Murphy, Murphy, and Newcomb put it, "We learn day by day the meaning of gestures, facial expression, tone of voice; but a great deal that we learn functions beneath the level of consciousness, or may be above the threshold of consciousness today and function just as well when below it tomorrow."[24]

Helene Deutsch has suggested that woman's intuition is due to the necessity for that greater inner alertness which a masculine society thrusts upon her, a sort of acute "listening in the dark." "Woman's understanding of other people's minds," she writes, "her intuition, is the result of an unconscious process through which the subjective experience of another person is made one's own by association and thus is immediately understood. The other person's subjective experience manifests itself in an external happening that is sometimes barely perceptible, but that in an intuitive person evokes by quick association a definite inner state."[25]

In other words, woman undergoes a better training in the interpretation of subliminal cues than man. The wit who remarked that woman's intuition is merely man's transparency was speaking wiser than he knew and at the same time exhibiting his own opacity.

The conditioned response is a preparatory or anticipatory response, a function of organic readiness or preparation for tension-reduction; it is, in brief, a redirected drive.[26]

IMITATION

Imitation is the most fundamental of all the forms of social learning. In all societies and at all ages of the developing person it is socially most highly rewarded. It is the principal way in which the developing person learns to behave and learns to modify his behavior. The importance of imitation in the socialization process has long been understood in every society, and in our own is given recognition in the saying that the child learns not by precept but by example.

As Piaget points out, the child learns to imitate, it is not born with a hereditary drive which causes it to imitate. The act by which a model is reproduced is imitation. Piaget has shown that imitation or the precursors of imitation begin quite early in the infancy of the person.[27] It is not a correct assumption that the child begins to imitate in the second half of the second year.

Imitation may be of the conditioned-response type, or imitation after a trial-and-error period, or deliberate imitation. Miller and Dollard have offered a convenient classification of the sub-mechanism involved in imitation which we shall here follow. The classification is threefold: (1) *same* behavior, (2) *matched-dependent* behavior, and (3) *copying*.

To imitate is to behave like another. In *same* behavior we are dealing with behavior which may be learned with or without imitative aids, it is of the trial-and-error variety. What is involved is the sameness of the cue to which but a single patterned response must be made if the reward is to be secured, and this results in a sameness of behavior which different individuals arrive at independently. Two persons follow the same route because they read the same route numbers leading to their destination.

Copying involves the act of one person learning to model his behavior on that of another. The copier must know when his behavior is the same, and he must have criteria for the sameness and difference of the acts he performs.

Matched-dependent behavior is important in social life. It arises preeminently in the dependent situation, wherever one person is older, shrewder, or more skilled than another. Children must perforce follow their elders, they must learn by reliance upon others to do what is required of them. In the process of socialization children match behavior with their elders and are dependent on them for cues as to what to do. Here is a simple illustration of matched-dependent behavior given by Miller and Dollard. Two children, Jim aged five and Bobby aged two, were playing in their bedroom which was adjacent to the family kitchen.

The kitchen opened upon a back stairway. It was six o'clock in the evening, the hour when father usually returned home, bearing candy for the two children. While playing in the bedroom, Jim heard a footfall on the stairs; it was the familiar sound of father's return. The younger child, however, had not identified this critical cue. Jim ran to the kitchen to be on hand when father came in the back door. Bobby happened on this occasion to be running in the direction of the kitchen and behind Jim. On many other occasions, probably many hundreds, he had not happened to run when Jim did. He had, for instance, remained sitting, continued playing with his toys, run to the window instead of the door, and the like; but on this occasion, he was running behind his brother. Upon reaching the kitchen, Jim got his candy and Bobby his.

On subsequent nights with similar conditions, the younger child ran more frequently at the mere sight of his brother running. When he ran, he received candy. Eventually, the behavior, under pressure of continued reward, became highly stabilized, and the younger child would run when the older ran, not only in this situation but in many others where time and place stimuli were different. He had learned in this one respect to *imitate* his older brother, but he had not learned to run at the sound of his father's footfall.[28]

Analysis of the behavior of these two children may be broken down into the following elements:

Leader

Drive: Appetite for candy
Cue: Father's football
Response: Running
Reward: Eating candy

Imitator

Drive: Appetite for candy
Cue: Leg-twinkle of brother
Response: Running
Reward: Eating candy

These acts of leader and imitator can be put together in one diagram:

Leader	*Imitator*
Drive: Appetite for candy	Appetite for candy
Cue: Father's football — — dependent— →Leg-twinkle of leader	
Response: Running━ — — — matched— — →Running	
Reward: Eating candy	Eating candy

The responses are *matched*. When the older brother runs the younger does likewise; in other words, the response of the imitator is elicited by cues from the act of the leader. This type of situation and this way of meeting it is of very common occurrence in human society. It should be clear that it actually represents a simple illustration of the conditioned response. A diagram will make this clear.

Leader: UCS=Father's football   UCR = Running ⎫ Reward
                                                                            ⎬ eat up
Imitator: CS=Leader's leg-twinkle   CR = Running ⎭ candy

Here the diagram is made with reference to the imitator. Actually the leader's response is quite as conditioned as the imitator's; there is simply a difference of cues involved. For the leader the father's football is the conditioned stimulus (CS) which starts as the sign for candy which motivates the response of running to secure it as the reward. In the case of the imitator, father's football has not yet been discriminated as a cue, but the brother's leg-twinkle has, and this, under certain conditions, becomes the sign for candy and motivates the running which leads to the candy reward. In diagrammatic form this is then properly represented as follows:

UCS = Candy   UCR = Running and eating candy
  CS = Leader's leg-twinkle   CR = Running and eating candy
This becomes under conditioning:

                          ⟶ CR = Running and eating candy
  CS = Leader's leg-twinkle ⟋

The real stimulus is the candy eaten after the first experience; later, the leader's leg-twinkle becomes associated as a sign of the candy and running as the proper response to secure it.

This is one of the commonest patterns of imitation which occurs in social life at every age level.

The social conditions under which imitative behavior normally occurs are those of hierarchy or rank with respect to specific skills and social statuses.

There are at least four classes of persons who are imitated by others. They are: (1) superiors in an age-grade hierarchy, (2) superiors in a hierarchy of social status, (3) superiors in an intelligence ranking system, and (4) superior technicians in any field.

Age-Grade Superiors

The fact that persons within any society are graded in age-groups provides the basic means by which imitation can take place. In our own society we recognize age-grading in such terms as "infant," "child," "adolescent," "college student," "grown man," "man in the prime of life," and "old man." These terms imply that a certain type of behavior may be expected from the persons they define. In the process of socialization the person makes the transition from one age-grade to another by learning the responses which are peculiar to each age-grade. It is important at this point to note that it is not always age or size which determines one's age-grade status in a particular community, but rather one's social readiness for the role of a person of a particular age-grade. Among the Australian aborigines a youth will not be initiated until he is considered socially developed or mature enough to be admitted to the first or second stages of initiation.[29] Among ourselves we tend to treat many persons as belonging to a much younger age-grade than their chronological age would suggest. We respond to such persons on the basis of their behavior. If they behave like young people we tend to regard them as belonging to the "young people" age-grade. Furthermore, in our society a single person can actually belong to several age-grades. In one group of that society such a person may be regarded as a youth, in another group as an adult, depending upon his behavior or the behavior that is thrust upon him by each group. A youth who can successfully imitate the behavior of a mature adult in one group will be accepted as such, whereas in another group, his home community group, he will be more diffident about acting as an adult and will tend to adhere to the behavior characteristics of his own particular age-grade.

The rewards held out by the higher age-grades are obvious: Greater freedom, more privileges and prestige. Consequently, children in all societies desire to enter the superordinal age-grades as soon as possible. Long trousers in early teen-agers and a cigarette carelessly depending from the lips of middle teen-agers are familiar evidences of this desire in our own society, and they are obvious examples of the deliberate imitation process. As Miller and Dollard point out, an age-grade system constitutes an approximate skill and prestige hierarchy.

Up to a point (perhaps old age), freedom and privilege increase with the advancement through different phases of the age cycle. As children moving up in the age-cycle are allowed or taught to make the responses of those in the next age-grade above them, and find that these responses lead to reward (for example, being permitted to stay up later and play longer), those above them acquire prestige—that is, they become leaders and models for matched-dependent and copying responses of wide range and variety. Rewarded matching or copying of particular responses institutes a tendency to match the behavior of superordinate persons over a wide range of responses. The tendency to match behavior with a superordinate person or group does not need to be conscious, willful or intentional. It can occur, and does frequently occur, automatically and without verbal aids. The imitative response is directly connected to the cue of the other person's behavior without intermediate mental links of response.[30]

It is unnecessary here to enter into all the ramifications of the imitative process in relation to age-grading; most readers will be familiar with this from their own experience. It will be clear that the age-grade limits imitation, that a member of one age-grade may do many things which are done in the superordinate age-grades but may not do others which are limited to the superordinate age-grades. Thus a child may imitate the table manners of his older brother but may not stay up as late as he does. An older person may be solemn, a younger person rarely. In young children the forbidden superior age-grade behavior finds expression in play imitating the behavior of adults.

In nonliterate societies age-grade differences in behavior are much more sharply drawn than in our own society. The age-grades are organized into a clear hierarchy, with definite privileges and obligations pertaining to membership in each. Definite ceremonies mark the entry into and the exit from each group.

It remains to be said that imitation is not a basic drive, but a socially acquired drive which occurs only under specific conditions and in response to definite rewarding goals. Finally, it must be remembered that imitation is efficient only insofar as it possesses meaning and functional significance for the imitator.

Social-status and Intelligence Superiors

Imitation of superiors in social status and imitation of the intelligent are obvious processes which need not detain us here. A few words may be said concerning *imitation of technicians*. Every society has its specialized divisions of labor, and no one person generally participates as a specialist in all of them. The more technologically complex a society is the more restricted is this participation. The category of technicians cuts across age-grading, social class, and intelligence hierarchies. Older persons may learn from younger, and upper class persons from lower class persons. Men in one field of techniques may learn from men in other fields. Children learn specialized techniques such as the three "R's" from their school teachers. College students learn from their professors. A surgeon may learn various useful devices from a plumber, and so on. We imitate technicians whenever we find it rewarding to do so.

NON-IMITATION

Learning not to imitate others under certain conditions is also an important process in socialization. When with reference to certain behavior non-imitation is rewarded negative imitation will occur. In this way perception of difference can become a secondary reward. This is the case when an upper class person compares himself with a social inferior, or when a cultivated person compares himself with an uncultivated one. Children learn not to behave like other children whose behavior is disapproved. The opposite behavior is approved; it will therefore tend to be adopted because it is rewarded.

IDENTIFICATION

A somewhat neglected and important factor in learning is what Freud described as the process of unconscious molding of a person's ego on a model. "First," writes Freud, "identification is the original form of emotional tie with an object. Secondly, in a regressive way it becomes a substitute for a libidinal object tie, as it were by means of the introjection of the object into the ego; and thirdly, it may arise with every new perception of a common quality shared with some other person who is not an object of the sexual instinct."[31] And again, "Our ego becomes like another, one which results in the first ego behaving itself in certain respects in the same way as the second; it imitates it, and as it were takes it into itself."[32]

Identification is not to be confused with imitation, even though Seward has recently defined identification as "a generalized disposition to imitate the behavior of a model."[33] Identification always involves some imitation, but whereas imitation is mostly conscious, identification is largely unconscious. As Alexander says, "Identification is the basis of all learning which is not acquired independently by trial and error. It is the most important mechanism in the development of the mature ego."[34] Children tend to take an active part in the development of their own ego by identifying themselves with parental figures, whom they endeavor to be like. It is because of the social stimuli that these figures as models provide that children strive to make something of themselves.[35] As Balint points out ". . . in relation to parents, love and identification are so much intermingled that any clear differentiation between the two seems hopeless." "A child can only become fond of something unknown . . . if he can succeed in identifying it with something known. The common basis of loving and of understanding is identification, and without it both would be impossible."[36]

EMOTIONS

In learning the emotions play a significant role, for in the process of conditioning any emotion which has been aroused may itself come to serve as a motive and source of reinforcement for new trial-and-error learning, generalization, discrimination, and even further (higher order) conditioning. Depending upon its strength an emotion may serve either as a cue or as a drive, or both. A strong emotion has drive value and a reduction in its strength acts as a reward. To the extent that an emotion is distinctive it has cue value. This, of course, illustrates a general principle which is true of any stimulus, whether originating externally or self-induced.

All the emotions are themselves subject to the laws of learning, and their connections with various cues and drives are practically entirely the result of prior training, contrary to the belief which prevailed but a short time ago that there existed an inherited disposition for particular instincts to be accompanied by particular emotions. The *mechanism* of the emotions is innate; their capacity to get attached to particular cues is acquired (or acquirable), and it is from this standpoint that emotions may be spoken of, in any social context, as acquirable drives. Thus, anxiety is one of the innate responses of pain, but "the physiological reactions producing the sensation of anxiety can easily be learned as responses to new situations, while those producing the original pain cannot. Therefore the anxiety is referred to as an acquirable drive and the pain as a primary drive."[37]

One of the ways in which acquired drives differ from innate or primary drives is that the former are much more difficult to define and specify. The fact that it is possible to attach different stimulus-producing responses to the same cue, so that both fear and anger may be aroused in the same situation, that different proportions of two or more stimulus-producing responses may be attached to different cues, so that one situation may make a person very angry and slightly anxious, whereas another may make him slightly angry and very anxious, and that different individuals may learn to respond to the same cue with different mixtures of stimulus-producing responses, so that one individual may be angry, disgusted, and afraid while another is only afraid, are some of the factors which make the definition of acquired drives difficult.

Rewards which are the goals of acquired drives can likewise vary. Another way in which acquired drives and rewards differ from innate drives and rewards is that acquired drives and rewards are much more changeable.

CANALIZATION

Up to as late as the twelfth postnatal month many of the child's drives are not clearly directed upon specific objects. A wide variety of stimuli even in the young child are capable of arousing many of his drives. But with the passage of time drives become attached to specific objects or aspects of experience which have frequently satisfied those drives, and such stimuli become more and more adequate initiators of the proper responses. In this process we see the mechanism for acquired tastes. In this process a direct relationship between the satisfying experience and the drive becomes established. In this way individual preferences and general cultural preferences develop by a process of fixation. The drive is channeled or *canalized* in a specific direction characteristic of the person and his culture. It is important to distinguish between canalization as a social process and conditioning. In canalization the object first eliciting a drive response, the original or unconditional response, remains the adequate direct cue; there is no entry of a substitute cue or associative reinforcement. In the conditioned response a new and often accidental stimulus, occurring while an adequate unconditioned stimulus is at work, acquires the power to call out a response. It is often relatively easy to extinguish the connection between a cue-response in simple conditioning, but much harder to produce such extinction in a canalized response.

The process of canalization is of great importance for learning theory, for a large proportion of our social motives are canalized drives. Indeed, it has been suggested by Murphy, Murphy, and Newcomb that "there is enormously less conditioning and more canalization in social life than most writers have recognized."[38] As these authors point out, a taste for beer or olives, for golf or politics, is not acquired solely through conditioning.

We start with an interest in food, or tone, or strenuous activity, or the interchange of gestures or facial expressions with our fellows; and these needs, supplemented by many others and guided by cultural processes, give us in time a specific craving for our game of golf or our political argument. We think it worth while to stress that the rudiments of response to tone, taste, smell, and the forms and features of people in the child's immediate world are clearly present and canalized by social experience until they become fairly definite and fixed.[39]

While conditioning is one of the processes which produce similar stabilization of habits, it is not the sole process by which such responses to given cues are produced. Canalization is at least an equally important means of securing such responses. The frequency and intensity of certain stimuli in rewarding situations is a fact which is alone sufficient to produce a connection between them and a drive; so that one can depend upon such cues to evoke the proper drive-response.

But while canalization plays an important role in the acquisition of social habits, that role is a minimal one in infancy compared with the part it plays later. For example, during early infancy the mother ministering to the child's needs is not specifically perceived as an independent object; what is perceived are the satisfactions which she provides in response to the infant's needs, in the form of food and care. These satisfactions are elicited by a large number of unconditioned stimuli that, as the child develops the image of the mother, gradually become associated with the satisfying situation. By associative reinforcement she becomes a symbol of present and anticipated satisfactions; by her presence she may serve to satisfy a number of drives. She, as an object, has become a satisfying substitute stimulus, she has become a conditioned stimulus producing satisfying responses. Though she cannot satisfy all drives by the fact of her presence alone, it is more than doubtful whether the infant sees it that way. What he comes to know is that when this object (the mother) is present, needs are satisfied. It is probable that this is the pattern of most of the learning of the infant, and that canalization does not really begin to take effect until the period of childhood has been reached. It is not by canalization but by conditioning that the mother becomes the object of love. The preference for certain foods, however, becomes established by sheer force of their repeated direct satisfying value, that is, by canalization.

LEARNING AND VALUES

When the process of canalization is complete, so that the person is prepared to satisfy a need with a definite response, a value has been established. In this sense a value may be defined as the maintenance of a set toward the attainment of a goal.[40] The person learns to want many goals. When these goals are remote and are strived for, value obtains. When the person blindly gropes for some undefined goal in a random manner, value does not obtain. Some definitely known goal must be held in view. This last statement implies that a value takes its existential form from the fact that a goal is being contemplated or approached, rather than from the actual achievement of the goal. The latter is the *reward*, the former the *value*. Thus, stimuli which act as cues and even drives, as well as the goal itself, may all become values. Value itself is not a reward; it is best regarded as a *potential rewarder*. We often strive for things we do not have, and may never have. That we value what we strive to attain is exhibited in the striving, not in the attainment.

An attitude and a value are ultimately one and the same thing. The distinction which is usually made between them is quite arbitrary, being based on the degree of verbalization involved: where verbalization is high we speak of an attitude, where it is low, of a value.

In the process of socialization the values of the person undergo integration, and it is this integration, indeed, which constitutes the basis of the integration of personality: the organization of values into a system derived from the history of the individual's own experience.

The conflicts between values constitute, in the social situation, important factors in the social development of the person. The resolution or nonresolution of these conflicts, the confusion of values, in terms of the social definition of goals, are processes which have very important influences upon the developing personality. Since by far the larger number of the person's values are learned, it is of the first order of importance for human beings to learn what values they should live by.

Appendix B THE EFFECTS UPON THE MOTHER OF REMOVAL OF THE INFANT IMMEDIATELY AFTER BIRTH

To the solid ground
Of Nature, trusts the mind which builds for aye.   —WORDSWORTH

Experimental data on the effects upon the mother of separating the infant from her immediately after birth have not, as far as I know, hitherto been published. The following observations are, therefore, extremely valuable, and are for this reason here reprinted by courtesy of the author, Betsy Marvin McKinney, and *Child-Family Digest*. It is to be hoped that Mrs. McKinney's interesting observations will prompt the further study, under experimental conditions, of the relationships she reports.

A CANINE DEMONSTRATION*

About four weeks ago our beloved collie, Jeanie, produced eight pups. The experience proved so interesting (in its implications) I thought you might like to hear about it. Theoretically she belongs to the three children, and since some of Jeanie's pups were whelped in the daytime hours before the children's bedtime, they were able to be on hand to watch, utterly fascinated, of course.

She began having them so fast and was also so fatigued trying to catch up with the cleaning and decording of each puppy before the next was on the way that I removed them one by one to a nearby box lined with soft flannel as soon as she had occupied that part of her maternal duties, thinking to help her and give her a rest, as well as to prevent her possible rolling on an earlier pup when she gave birth to a later one. She's such a trusting soul where we are concerned that she permitted this human interference without too much anxiety, and continued with her whelping until all eight had arrived. When it seemed that no more pups would be forthcoming, I returned them to her for a few seconds for reassurance purposes, and then removed them all again, this time for an hour or so, to give her a "real rest." She was very tired, and had been working hard for some hours.

* Reprinted by permission of the author, Betsy Marvin McKinney, and *Child-Family Digest*, vol. 10, 1954, pp. 63–65.

Last year, as soon as the fourth and last pup of her first litter was born, she was eager to leave her whelping box for an airing and needed no urging, but this time she wouldn't budge. She would *not* get out and seemed, moreover, to be getting more and more anxious about her squirming little pups. So I put them back beside her, whereupon they began to root around and nuzzle and in very short order, to nurse. I suddenly realized that this was the first real opportunity I'd given her puppies to nurse her despite the fact that several hours had elapsed since the first birth.

I stayed with her a few hours more in case any more pups might still arrive (went to bed around dawn that day!) and when at the end of that time and despite all the wiles I knew I *still* couldn't get that listless dog out of her whelping box for the relief I knew she must need by then, the full impact of what I had done began to dawn.

Finally, by means of really stern scolding, I forced her to go outdoors for a few necessary seconds, after which she returned to her box to stay there, nursing those pups, *for over 24 hours!*

It was a shock to realize with shame and abashment that I had performed on Jeanie the same type of cultural deprivation and damage that is performed on many human mothers when their babies are taken away from them at birth without permitting the immediate nursing that is an instinctive urge of the newborn.

As for Jeanie, that poor animal was in bad internal shape, and I am afraid it was all due to me. She *had* to stay there hours longer than she'd otherwise have needed to, to be nursed back into reasonable internal health by her puppies. She was in a bad way, hemorrhaged during the night, and I could have kicked myself for being so stupid. As it was, it took our Jeanie a pretty long time to come back to normal—and in all probability because I'd deprived her of the immediate therapeutic suckling which would have pulled her together when she needed it most—directly following the birth and clean-up of each puppy!

You know I wonder sometimes if this same situation occurs without anyone realizing it, in the case of human mothers; if there is any tie-in between slow recoveries from childbirth and the removal, sometimes for long periods, of the new mother's baby? I wonder if the standard injection of pituitrin routinely used to contract the uterus following delivery could, despite its possible need in many cases, have the long-term effect that immediate and continued nursing has, wherein the baby and mother answer each other's needs at exactly the tempo and to the exact extent that both require, over an extended period of time? It is almost symbiotic, that early relationship, the mother giving her baby security along with the stimulus to nourishment while the baby serves her as a therapeutic agent speeding her recovery from her own recent tiring labors in bringing her baby forth.

At any rate, Jeanie certainly demonstrated this principle in an unmistakable way and I felt very badly at my own share in her discomfort.

Appendix C   REFERENCES

Chapter 1. INTRODUCTION

1. C. Kluckhohn and H. R. Murray, "A conception of personality," in *Personality in Nature, Society, and Culture*, 2d ed., New York, A. A. Knopf, 1953, p. 43.
2. R. Linton, *The Cultural Background of Personality*, New York, Appleton-Century, 1945, p. 18.
3. E. R. Hilgard and D. G. Marquis, *Conditioning and Learning*, New York, Appleton-Century, 1940, p. 347.
4. J. Deese, *Psychology of Learning*, New York, McGraw-Hill, 1952, p. 342.
5. E. R. Guthrie, "Conditioning: A theory of learning in terms of stimulus, response and association," *Forty-First Yearbook of the National Society for the Study of Education*, Part II, Bloomington, Illinois, Public School Publishing Company, 1942, chap. I, p. 17.
6. Deese, *op. cit.*
7. Ives Hendrick, "Early development of the ego," *Psychoanalytic Quarterly*, vol. 20, 1951, pp. 41–61.
8. Kimball Young, *Personality and Problems of Adjustment*, New York, Crofts & Co., 1940, p. 124.
9. L. O. Kattsoff, *The Design of Human Behavior*, St. Louis, Mo., Educational Publishers, 1953, p. 28.
10. See B. F. Skinner, *Science and Human Behavior*, New York, Macmillan, 1953; A. F. C. Wallace, "A science of human behaviour," *Explorations*, no. 3, 1954, pp. 127–136.
11. For an excellent discussion of law from this point of view see Felix Kaufmann, *Methodology of the Social Sciences*, New York, Oxford University Press, 1944; also chapter 4, "Sociological law," in George A. Lundberg's *Foundations of Sociology*, New York, Macmillan, 1939, pp. 133, *et seq.*; see also P. Sorokin, *Sociocultural Causality, Space, Time*, Durham, North Carolina, Duke University Press, 1943; Douglas G. Haring, "Science and social phenomena," *American Scientist*, vol. 35, 1947, pp. 351–363; Lewis W. Beck, "The 'Natural Science Ideal' in the social sciences," *Scientific Monthly*, vol. 48, 1949, pp. 386–394; E. W. Leaver and J. J. Brown, "The need for general laws in the social sciences," *Science*, vol. 114, 1951, pp. 339–382; Florian Znaniecki, *Cultural Sciences*, Urbana, University of Illinois Press, 1952.
12. Similar phenomena have been observed among numerous other animals. In fishes, for example, it has been observed that in overpopulated aquaria infanticide increases in direct proportion to crowding, and a population suited to the volume of water is thus maintained (C. M. Brader and C. W. Coates, "A preliminary study of population stability and sex ratio of *Lebistes*," *Copeia*, no. 3, pp. 147–155, 1932). See also J. B. Calhoun, "The social aspects of population dynamics," *Journal of*

Mammalogy, vol. 33, 1952, pp. 129–159; M. F. Ashley Montagu, *Coming Into Being Among the Australian Aborigines*, London, Routledge, 1937.

13. See G. P. Murdock, *Social Structure*, New York, Macmillan, 1949; and S. F. Nadel, *The Foundations of Social Anthropology*, Glencoe, Illinois, Free Press, 1951. For a contrary view see E E. Evans-Pritchard, *Social Anthropology*, Glencoe, Illinois, Free Press, 1951.

14. See P. F. Lazarsfeld, *Mathematical Thinking in the Social Sciences*, Glencoe, Illinois, Free Press, 1954; S. C. Dodd, *The Dimensions of Society*, New York, Macmillan, 1942; and N. Rashevsky, *Mathematical Biology of Social Behavior*, Chicago, University of Chicago Press, 1951. See the writings of W. R. Ashby, "Effect of controls on stability," *Nature*, vol. 155, 1945, p. 242; "Dynamics of the cerebral cortex: The behavioral problems of systems in equilibrium," *American Journal of Psychology*, vol. 59, 1946, pp. 682–685; *Design For a Brain*, New York, John Wiley, 1952. See also E. F. Haskell, "A natural classification of societies," *Transactions of the New York Academy of Sciences*, Ser. II, vol. 9, 1947, pp. 186–196.

15. E. G. Miller, Jr., "Scientific method and social problems," *Science*, vol. 109, 1949, pp. 290–291.

16. D. L. Watson, *The Study of Human Nature*, Yellow Springs, Ohio, Antioch Press, 1953, p. 109.

17. P. W. Bridgman, "The prospect for intelligence," in *Reflections of a Physicist*, New York, Philosophical Library, 1950, pp. 342–368.

18. Gerald Holton, "On the duality and growth of physical science," *American Scientist*, vol. 41, 1953, pp. 89–99.

19. R. H. Seashore, "Physiological psychology," in *Annual Review of Physiology*, vol. 8, 1946, pp. 515–534.

20. See Hans Vaihinger, *The Philosophy of "As If,"* New York, Harcourt, Brace & Co., 1924.

21. Richard Hofstadter, *Social Darwinism in American Thought 1860–1905*, Philadelphia, University of Pennsylvania Press, 1944, p. 176.

22. Whether one refers to the duplicated organisms as maternal and daughter or sister cells depends upon the school of philosophy in these matters to which one belongs. It makes not the least difference what terminology one adopts. The problem is perhaps best resolved in the limerick:

> An ameba named Sam and his brother
> Were drinking a toast to each other;
> In the midst of their quaffing
> They split themselves laughing
> And now each of them is a mother.

23. W. M. Wheeler, *Social Life Among Insects*, New York, Harcourt, Brace, 1923.

24. T. C. Schneirla, "The 'levels' concept in the study of the social organization of animals," in J. H. Rohrer and M. Sherif (editors), *Social Psychology at the Crossroads*, New York, Harper, 1951, p. 89. See also J. B. Calhoun, "The social aspects of population dynamics," *Journal of Mammalogy*, vol. 33, 1952, pp. 139–159.

25. W. C. Allee, *Cooperation Among Animals*, New York, Henry Schuman, 1951, p. 21.

26. "There is something fundamentally social in living things, and closer scrutiny shows that this must be a characteristic of all life, since every organism is, at least temporarily, associated with other organisms, even if only with members of the opposite sex and with its parents. . . . This statement holds good even of such supposedly unsocial creatures as lions, eagles, sharks, tiger-beetles, and spiders. There are,

in fact, no truly solitary organisms. We may say, therefore, that the social is a correlate as well as an emergent of all life in the sense in which Morgan speaks of the mind as being both a correlate and an emergent of life. . . . Indeed, the correlations of the social—using the term in its most general sense—even extend down through the non-living to the very atom with its organization of component electrons." (William M. Wheeler, "Emergent evolution and the development of societies," in *Essays in Philosophical Biology*, Cambridge, Harvard University Press, 1939, pp. 158–159.)

27.   T. Dobzhansky, *Genetics and the Origin of Species*, 3d ed., New York, Columbia University Press, 1951, pp. 78–79.

28.   G. G. Simpson, *Life of the Past*, New Haven, Yale University Press, 1953, p. 56.

29.   J. P. Scott, "Social behavior, organization and leadership in a small flock of domestic sheep," *Comparative Psychology Monographs*, vol. 18, 1945, pp. 1–29.

30.   C. F. Jacobsen, M. M. Jacobsen, and J. G. Yoshioka, "Development of an infant chimpanzee during her first year," *Comparative Psychology Monographs*, vol. 9, 1932, pp. 1–94.

31.   Personal communication from Dr. J. A. Reyniers, November 10, 1951.

32.   Charles H. Cooley, *The Social Process*, New York, Scribner's, 1918, p. 28.

33.   T. Dobzhansky and M. F. Ashley Montagu, "Natural selection and the mental capacities of mankind," *Science*, vol. 105, 1947, pp. 587–590; N. C. Tappen, "A mechanistic theory of human evolution," *American Anthropologist*, vol. 55, 1953, pp. 605–607; M. F. Ashley Montagu, "Cultural and physical evolution," *American Anthropologist*, vol. 56, 1954, p. 290; W. Etkin, "Social behavior and the evolution of man's mental faculties," *American Naturalist*, vol. 88, 1954, pp. 129–142.

Chapter 2.   THE BIOLOGICAL BASIS OF COOPERATION

1.   N. Tinbergen, *Social Behaviour in Animals*, New York, Wiley, 1953, p. 53; W. C. Allee, *Cooperation Among Animals*, New York, Henry Schuman, 1951.

2.   N. R. F. Maier and T. C. Schneirla, *Principles of Animal Psychology*, New York, McGraw-Hill, 1935, pp. 1–7. See also L. K. Frank, *Nature and Human Nature*, New Brunswick, New Jersey, Rutgers University Press, 1951.

3.   E. S. Russell, *The Directiveness of Organic Activities*, New York, Cambridge University Press, 1945, p. 191.

4.   N. Tinbergen, *op. cit.*, p. 2.

5.   For critical surveys of this literature see the references in footnotes 20 and 25.

6.   H. V. Wilson, "Development of sponges from dissociated tissue cells," *Bulletin of U. S. Bureau of Fisheries*, vol. 39, 1910, pp. 1–30; P. S. Galtsoff, "Regeneration after dissociation," *Journal of Experimental Zoology*, vol. 42, 1925, pp. 183–251.

7.   C. M. Child, "Axial development in aggregates of dissociated cells from *Corymorpha*," *Physiological Zoology*, vol. 1, 1928, pp. 419–461.

8.   I. E. Wallin, *Symbionticism and the Origin of Species*, Baltimore, Williams & Wilkins, 1927. See particularly H. S. Jennings, *The Behavior of Lower Organisms*, New York, Columbia University Press, 1906.

9.   P. Deegener, "Soziologische beobachtungen an *Hyponomeuta cognatellus*," *Hb. Biol. Centralbl.*, vol. 42, 1922, pp. 241–253.

10.   See R. Redfield (editor), "Levels of integration in biological and social systems," *Biological Symposia*, vol. 8, Lancaster, Pennsylvania, Jaques Cattell Press, 1942.

352　Appendix C

11. J. T. Bonner, *Morphogenesis*, Princeton, Princeton University Press, 1952, pp. 173 *et seq.*

12. For a survey of the literature see W. C. Allee, *op. cit.*; W. C. Allee, *Animal Aggregations*, Chicago, University of Chicago Press, 1931; W. C. Allee, *et al.*, *Principles of Animal Ecology*, Philadelphia, Saunders, 1949. See also the references quoted in footnotes 20 and 25.

13. W. S. Allee, *Cooperation Among Animals, loc. cit.*

14. W. C. Allee, K. P. Schmidt, and R. Hesse, *Ecological Animal Geography*, New York, Wiley, 1951.

15. W. C. Allee, *Cooperation Among Animals, loc. cit.*, p. 35.

16. *Ibid.*, pp. 106–107; J. B. Calhoun, "The social aspects of population dynamics," *Journal of Mammalogy*, vol. 33, 1952, pp. 139–159; N. Tinbergen, *op. cit.*

17. E. Fraser Darling, *Bird Flocks and the Breeding Cycle*, New York, Cambridge University Press, 1938.

18. T. Brailsford Robertson, "Experimental studies on cellular multiplication: II. The influence of mutual contiguity upon reproductive rate and the part played therein by the 'x-substance' in bacterised infusions which stimulate the multiplication of infusoria," *Biochemical Journal*, vol. 15, 1921, pp. 612–619.

19. In *The Origin of Species* (1859) Darwin wrote: "I should premise that I use the term Struggle for Existence in a large and metaphorical sense, including dependence of one being on another, and including (which is more important) not only the life of the individual, but success in leaving progeny" (chap. III, p. 62). Having mentioned "dependence" here Darwin thereafter neglects to develop the notion. In *The Descent of Man* (1871), however, he to some extent made up for this neglect. See Ashley Montagu " 'Social instincts,' " *Scientific American*, vol. 182, 1950, pp. 54–56.

20. For a discussion of this subject see M. F. Ashley Montagu, *Darwin, Competition, and Cooperation*, New York, Schuman, 1952.

21. A. V. Espinas, *Des Sociétés Animales*, Paris, Librairie Ballière, 1878, 3d ed., 1924; Kessler, "Mutual aid as a law of nature and the chief factor of evolution," *Memoirs (Trudy) of the St. Petersburg Society of Naturalists*, vol. 9, 1880, a lecture delivered at the annual meeting of the St. Petersburg Society of Naturalists, January 8, 1880, noticed in *Nature*, London, January 21, 1880; J. M. A. Lanessan, "La lutte pour l'existence et l'association pour la lutte," *Bibliotheque Biologique*, Paris, 1881; L. Büchner, *Liebe und Liebes-Leben in der Thierwelt*, Berlin, 1883; P. Geddes and A. Thomson, *The Evolution of Sex*, London, Scott, 1889; Menzbir, *Darwinism in Biology* (in Russian); J. Novikoff, *Les Luttes Entre Sociétés Humaines et Leur Phases Successives*, Paris, 1893, 2d ed., 1896. See also Novikoff's *La Guerre et ses Prétendus Bienfaits*, Paris, 1894.

22. T. H. Huxley, "The struggle for existence: a programme," *Nineteenth Century*, vol. 23, 1888, pp. 161–180.

23. Many times reprinted, but now out of print.

24. Henry George, *Progress and Poverty*, New York, 1897, book X, chap. III.

25. J. M. A. Lanessan, *La Lutte Pour l'Existence et l'Evolution des Sociétés*, Paris, Alcan, 1903; J. W. L. Jones, "Sociality and sympathy," *Psychological Review*, vol. 5, 1903, pp. 1–98; L. M. Keasbey, "Co-operation, coercion and competition," *Science*, vol. 17, 1903, pp. 922 *et seq.*; C. Bouglé, "Darwinism and sociology," in *Darwin and Modern Science* (edited by A. C. Seward), Cambridge, at the University Press, 1909, pp. 465–476; Henry M. Bernard, *Some Neglected Factors in Evolution*, New York, Putnam, 1911; Patrick Geddes and J. Arthur Thomson, *Sex*, London, Williams &

Norgate, 1911; Yves Delage and Marie Goldsmith, *The Theories of Evolution*, New York, Huebsch, 1912; Hermann Reinheimer, *Evolution by Co-operation: A Study of Bioeconomics*, London, Kegan Paul, 1913; William Patten, "Co-operation as a factor in evolution," *Proceedings of the American Philosophical Society*, vol. 55, 1916, pp. 505–532; George Nasmyth, *Social Progress and the Darwinian Theory*, New York, Putnam, 1916; P. Deegener, *Die Formen der Vergesellschaftung im Tier-reiche*, Leipzig, Veit, 1918; John M. Macfarlane, *The Causes and Course of Evolution*, New York, Macmillan, 1918; William Patten, *The Grand Strategy of Evolution*, Boston, Richard Badger, 1920; Hermann Reinheimer, *Symbiosis: A Socio-Physiological Study of Evolution*, London, Headley Bros., 1920; William M. Wheeler, *Social Life Among Insects*, New York, Harcourt, Brace & Co., 1923; Robert W. Gibson, *The Morality of Nature*, New York, Putnam, 1923; Leo S. Berg, *Nomogenesis, or Evolution Determined by Law*, London, Constable, 1926; William M. Wheeler, "Social evolution," in *Human Biology and Racial Welfare* (edited by Edmund V. Cowdry), New York, Hoeber, 1930; Herbert F. Standing, *Spirit in Evolution*, London, Allen & Unwin, 1930; W. E. Allee, *Animal Aggregations, loc. cit.*; W. C. Allee, *The Social Life of Animals*, New York, W. W. Norton, 1938; Christopher Caudwell, "Love," in *Studies in a Dying Culture*, London, Bodley Head, 1938; William Galt, "The principle of cooperation in behavior," *Quarterly Review of Biology*, vol. 15, 1940, pp. 401–410; Robert Redfield (editor), "Levels of integration in biological and social systems," *loc. cit.*; Charles Sherrington, *Man on His Nature*, New York, Cambridge University Press, 1941; Alfred E. Emerson, "Basic comparisons of human and insect societies," in *Biological Symposia*, vol. 8, 1942, pp. 163–177; R. Gerard, "Higer levels of integration," in *Biological Symposia*, vol. 8, 1942, pp. 67–87; Ralph Lillie, *General Biology and Philosophy of the Organism*, Chicago, University of Chicago Press, 1945; John Hewetson, *Mutual Aid and Social Evolution*, London, Freedom Press, 1946; Alfred E. Emerson, "The biological basis of social cooperation," *Illinois Academy of Science Transactions*, vol. 39, 1946, pp. 9–18; L. R. Wheeler, *Harmony of Nature: A Study of Co-operation for Existence*, New York, Longmans, 1947; Thomas H. Huxley and Julian S. Huxley, *Touchstone For Ethics*, New York, Harper, 1947; Henry G. Maurice, *Ask Now the Beasts*, London, Society for the Preservation of the Fauna of the Empire, 1948; L. L. Whyte, *Everyman Looks Forward*, New York, Holt, 1948; Samuel J. Holmes, *Life and Morals*, New York, Macmillan, 1948; M. F. Ashley Montagu, "The origin and nature of social life and the biological basis of cooperation," *Journal of Social Psychology*, vol. 29, 1949, pp. 267–283; Hugh Miller, *The Community of Man*, New York, Macmillan, 1949; E. Morton Miller, "A look at the anatomy and physiology of groups," *Bios.*, vol. 20, 1949, pp. 24–31; W. C. Allee, *et al.*, *Principles of Animal Ecology, loc. cit.*; George G. Simpson, *The Meaning of Evolution*, New Haven, Yale University Press, 1949; Herman J. Muller, "Genetics in the scheme of things," *Hereditas*, supplementary volume, 1949, pp. 96–127; F. J. Trembley, "Evolution and human affairs," *Proceedings of the Pennsylvania Academy of Science*, vol. 23, 1949, pp. 181–195; Alfred Korzybski, *Manhood of Humanity*, Lakeville, Connecticut, Institute of General Semantics, 1950; Ashley Montagu, *On Being Human*, New York, Schuman, 1950; Ashley Montagu, " 'Social instincts,' " *loc. cit.*; Michael Graham, *Human Needs*, London, Cresset Press, 1951; Ashley Montagu, *Darwin, Competition, and Cooperation, loc. cit.*; Vera Daniel, "Physical principles in human co-operation," *Sociological Review* (London), vol. 44, 1952, pp. 107–134; R. A. M. Bergman, "The biological foundations of society," *Civilizations*, vol 2, 1952, pp. 1–15; Alfred E. Emerson, "The supraorganismic aspects of the society," *Colloques*

Internationaux du Centre National de la Recherche Scientifique, vol. 34, 1952, pp. 333–353; A. Campbell Garnett, *The Moral Nature of Man,* New York, Ronald Press, 1952; Julian Huxley, *Evolution in Action,* New York, Harper, 1953; Edmund W. Sinnott, *Two Roads to Truth,* New York, Viking, 1953; Louis O. Kattsoff, *The Design of Human Behavior,* St. Louis, Educational Publishers, 1953; Alfred E. Emerson, "Dynamic homeostasis: A unifying principle in organic, social, and ethical evolution," *Scientific Monthly,* vol. 78, 1954, pp. 67–85; Edmund W. Sinnott, "Biology and teleology," *Bios,* vol. 25, 1954, pp. 35–43; Pitirim A. Sorokin, *The Ways and Power of Love,* Boston, Beacon Press, 1954; Umberto D'Ancona, *The Struggle For Existence,* Leiden, Brill, 1954; T. A. Goudge, "The concept of evolution," *Mind,* vol. 43, 1954, pp. 16–25; T. A. Goudge, "Some philosophical aspects of the theory of evolution," *University of Toronto Quarterly,* vol. 8, 1954, pp. 386–401; Max Scheler, *The Nature of Sympathy,* New Haven, Yale University Press, 1954; G. Witt, "Primary love therapy," *Psychonalysis,* vol. 3, 1954, pp. 63–73.

26. W. C. Allee, "Where angels fear to tread: A contribution from general sociology to human ethics," *Science,* vol. 97, 1943, p. 521.

27. *Ibid.,* p. 520.

28. J. B. Calhoun, *op. cit.*

29. T. C. Schneirla, "Problems in the biopsychology of social organization," *Journal of Abnormal and Social Psychology,* vol. 41, 1946, pp. 385–402.

30. C. D. Leake, "Ethicogenesis," *Scientific Monthly,* vol. 60, 1945, pp. 245–253. See also a revision of this article in *Studies and Essays in the History of Science and Learning* (edited by M. F. Ashley Montagu), New York, Schuman, 1946, pp. 261–275. A further reprinting of this article together with a criticism and discussion of it will be found in C. D. Leake and P. Romanell, *Can We Agree?* Austin, University of Texas Press, 1950.

31. P. R. Burkholder, "Cooperation and conflict among primitive organisms," *American Scientist,* vol. 40, 1952, p. 603. See also C. L. Birch, "Experimental background to the study of the distribution and abundance of insects," *Evolution,* vol, 7, 1953, pp. 136–144.

32. T. Dobzhansky and M. F. Ashley Montagu, "Natural selection and the mental capacities of mankind," *Science,* vol. 105, 1947, pp. 587–590.

33. Robert W. Gibson, *op. cit.,* p. 30.

34. *Ibid.,* p. 95.

35. A. E. Emerson, "The biological basis of social cooperation," *loc. cit.,* pp. 8–18. See also W. C. Allee, "Biology and international relations," *New Republic,* vol. 112, 1945, pp. 816–817.

36. "The care of the eggs might be called social behaviour, for from the time of being laid the eggs are individuals. Usually we do not consider such one-sided relations as really social, but we must not forget that the egg, although not moving, does give special stimuli which have a profound influence on the parent bird," N. Tinbergen, *op. cit.,* p. 6.

37. Ralph Linton, "Culture, society, and the individual," *Journal of Abnormal and Social Psychology,* vol. 33, 1938, pp. 425–436.

38. Carl J. Warden, *The Emergence of Human Culture,* New York, Macmillan, 1936.

39. This account of the hunting habits of lions is taken from Ralph Linton's *The Study of Man,* New York, (Appleton-Century, 1936, p. 78). Desiring to check on the accuracy of this account I wrote to Dr. L. S. B. Leakey, Director of the Coryndon Museum, at Nairobi, Kenya Colony. Dr. Leakey was born and brought up

in Kenya Colony and has always had a keen interest in its natural history, and his reply—for which I am much indebted to him—raises more than a doubt as to the accuracy of the alleged change in lions' habit of hunting. However, the possibility does exist that the way of hunting referred to was adaptively devised by the lions, at some earlier time, to meet the appropriate conditions. Under date of November 2, 1953, Dr. Leakey writes: "I do not think there is any question of lion having altered their traditional way of hunting. So far as I can tell you lions have always had several different methods of hunting. One of which was the hunting solo or in pairs, and the other the hunting by a 'pride' of lion, in which some of the lion remained hidden while the other lions quite openly walked towards the game and edged them towards the hidden member of the 'pride.' I am practically certain records of both methods of hunting can be found, even in the earliest literature dealing with lions in Africa."

40. Zing Y. Kuo, "Genesis of cat's responses to the rat," *Journal of Comparative Psychology*, vol. 11, 1931, pp. 1–35.

41. *Ibid.*, p. 35.

42. Loh Seng Tsai, "Peace and cooperation among natural enemies," reported at the St. Louis, December 30, 1952, meeting of the American Association for the Advancement of Science.

43. J. Fisher and R. A. Hinde, "The opening of milk bottles by birds," *British Birds*, vol. 42, 1949, pp. 347–357; see also T. H. Hawkins, "Opening of milk bottles by birds," *Nature*, vol. 165, 1950, pp. 435–436.

44. R. A. Hinde and J. Fisher, "Further observations on the opening of milk bottles by birds," *British Birds*, vol. 44, 1952, pp. 392–396. In Sweden the spotted woodpecker (*Dendrocopus major*) has been observed opening milk bottles, and in the *Seattle Times*, June 7, 1937, there is a photograph of Steller's jay (*Cyanocitta stelleri*) opening a milk bottle.

45. W. H. Thorpe, "The learning abilities of birds," *Ibis*, vol. 93, 1951, pp. 1–52, 252–296; W. H. Thorpe, "The definition of some terms in animal behavior studies," *Bulletin of Animal Behavior*, vol. 9, 1951, pp. 34–40; Konrad Z. Lorenz, *King Solomon's Ring*, New York, Crowell, 1952, pp. 140, 144–145.

46. W. E. D. Scott, "Data on song in birds," *Science*, n. s., vol. 14, 1901, pp. 522–526.

47. E. Conradi, "Song and call-notes of English sparrows when reared by canaries," *American Journal of Psychology*, vol. 16, 1905, pp. 190–199.

48. See M. Metfessel, "Relationships of heredity and environment in behavior," *Journal of Psychology*, vol. 10, 1940, pp. 177–198.

49. Konrad Z. Lorenz, *op. cit.*, p. 140.

50. Robert M. Yerkes, *Chimpanzees*, New Haven, Yale University Press, 1943, p. 52.

51. The scientist-compeer of St. Francis, Professor Konrad Z. Lorenz, has given us a profound insight into the nature of the "beast" in his delightful book *King Solomon's Ring*, (*loc. cit.*). See also H. G. Maurice, *op. cit.*, and Ruth C. Noble, *The Nature of the Beast*, New York, Doubleday, 1946.

52. T. H. Langlois, "A Study of the small-mouth bass, *Micropterus dolomieu* (Lacepede) in rearing ponds in Ohio," *Ohio Biological Survey, Ohio State University Studies. Bulletin* No. 33, vol. 6, 1936; T. H. Langlois, "Sociological succession," *Ecology*, vol. 18, 1937, pp. 458–461.

53. E. Fredericson, "Competition: the effects of infantile experience upon adult behavior," *Journal of Abnormal and Social Psychology*, vol. 46, 1951, pp. 406–409.

54. J. B. Calhoun, *op. cit.*, p. 143.

55. T. C. Schneirla, "Levels in the psychological capacities of animals," in *Philosophy For the Future* (R. W. Sellars *et al.*, editors), New York, Macmillan, 1949, pp. 243–286.

56. T. Dobzhansky and M. F. Ashley Montagu, *op. cit.* See also P. R. David and L. H. Snyder, "Genetic variability and human behavior," in *Social Psychology at the Crossroads* (edited by J. H. Rohrer and M. Sherif), New York, Harper, 1951, pp. 53–82. In the same volume see also T. C. Schneirla, "The 'levels' concept in the study of social organization in animals," pp. 83–120.

57. See K. Lorenz, *op. cit.*, and N. Tinbergen, *op. cit.*

58. Leslie A. White, *The Science of Culture*, New York, Farrar Straus, 1949, p. 27.

59. Ernst Cassirer, *An Essay on Man*, New Haven, Yale University Press, 1944, p. 32.

60. See J. Ruesch and G. Bateson, *Communication*, New York, Norton, 1951; T. C. Schneirla, "Comparative psychology," *Encyclopedia Britannica*, vol. 17, 1948, pp. 690–708; Karl Deutsch, "Mechanism, teleology, and mind," *Philosophy and Phenomenological Research*, vol. 12, 1951, pp, 185–222.

61. Robert M. Yerkes and Henry W. Nissen, "Pre-linguistic sign behavior in chimpanzee," *Science*, vol. 89, 1939, pp. 585–587.

62. Clifford T. Morgan, *Physiological Psychology*, New York, McGraw-Hill, 1943, p. 551; James Deese, *The Psychology of Learning*, New York, McGraw-Hill, 1953, pp. 254–259.

63. Leslie A. White, "The symbol: The origin and basis of human behavior," *Philosophy of Science*, vol. 8, 1940, pp. 451–463; reprinted in the same author's *The Science of Culture, loc. cit.*, pp. 22–39.

64. Cathy Hayes, *The Ape in the House*, New York, Harper, 1951.

65. For a brilliant discussion of this subject see G. H. Mead, *Mind, Self, and Society*, Chicago, University of Chicago Press, 1944, pp. 32–134.

66. George Kelemen, "The anatomical basis of phonation in the chimpanzee," *Journal of Morphology*, vol. 82, 1948, pp. 229–256. Students have long been puzzled by the apes' inability to talk. The suggestion most often made is that cerebrally these animals are not developed sufficiently to be able to talk, and this is probably true. Kelemen has, however, stated on the basis of a study of the larynx in a chimpanzee that "even with the help of the high grade of intelligence of this animal every attempt to make him utter human voice and speech must fail on the basis of anatomy. An imaginary being equipped with a human brain and the larynx of the chimpanzee could not produce any other phonetic effect than this animal actually does" (p. 254). Much earlier see Peter Camper, "Account of the organs of speech of the Orang-Outang," *Philosophical Transactions*, vol. 69, 1779, pp. 135–159. "Having dissected the whole organ of voice in the Orang, in apes, and several monkies, I have a right to conclude, that Orangs and apes are not made to modulate the voice like men: for the air passing by the *rima glottidis* is immediately lost in the ventricles or ventricle of the neck, as in apes and monkies, and must consequently return from thence without force and melody within the throat and mouth of these creatures: and this seems to me the most evident proof of the incapacity of Orangs, apes and monkies, to utter any modulated voice, as indeed they have never been observed to do" (pp. 155–156).

67. G. H. Mead, *op. cit.*, p. 50.

68. Ernst Cassirer, *op. cit.*

69. Howard Becker, "Science, culture, and society," *Philosophy of Science*, vol. 19, 1952, pp. 282–283.

70. Konrad Z. Lorenz, *op. cit.*

71. Wolfgang Koehler, *The Mentality of the Apes*, New York, Harcourt, Brace, 1925, p. 317.

72. Clifford T. Morgan, *op. cit.*, p. 531.

73. Kurt Goldstein, *Human Nature in the Light of Psychopathology*, Cambridge, Harvard University Press, 1940.

74. John F. Markey, *The Symbolic Process and Its Integration in Children*, New York, Harcourt, Brace, 1928, p. 156.

75. John B. Watson, *Behaviorism*, 2d ed., Philadelphia, Lippincott, 1930.

76. See D. O. Hebb, *The Organization of Behavior*, New York, Wiley, 1949, p. 117, for a pointed discussion of the conditioned reflex theory of language.

77. See Edward Sapir, *Language*, New York, Harcourt, Brace, 1921; *Selected Writings of Edward Sapir* (David Mandelbaum, editor), Berkeley, University of California Press, 1949; L. Bloomfield, *Language*, New York, Holt, 1933; Franz Boas, *Language*, in F. Boas (editor), *General Anthropology*, Boston, Heath, 1938. See also W. M. Urban, *Language and Reality*, New York, Macmillan, 1939.

78. "Who knows not foreign languages, knows not his own."

79. Bronislaw Malinowski, *Coral Gardens and Their Magic*, New York, American Book Co., 1935, vol. 2, p. 7. See Malinowski "The problem of meaning in primitive languages," in C. K. Ogden and I. A. Richards, *The Meaning of Meaning*, New York, Harcourt, Brace, 1923, pp. 451–510.

80. Carl J. Warden, *op. cit.*, p. 7.

81. B. Malinowski, *Coral Gardens and Their Magic, op. cit.*, p. 52.

82. K. J. W. Craig, *The Nature of Explanation*, New York, Cambridge University Press, 1943.

83. James Deese, *op. cit.*, p. 254.

84. *Ibid.*, p. 259.

85. A. L. Kroeber, "Culture, events, and individuals," in *The Nature of Culture*, Chicago, University of Chicago Press, 1952, p. 104.

86. The mores are the more explicitly defined and emphasized moral standards and customs of the group as compared with the implicit spontaneous unpremeditated ways (folkways) of doing things such as greeting, eating three meals a day, manner of dress, courtship, and the like.

87. This description of culture is based on that given by A. L. Kroeber and C. Kluckhohn in their joint work "Culture," *Papers of the Peabody Museum* (Cambridge), vol. 47, 1952, p. 181.

88. O. K. Moore, "Nominal definitions of 'culture,'" *Philosophy of Science*, vol. 19, 1952, pp. 245–256.

89. J. L. Myres, *Political Ideas of the Greeks*, New York, Abingdon Press, 1927, p. 16.

Chapter 3.   THE MEANING OF MAN'S NERVOUS SYSTEM

1. See G. L. Freeman, *Physiological Psychology*, New York, Van Nostrand, 1948.

2. L. Monné, "Structure and function of neurones in relation to mental activity," *Biological Reviews*, vol. 24, 1949, pp. 297–315. See also Edmund W. Sinnott, *Cell and Psyche*, Chapel Hill, University of North Carolina Press, 1950, p. 60: "In any

living system one cannot separate the processes of growth which lead to the development of the body from those by which the life of the body is maintained." Or, as von Bonin puts it: "structure should be understood as an enduring order impressed upon a flow of energy." Gerhardt von Bonin, *Essay on the Cerebral Cortex,* Springfield, Illinois, Thomas, 1950, p. ix.

3.   C. Judson Herrick, *Brains of Rats and Men,* Chicago, University of Chicago, Press, 1926, p. 4.

4.   J. C. Eccles, "Hypotheses relating to the brain-mind problem," *Nature,* vol. 168, 1951, p. 3.

5.   Ralph Gerard, "Neurophysiology in relation to behavior," in Roy Grinker (editor), *Mid-Century Psychiatry,* Springfield, Ill., Thomas, 1954, pp. 23–32.

6.   Paul Weiss (editor), *Genetic Neurology,* Chicago, University of Chicago Press, 1950.

7.   S. H. Gasser, "The classification of nerve fibers," *Ohio Journal of Science,* vol. 41, 1941, pp. 145–149.

8.   O. S. English and G. H. J. Pearson, *Emotional Problems of Living,* New York, Norton, 1945, p. 45.

9.   A. W. Angulo y Gonzalez, "Is myelinogeny an absolute index of behavioral capability?" *Journal of Comparative Neurology,* vol. 48, 1929, pp. 459–464.

10.   Hans Held, "Die Lehre von den Neuronen," *Fortschritte der Naturwissenschaftlichen Forschung, n.f.,* vol. 8, 1929, pp. 41–44.

11.   Walter B. Cannon, *The Wisdom of the Body,* New York, Norton, 1939.

12.   G. von Bonin, *op. cit.,* p. 124. See Nina Bull, "Toward a clarification of the concept of emotion," *Psychosomatic Medicine,* vol. 7, 1945, pp. 210–214. See also Stanley Cobb, *Emotions and Clinical Medicine,* New York, Norton, 1950.

13.   Kurt Goldstein, "On emotions considered from the organismic point of view," *Journal of Psychology,* vol. 31, 1951, pp. 37–49.

14.   Russell Myers, "Semantic dilemmas in neurology, psychology, and general semantics," *General Semantics Bulletin,* nos. 10 and 11, 1952/53, p. 49.

15.   H. R. Miller, *Central Autonomic Regulations in Health and Disease,* New York, Grune & Stratton, 1942, p. 21; J. S. Bockoven, "Social behavior and autonomic physiology in long-standing mental illness: Its relation to the problem of altruism," in P. Sorokin (editor), *Forms and Techniques of Altruistic and Spiritual Growth,* Boston, Beacon Press, 1954, pp. 283–289.

16.   J. H. Masserman, "The hypothalamus in psychiatry," *American Journal of Psychiatry,* vol. 98, 1942, pp. 633–637.

17.   James C. White and Reginald Smithwick, *The Autonomic Nervous System,* 2d ed., New York, Macmillan, 1941, pp. 62–76.

18.   H. Selye, *Stress,* Montreal, Acta Endocrinologica, 1950; H. G. Wolff *et al* (editors), *Life Stress and Bodily Disease,* Baltimore, Williams & Wilkins, 1950; H. G. Wolff, *Stress and Disease,* Springfield, Illinois, Thomas, 1954; N. B. Talbot *et al., Functional Endocrinology,* Cambridge, Harvard University Press, 1952.

19.   M. F. Ashley Montagu, "Constitutional and prenatal factors in infant and child health," in M. J. E. Senn (editor), *The Healthy Personality,* New York, Josiah Macy Jr. Foundation, 1950, pp. 148–210.

20.   R. A. Spitz, "Infantile depression and the general adaptation syndrome," *Proceedings of the 42nd Annual Meeting American Psychopathological Association,* 1953, pp. 93–108.

21.   Judson Herrick, *op. cit.,* pp. 146–147.

22.   For an admirable critical discussion of this subject see Russell Myers, *op. cit.,* pp. 35–51.

23. J. W. Macfarlane, "The guidance study," *Sociometry*, vol. 2, 1939, pp. 1–33.

24. H. E. Jones, "The galvanic skin reflex," *Child Development*, vol. 1, 1930, pp. 106–110.

25. O. H. Mowrer, *Learning Theory and Personality Dynamics*, New York, Ronald Press, 1950, p. 240.

26. L. S. Kubie, "The ontogeny of anxiety," *Psychoanalytic Review*, vol. 28, 1941, p. 81.

27. Karl S. Lashley, "The problem of serial order in behavior," in *Cerebral Mechanisms of Behavior* (L. A. Jeffress, editor), New York, Wiley, 1951, pp. 71, 131.

28. W. Grey Walter, *The Living Brain*, New York, Norton, 1953.

29. Herrick, *op. cit.*, pp. 264–265.

30. L. Monné, *op. cit.*, pp. 297–315.

31. *Ibid.*, p. 311.

32. Ward C. Halstead (editor), "Brain and behavior: A symposium," *Comparative Psychology Monographs*, vol. 20, 1950; W. C. Halstead, "Brain and intelligence," in *Cerebral Mechanisms in Behavior* (L. A. Jeffress, editor), New York, Wiley, 1951, pp. 244–288.

33. H. Hydén and H. Hartelius, "Stimulation of nucleoprotein production in the nerve cell by malononitrile, and its effect on psychic functions in mental disorder," *Acta Psychiatrica et Neurologica*, Supplement 47, 1948, pp. 1–117. See also J. Mendelson, *et al.*, "Stability and absorption spectrum of malononitrile," *Science*, vol. 120, 1954, pp. 266–269.

34. Percival Bailey, "Concerning the organization of the cerebral cortex," *Texas Reports on Biology and Medicine*, vol. 6, 1948, pp. 34–56; Percival Bailey, "Cortex and mind," in R. Grinker (editor), *Mid-Century Psychiatry*, Springfield, Ill., 1953, pp. 8–22.

35. L. S. Kubie, "Instincts and homeostasis," *Psychosomatic Medicine*, vol. 10, 1948, pp. 15–30.

36. Gerhardt von Bonin, *op. cit.*, pp. 131–132.

37. A. Tustin, "Feedback," *Scientific American*, vol. 187, 1952, pp. 48–54.

38. Gardner B. Murphy, *Personality*, New York, Harper, 1947, p. 84.

Chapter 4. HEREDITY AND ENVIRONMENT

1. By other methods other observers have arrived at very similar estimates: See J. N. Spuhler, "On the number of genes in man," *Science*, vol. 108, 1948, p. 279, and R. D. Evans, "Quantitative inferences concerning the genetic effects of radiation on human beings," *Science*, vol. 109, 1949, pp. 299–304.

2. G. W. Beadle, "Genes and biological enigmas," in *Science in Progress*, 6th Series (edited by G. Baitsell), New Haven, Yale University Press, 1949, pp. 184–249; M. Demerec, "What makes genes mutate?" *Proceedings American Philosophical Society*, vol. 98, 1954, pp. 318–322; L. J. Stadler, "The gene," *Science*, vol. 120, 1954, pp. 811–819; H. J. Muller, "Life," *Science*, vol. 121, 1955, pp. 1–9.

3. See Sir Charles Sherrington, *Man On His Nature*, 2d ed., New York, Cambridge University Press, 1951, p. 103: "Each gene in the egg-cell embodies a unit 'character' in the make-up of the individual springing from the ovum."

4. Carl von Naegeli, *Mechanische-physiologische Theorie der abstammungslehre*, Munich and Leipzig, 1884. J. Clausen, D. D. Keck, and W. M. Hiesy, *Experimental Studies on the Nature of Species*, Carnegie Institution of Washington, D.C., 1940, 1945.

5. R. S. Lillie, "Directive action and life," *Philosophy of Science*, vol. 4, 1939, pp. 202–226.

6. "Heredity . . . may be defined as the influence on the individuals of the materials which they receive from their parents at the beginning of their lives." Herbert S. Jennings, *Genetics*, New York, Norton, 1935, p. 4.

7. See pp. 249–266.

8. T. Dobzhansky, "What is heredity?" *Science*, vol. 100, p. 406.

9. M. F. Ashley Montagu, "Our changing concept of human nature," *Impact of Science on Society* (Unesco, Paris), vol. 3, 1952, pp. 219–232.

10. Beautifully stated by John Donne in *Love's Deity*, where he speaks of "that vice-nature, custom."

11. J. B. Scott, "The magnification of differences by a threshold," *Science*, vol. 100, 1944, pp. 569–570; J. P. Scott and M. S. Charles, "Genetic differences in the behavior of dogs: a case of magnification by thresholds and by habit formation," *Journal of Genetic Psychology*, vol. 84, 1954, pp. 175–188; John Fuller and J. P. Scott, "Genetic factors affecting intelligence," *Eugenics Quarterly*, vol. 1, 1954, pp. 28–43.

12. M. F. Ashley Montagu, *Man's Most Dangerous Myth. The Fallacy of Race*, 3rd ed., New York, Harper, 1953.

Chapter 5.   LIFE IN THE WOMB AND THE TRAUMA OF BIRTH

1. George W. Corner, *Ourselves Unborn*, New Haven, Yale University Press, 1944, pp. 51–55; William F. Windle, *Physiology of the Fetus*, Philadelphia, Saunders, 1940, p. 206.

2. L. W. Sontag and T. W. Richards, "Studies in fetal behavior," *Monographs of the Society for Research in Child Development*, vol. 3, no. 4, 1938.

3. For a good summary of the whole subject of prenatal behavior see Leonard Carmichael, "The onset and early development of behavior," in *Manual of Child Psychology* (edited by Leonard Carmichael), New York, Wiley, 1954, pp. 60–185; M. F. Ashley Montagu, "Constitutional and prenatal factors in infant and child health," in *The Healthy Personality* (edited by M. J. E. Senn), New York, Josiah Macy, Jr., Foundation, 1950, pp. 148–210.

4. H. S. and H. B. Forbes, "Fetal sense reaction: hearing," *Journal of Comparative Psychology*, vol. 7, 1927, pp. 353–355.

5. L. W. Sontag and T. W. Richards, *op. cit.*, pp. 49–60.

6. Jack Bernard and L. W. Sontag, "Fetal reactivity to tonal stimulation: a preliminary report," *Journal of Genetic Psychology*, vol. 70, 1947, pp. 205–210.

7. L. W. Sontag and R. F. Wallace, "Study of fetal activity," *American Journal of Diseases of Children*, vol. 48, 1934, pp. 1050–1057; L. W. Sontag, "Differences in modifiability of fetal behavior and physiology," *Psychosomatic Medicine*, vol. 6, 1944, pp. 151–154.

8. L. W. Sontag, "The significance of fetal environmental differences," *American Journal of Obstetrics and Gynecology*, vol. 42, 1941, pp. 996–1003.

9. L. W. Sontag, "War and the fetal maternal relationship," *Marriage and Family Living*, vol. 6, 1944, pp. 1–5.

10. J. L. Halliday, *Psychosocial Medicine*, New York, Norton, 1948, p. 91.

11. Phyllis Greenacre, "The predisposition to anxiety," *Psychoanalytic Quarterly*, vol. 10, 1941, pp. 610–638.

12. Samuel Taylor Coleridge, *Miscellanies, Aesthetic and Literary* (collected and arranged by Thomas Ashe), London, Bohn Standard Library, 1885, p. 301.

13. Otto Rank, *The Trauma of Birth*, New York, Robert Brunner, 1952. This work was originally published in German in 1924 and in English translation in 1929. A good summary of the theory will be found in Patrick Mullahy, *Oedipus Myth and Complex*, New York, Hermitage Press, 1948, pp. 162–168, and also in Rollo May, *The Meaning of Anxiety*, New York, Ronald Press, 1950, pp. 128–131.

14. Sigmund Freud, *The Problem of Anxiety*, London, Hogarth Press, 1936.

15. Stanley Cobb, *Borderlands of Psychiatry*, Cambridge, Harvard University Press, 1944, p. 88.

16. W. E. Le Gros Clark, "Ignorances in the anatomical field," *Prospects In Psychiatric Research* (edited by J. M. Tanner), Oxford, Blackwell, 1953, pp. 5–29.

17. Nandor Fodor, *In Search of the Beloved: A Clinical Investigation of the Trauma of Birth and Pre-Natal Conditioning*, New York, Hermitage Press, 1949, p. 383.

18. Margaret Ribble, *The Right of Infants*, New York, Columbia University Press, 1943, p. 15.

19. M. Kenworthy, "The pre-natal and early post-natal phenomena of consciousness," in E. Dummer (editor), *The Unconscious*, New York, Knopf, 1927, p. 181. In this remarkably prescient study Kenworthy states that "The interesting comparative studies of the emotional and nervous reactions of the new-born babies of Caesarian section and those born through the birth canal of primiparous and multiparous mothers indicates the relative effects of such births." I have not been able to trace such studies.

20. Mary Shirley, "A behavior syndrome characterizing prematurely-born children," *Child Development*, vol. 10, 1939, pp. 115–128.

21. Mary C. Drillien, "Studies in prematurity, stillbirth and neonatal death, factors affecting birth-weight and outcome, delivery, and its hazards," *Journal of Obstetrics and Gynaecology of the British Empire*, vol. 54, 1947, pp. 300–323, 443–468; Mary C. Drillien, "Studies in prematurity; development and progress of prematurely born children in pre-school period," *Archives of the Diseases of Childhood*, vol. 23, 1948, pp. 69–83.

22. Philip J. Howard and Calier H. Worrell, "Premature infants in later life," *Pediatrics*, vol. 9, 1952, pp. 577–584; B. Beskow, "Mental disturbances in premature children of school age," *Acta Pediatrica*, vol. 37, 1949, pp. 125–130; Julius H. Hess, "Experiences gained in a thirty year study of prematurely born infants," *Pediatrics*, vol. 11, 1953, pp. 425–434.

23. Sigmund Freud, *Inhibitions, Symptoms and Anxiety*, London, Hogarth Press, 1936.

24. Otto Rank, *op. cit.*, p. 11.

25. *Ibid.*, p. 212.

26. For another interpretation see Ernest Jones, *Nightmare, Witches, and Devils*, New York, Norton, 1931.

27. Denys E. R. Kelsey, "Phantasies of birth and prenatal experiences recovered from patients undergoing hypnoanalysis," *Journal of Mental Science* (London), vol. 99, 1953, pp. 212–223.

28. M. L. Peerbolte, *Prenatal Dynamics*, Leyden, Sijthoff, 1954.

29. L. W. Sontag, "Evidences of disturbed prenatal and neonatal growth in bones of infants at one month," *American Journal of Diseases of Children*, vol. 53, 1938, p. 1248; L. W. Sontag and L. M. Harris, "Evidences of disturbed prenatal and

neonatal growth in bones of infants aged one month," *American Journal of Diseases of Children,* vol. 56, 1938, pp. 1248–1255.

30. Ira S. Wile and R. Davis, "The relation of birth to behavior," *American Journal of Orthopsychiatry,* vol. 11, 1941, pp. 320–324.

31. Phyllis Greenacre, "The biological economy of birth," in *Psychoanalytic Study of the Family,* vol. 1, pp. 31–51, New York, International Universities Press, 1945.

32. P. L. Schroeder, "Behavior difficulties in children associated with the results of birth trauma," *Journal of the American Medical Association,* vol. 92, 1929, pp. 100–104.

33. J. L. Despert, "Anxiety, phobias, and fears in young children," *The Nervous Child,* vol. 5, 1946, pp. 8–24.

34. J. L. Boland, "Type of birth as related to stuttering," *Journal of Speech and Hearing Disorders,* vol. 16, 1951, pp. 40–43.

35. O. Hobart Mowrer, *Learning Theory and Personality Dynamics,* New York, Ronald Press, 1950, p. 559.

Chapter 6.   THE BASIC AND ACQUIRED NEEDS

1. Bronislaw Malinowski, *A Scientific Theory of Culture and Other Essays,* Chapel Hill, University of North Carolina Press, 1944, p. 74.

2. *Ibid.,* p. 75.

3. Frank A. Beach, *Hormones and Behavior,* New York, Hoeber, 1948.

4. Otto Klineberg, *Social Psychology,* 2d ed., New York, Holt, 1954, p. 69.

5. For a stimulating though quite different discussion of needs and drives—the author preferring the noncommittal *drives*—see B. F. Skinner, *Science and Human Behavior,* New York, Macmillan, 1953, pp. 143–159.

6. Lawrence S. Kubie, "Instincts and homeostasis," *Psychosomatic Medicine,* vol. 10, 1948, pp. 15–30.

7. G. L. Freeman, *The Energetics of Human Behavior,* Ithaca, Cornell University Press, 1948, pp. 49–50.

8. Walter B. Cannon, *The Wisdom of the Body,* New York, Norton, 1939, p. 24.

9. For a valuable criticism and clarification of the concept of homeostasis, see J. R. Maze, "On some corruptions of the doctrine of homeostasis," *Psychological Review,* vol. 60, 1953, pp. 405–412.

10. C. A. Mace, "Homeostasis, needs and values," *British Journal of Psychology,* vol. 44, 1953, pp. 200–210.

11. L. S. Kubie, *op. cit.,* pp. 19–20.

12. *Ibid.,* p. 20.

13. K. S. Lashley, "Experimental analysis of instinctive behavior," *Psychological Reviews,* vol. 46, 1928, p. 445.

14. L. S. Kubie, *op. cit.,* pp. 21–23.

15. L. S. Kubie, "A physiological approach to the concept of anxiety," *Psychosomatic Medicine,* vol. 3, 1941, pp. 263–267.

16. L. S. Kubie, "Instincts and homeostasis," *loc. cit.,* pp. 21–22.

17. R. Stagner, "Homeostasis as a unifying concept in personality theory," *Psychological Review,* vol. 58, 1951, pp. 5–17.

18. L. S. Kubie, "Instincts and Homeostasis," *loc. cit.,* p. 23.

19. Sigmund Freud, *An Outline of Psychoanalysis*, New York, Norton, 1949, p. 19.

20. For what it may be worth it is interesting in passing to note that the consonant (really partially vowel—"em") sound "m" followed by a vowel forms the first letters of the word for "mother" in many languages. These sounds are incorporative, internalizing ones, akin to the "mmmm" sound that one often makes while consuming a particularly tasty dish. On the other hand the word for father usually commences with an externalizing rejecting "fricative" "f" or plosive "p" or "b." The word "mamma," meaning "mother" and the Latin word for breast "mamma," may here afford a clue to a very ancient connection.

21. Ian D. Suttie, *The Origins of Love and Hate*, New York, Julian Press, 1953, p. 35.

22. R. Linton, *The Cultural Background of Personality*, New York, Appleton-Century, 1945, p. 8.

23. Davenport Hooker, "Reflex activities in the human fetus," in *Child Behavior and Development* (edited by R. G. Barker, *et al.*), New York, McGraw-Hill, 1943, pp. 17–28. See W. F. Windle, *Physiology of the Fetus*, Philadelphia, Saunders, 1940, p. 185.

24. It would seem that some, at least, of the aquatic mammals are equally fond of cutaneous stimulation. McBride and Kritzler of the Duke University Marine Laboratory at Beaufort, North Carolina, write that "Dolphins are very fond of rubbing their bodies on various objects, so a backscratcher, constructed of three stout sweeper's brushes fixed to a slab of rock with the bristles directed upward, was installed in the tank. The young dolphins took to rubbing themselves on these brushes as soon as the adults discovered their purpose. The 1947 female, at the age of two years, became so fond of being caressed by the observer that she would frequently rear cautiously out of the water to rub her chin on the knuckles of his clenched fist." A. F. McBride and H. Kritzler, "Observations on pregnancy, parturition, and post-natal behavior in the Bottlenose Dolphin," *Journal of Mammalogy*, vol. 32, 1951, p. 261, pp. 251–266.

25. It is well known among experts and dairy farmers that hand-milked cows give more, and richer, terminal milk than machine-milked cows.

26. This seems to happen particularly frequently among chihuahua dogs, the mothers often making little or no attempt to lick their young. Hence their high mortality rate unless some substitute for maternal licking, such as stroking by the human hand, in introduced.

27. These experiments are reported in "Germ-free life studies," *Lobund Reports*, no. 1, 1946, and no. 2, 1949, University of Notre Dame.

28. *Ibid.*, no. 1, p. 20.

29. Personal communication from Professor Reyniers, November 10, 1950.

30. See Larry Rhine, "One little kitten and how it grew," *McCall's Magazine*, vol. 80, July, 1953, pp. 4–6: "The A.S.P.C.A. woman said, 'Your problem is not with the eating. You see, a kitten's first eliminations are stimulated by the mother cat. Now, if you'd like to try to do the same with a cotton swab dipped in warm water you might be able to . . .' "

31. W. F. Windle, *op. cit.*

32. Frederick S. Hammet, "Studies of the thyroid apparatus," *Endocrinology*, vol. 4, 1922, pp. 221–229.

33. M. J. Greenman and F. L. Duhring, *Breeding and Care of the Albino Rat for Research Purposes*, 2d ed., Philadelphia, Wistar Institute, 1931.

34. Otto Weininger, "Physiological damage under emotional stress as a function of early experience," *Science*, vol. 119, 1954, pp. 285–286; Otto Weininger *et al.*, "Gentling and weight gain in the albino rat." *Canadian Journal of Psychology*, vol. 8, 1954, pp. 147–151. See pp. 199–223 this book.

35. Sir William Osler, *Aphorisms* (collected by R. B. Bean and edited by W. B. Bean), New York, Schuman, 1950, p. 126.

36. On the allergic relationships between the skin and breathing see Bret Ratner, C. Collins-Williams, and S. Untracht, "Allergic-dermal respiratory syndrome in children," *American Journal of Diseases of Children*, vol. 82, 1951, pp. 666–676.

37. Mary Drillien, "Studies in prematurity. Part 4: Development and progress of the prematurely born child in the pre-school period," *Archives of the Diseases of Childhood*, vol. 23, 1948, pp. 69–83.

38. Mary Shirley, "A behavior syndrome characterizing prematurely-born children," *Child Development*, vol. 10, 1939, pp. 115–128.

39. Margaret A. Ribble, "Disorganizing factors of infant personality," *American Journal of Psychiatry*, vol. 98, 1941, pp. 459–463.

40. For a graphic and significant account of the same phenomenon in dogs, see B. M. McKinney, "A canine demonstration," *Child Family Digest*, vol. 10, 1954, pp. 63–65. Reprinted in this volume, pp. 346–348.

41. S. Lóránd and J. Asbót, "Ueber die durch Reizüng der Brustwarze angeregten reflektorischen Uteruskontraktionen," *Zentralblatt für Gynäkologie*, vol. 74, 1952, pp. 345–352.

42. Toward the end of the eighteenth century Erasmus Darwin pointed out that our fondness for rolling hills and gently undulating landscapes was probably derived from our conditioning upon the cushion of our mother's breasts. This also recalls the lines from Psalm 12, "I will lift up mine eyes unto the hills/ From whence cometh my help."

43. It is interesting to note that female fish will not spawn unless they are repeatedly touched—usually by the male. See N. Tinbergen, *Social Behaviour in Animals*, New York, Wiley, 1953, pp. 29, 83.

44. However, Tinbergen tells us that "In many higher animals, particularly land animals, fertilization involves mating, or copulation. This requires more than mere synchronization. It means bodily contact. This is a thing most animals avoid. This avoidance is an adaptation, part of their defence against predators. Being touched usually means being captured." Tinbergen, *op. cit.*, p. 22.

45. O. Spurgeon English, "Sex and human love," in *About the Kinsey Report* (edited by Donald P. Geddes and E. Curie,) New York, New American Library, 1948, pp. 101–102.

46. Charlotte Wolff, *A Psychology of Gesture*, London, Methuen, 1948, p. 49.

47. M. F. Ashley Montagu, "The sensory influences of the skin," *Texas Reports on Biology and Medicine*, vol. 11, 1953, pp. 291–301.

Chapter 7. NEEDS, CULTURE, AND VALUES

1. In many nonliterate societies "no very clear-cut line is drawn between social service and economic service." See Raymond Firth, *Elements of Social Organization*, London, Watts, 1951, p. 193.

2. Bronislaw Malinowski, *A Scientific Theory of Culture*, Chapel Hill, University of North Carolina, 1944, p. 38.

3. Ralph Linton, "Culture, society and the individual," *Journal of Abnormal and Social Psychology*, vol. 33, 1938, pp. 425–436.

4. David B. Dill, *Life, Heat, and Altitude*, Cambridge, Harvard University Press, 1938.

5. Bronislaw·Malinowski, *op. cit.*, p. 86.

6. S. Rosenzweig, "Babies are taught to cry: A hypothesis," *Mental Hygiene*, vol. 38, 1954, pp. 81–84.

7. H. D. Renner, *The Origin of Food Habits*, London, Faber and Faber, 1944.

8. Alfred C. Kinsey, *et al.*, *Sexual Behavior in the Human Female*, Philadelphia, Saunders, 1953; M. F. Ashley Montagu, *The Natural Superiority of Women*, New York, Macmillan, 1953.

9. N. Tinbergen, *Social Behaviour In Animals*, New York, Wiley, 1953, p. 22.

10. Geoffrey May, *Social Control of Sex Expression*, New York, Morrow, 1931; Clellan S. Ford and Frank A. Beach, *Patterns of Sexual Behavior*, New York, Harper, 1951.

11. See M. F. Ashley Montagu, *Coming Into Being Among the Australian Aborigines*, London, Routledge, 1937; M. F. Ashley Montagu, *Adolescent Sterility*, Springfield, Illinois, Thomas, 1946.

12. W. H. R. Rivers (editor), *Essays on the Depopulation of Melanesia*, Cambridge, Cambridge University Press, 1922.

13. A. Lommell, "Modern culture influences on Australian Aborigines," *Oceania*, vol. 21, 1950, pp. 14–24; R. M. Berndt, "Influence of European culture on Australian Aborigines," *Oceania*, vol. 21, 1951, pp. 229–235; B. B. Rubenstein, "An emotional factor in infertility," *Fertility and Sterility*, vol. 2, 1951, pp. 80–86.

14. H. Schuermann, "Ueber die Zuhnahme männlicher Fertilitätsstorungen und ueber die Bedeutung psychischer Einflüsse für zentralnervöse Regulation der Spermiogenese," *Medizinische Klinik*, no. 13, 1948, p. 366; W. H. Gantt, "Disturbances in sexual functions during periods of stress," in *Life Stress and Bodily Disease* (edited by H. G. Wolff, *et al.*), Baltimore, Williams & Wilkins, 1950, pp. 1030–1056; W. R. Miles, "The sex expression of men living on a lowered nutritional level," *Journal of Nervous and Mental Disorders*, vol. 49, 1919, pp. 208–224. Under conditions of stress or starvation the functions of the pituitary gland are disturbed and it fails to produce its hormones, as a result the sex glands, the thyroid, and the adrenal glands show decreased activity. See W. H. Perloff *et al.*, "The starvation state and functional hypopituitarism," *Journal of the American Medical Association*, vol. 155, 1954, pp. 1307–1313.

15. Walter B. Cannon, " 'Voodoo' death," *American Anthropoligist*, vol. 44, 1942, pp. 169–181. See also the symposium volume *Life Stress and Bodily Disease*, *loc. cit.*

16. Hans Selye, *Stress*, Montreal, Acta Endocrinologica, 1950; Hans Selye, "The general adaptation syndrome and the diseases of adaptation," *Journal of Clinical Endocrinology*, vol. 6, 1946, pp. 117–230; Hans Selye, *Textbook of Endocrinology*, Montreal, Acta Endocrinologica, 1947, pp. 837–867; O. Weininger, "Mortality of albino rats under stress as a function of early handling," *Canadian Journal of Psychology*, vol. 7, 1953, pp. 111–114; H. G. Wolff, *Stress and Disease*, Springfield, Illinois, Thomas, 1954; E. W. Bovard, "A theory to account for the effects of early handling on viability of the albino rat," *Science*, vol 120, 1954, p. 187.

17. There now exists a very large amount of experimental evidence to support this statement. See H. S. Liddell, "Conditioned reflex method and experimental neurosis," in *Personality and the Behavior Disorders* (edited by J. McV. Hunt), vol. 1, pp. 389–412, New York, Ronald, 1944.

18. "It seems that neuroses are only acquired during early childhood (up to the age of six), even though their symptoms may not make their appearance until much later," Sigmund Freud, *An Outline of Psychoanalysis*, New York, Norton, 1949, p. 83.

19. "Clinical data indicate that it is always more physiologically relaxing to react to frustration as directly as the situation will allow. This includes talking back politely to the boss rather than raving about mistreatment to friends, taking up a job that has to be redone rather than crying over it, and concentrating upon improving upon a necessary skill rather than to get in another person to help out," G. L. Freeman, *The Energetics of Human Behavior*, Ithaca, Cornell University Press, 1948, p. 125.

20. Henry A. Murray, *Explorations in Personality*, New York, Oxford University Press, 1938, p. 130.

21. Flanders Dunbar, *Psychosomatic Diagnosis*, New York, Hoeber, 1944; Flanders Dunbar, *Emotions and Bodily Changes*, 5th ed., New York, Columbia University Press, 1955.

22. An innovation has been defined as "any thought, behavior, or thing that is new because it is qualitatively different from existing forms. Strictly speaking an innovation is an idea, or a constellation of ideas," which may or may not be given overt or tangible expression. See H. G. Barnett, *Innovation: The Basis of Cultural Change*, New York, McGraw-Hill, 1953, p. 7.

23. David Bidney, *Theoretical Anthropology*, New York, Columbia University Press, 1953, p. 17.

24. See Edmund Burgler, "The gambler: a misunderstood neurotic," *Journal of Criminal Psychopathology*, vol. 4, 1943, pp. 379–393. See also Robert Lindner, "The psychodynamics of gambling," in R. Lindner (editor), *Explorations in Psychoanalysis*, New York, Julian Press, 1953, pp. 197–217.

25. See *The Diary of Dostoyevsky's Wife* (edited by R. Fülöp-Miller and Fr. Eckstein), New York, Macmillan, 1928, pp. 232–241. Madame Dostoyevsky remarks: "It was a habit of Fyodor's [Dostoyevsky] to make one feel first terrified and then delighted" (p. 257). He would, as it were, prolong the pain in order to heighten the pleasure. See also Dostoyevsky's very revealing short novel *The Gambler*, New York, Dutton, 1948.

26. Margaret Mead (editor), *Competition and Cooperation Among Primitive Peoples*, New York, McGraw-Hill, 1937; Ruth Benedict, *Patterns of Culture*, New York, Mentor Books, 1946; John J. Honigmann, *Culture and Personality*, New York, Harper, 1954.

27. Ralph Linton, *The Cultural Background of Personality*, New York, Appleton-Century, 1945, pp. 7–10.

28. Abraham H. Maslow, "Some theoretical consequences of basic-need gratification," *Journal of Personality*, vol. 16, 1948, pp. 402–416.

29. Abraham H. Maslow, " 'Higher' and 'lower' needs," *Journal of Psychology*, vol. 25, 1948, pp. 433–436. Reprinted in the same author's *Motivation and Personality*, New York, Harper, 1954, pp. 146–154.

30. Hadley Cantril, "Toward a scientific morality," *Journal of Psychology*, vol. 27, 1949, pp. 363–376.

31. Maslow, *op. cit.*, p. 150.

32. John Dewey, *Problems of Men*, New York, Philosophical Library, 1946, p. 258.

33. Julian Huxley, *Evolution in Action*, New York, Harper, 1953, p. 150.

34. See Wolfgang Kohler, *The Place of Value in a World of Facts*, New York, Liveright, 1938, pp. 31 *et seq.*, for a discussion of "intrinsic requiredness."

35.   Samuel Alexander, *Beauty and Other Forms of Values,* New York, Macmillan, 1933, p. 10; K. G. Collier, "The inheritance of values," *Sociological Review* (London), vol. 40, 1948, pp. 97–112; Dorothy D. Lee, "Are basic needs ultimate?" *Journal of Abnormal and Social Psychology,* vol. 43, 1948, pp. 391–395; Nina Bull, "The biological basis of value," *Scientific Monthly,* vol. 53, 1941, pp. 170–174; Sol W. Ginsburg, "Values and the psychiatrist," *American Journal of Orthopsychiatry,* vol. 20, 1950, pp. 466–478; Bronislaw Malinowski, "Value and derived needs," in his *Freedom and Civilization,* New York, Roy Publishers, 1944, pp. 124–137; Hadley Cantril, *The "Why" of Human Experience,* New York, Macmillan, 1950; C. A. Mace, "Homeostasis, needs and values," *British Journal of Psychology,* vol. 44, 1953, pp. 200–210.

36.   Professor L. O. Kattsoff has independently arrived at a precisely similar conclusion. "The concept of health," he writes, "is the absolute criterion for the evaluation of modes of behavior." See his *The Design of Human Behavior,* St. Louis, Educational Publishers, 1953, p. 115.

37.   Abraham H. Maslow, "The instinctoid nature of basic needs," *Journal of Personality,* vol. 22, 1954, pp. 326–347.

38.   L .O. Kattsoff, *op. cit.,* p. 69.

39.   Samuel L. Hart, *Treatise on Values,* New York, Philosophical Library, 1949, p. 56.

40.   Abraham H. Maslow, "Our maligned human nature," *Journal of Psychology,* vol. 28, 1949, p. 273.

41.   Trygve Braatøy, *Fundamentals of Psychoanalytic Technique,* New York, John Wiley, 1954, p. 49. See particularly the admirable first chapter "Love—the basis of personal psychotherapy."

42.   Sol. W. Ginsburg, *op. cit.,* p. 478.

43.   E. W. Fellows, "Science and values: A survey of current points of view," *Scientific Monthly,* vol. 73, 1951, pp. 111–113.

44.   Henry Margenau, "Scientific basis of ethics," *Main Currents in Modern Thought,* vol. 9, 1952, pp. 82–83.

Chapter 8.   Dependency, Interdependency, and Love

1.   See M. F. Ashley Montagu, "Constitutional and prenatal factors in infant and child health," in *The Healthy Personality* (edited by M. J. E. Senn), New York, Josiah Macy, Jr., Foundation, 1952, pp. 148–210. Reprinted in W. E. Martin and C. B. Stendler, *Readings in Child Development,* New York, Harcourt Brace, 1954, pp. 15–29.

2.   M. A. Wenger, "An investigation of conditioned responses in human infants," in M. A. Wenger, J. M. Smith, and O. C. Irwin, "Studies in infant behavior," *University of Iowa Studies in Child Welfare,* vol. 12, 1936, pp. 7–90. See also Karl C. Pratt, "The neonate," in *Manual of Child Psychology* (edited by Leonard Carmichael), New York, Wiley, 1954, pp. 216–217, N. L. Munn, "Learning in children," same volume, pp. 374–458.

3.   See Karl C. Pratt, *op. cit.,* pp. 215–291. See also, P. F. Durham Seitz, "Psychocutaneous conditioning during the first two weeks of life," *Psychosomatic Medicine,* vol. 12, 1950, pp. 187–188.

4.   David K. Spelt, "The conditioning of the human fetus *in utero,*" *Journal of Experimental Psychology,* vol. 38, 1948, pp. 338–346.

5.   See Phyllis Greenacre, *Trauma, Growth and Personality,* New York, Norton, 1952; Rollo May, *The Meaning of Anxiety,* New York, Ronald Press, 1950.

6. See pp. 88–104.

7. Otto Rank, *The Trauma of Birth*, New York, Brunner, 1952, pp. 11–12.

8. S. Freud, *Three Contributions to the Theory of Sex*, Nervous and Mental Diseases Publishing Co., New York, 1910.

9. Rank, *op. cit.*, p. 17.

10. For a good account of the neonate see Karl C. Pratt, *op. cit.*, pp. 215–291.

11. See M. F. Ashley Montagu, "Some factors in family cohesion," *Psychiatry*, vol. 7, 1944, pp. 349–352; M. F. Ashley Montagu, "The sensory influences of the skin," *Texas Reports on Biology and Medicine*, vol. 11, 1953, pp. 291–301.

12. *Time*, August 12, 1954, p. 46.

13. See Grantly Dick Read, *Childbirth Without Fear*, New York, Harper, 1953, pp. 199–200. For detailed evidence see Betsy McKinney, "A canine demonstration," *Child Family Digest*, vol. 16, 1954, pp. 63–65, and the present book, pp. 346–348.

14. M. Bevan-Brown, *The Sources of Love and Fear*, New York, Vanguard Press, 1950, p. 15.

15. Alfred Adler, *Social Interest: A Challenge to Mankind*, New York, Putnam, 1938, p. 214.

16. M. Bevan-Brown, *op. cit.*

17. Alfred Adler, *op. cit.*, pp. 220–221.

18. M. Bevan-Brown, *op. cit.*, p. 10.

19. See L. L. Lemak, "Roentgenological manifestations of gastrointestinal ulceration in the newborn," *American Journal of Roentgenology*, vol. 66, 1951, pp. 191–199; E. Kezur, F. T. Kapp, and M. Rosenbaum, "Psychological factors in women with ulcers," *American Journal of Psychiatry*, vol. 108, 1951, pp. 368–373; B. R. Girdany, "Peptic ulcer in childhood," *Pediatrics*, vol. 12, 1953, pp. 56–61.

20. Franz Alexander, "Psychogenic factors in bronchial asthma," Part I, *Psychosomatic Medicine Monograph*, No. 4, 1941, p. 58; I. D. Harris, L. Rapoport, M. A. Rynerson, and Samter, M., "Observations on asthmatic children," *American Journal of Orthopsychiatry*, vol. 20, 1950, pp. 490–505.

21. E. Kezur, F. T. Kapp and M. Rosenbaum, *op. cit.*, pp. 368–373. See also O. Spurgeon English and Florence Foster, *Fathers Are Parents Too*, New York, Putnam, 1951.

22. For a discussion of the organ neuroses, see Otto Fenichel, *The Psychoanalytic Theory of the Neuroses*, New York, Norton, 1945, pp. 236–267; also the same author's *The Collected Papers of Otto Fenichel*, First Series, New York, Norton, 1953, Second Series, New York, Norton, 1954; Irving D. Harris, "Mood, anger and somatic dysfunction," *Journal of Nervous and Mental Disease*, vol. 113, 1951, pp. 152–158; Joseph J. Michaels, "A psychiatric adventure in comparative patho-physiology of the infant and adult," *Journal of Nervous and Mental Disease*, vol. 100, 1944, pp. 49–63.

23. Irving D. Harris, *op. cit.*, H. Hartmann, E. Kris, and R. M. Loewenstein, "Notes on the theory of aggression," in *The Psychoanalytic Study of the Child*, vol. 3/4, New York, International Universities Press, 1949, pp. 9–42.

24. B. Bettelheim and Emmy Sylvester, "Physical symptoms in emotionally disturbed children," *The Psychoanalytic Study of the Child*, *loc. cit.*, pp. 353–368.

25. Emory S. Bogardus (discussion), in Floyd H. Allport, "The group fallacy in relation to social science," *American Journal of Sociology*, vol. 29, 1924, p. 704.

26. Harry S. Sullivan, "The illusion of personal individuality," *Psychiatry*, vol. 13, 1950, p. 329.

27. A. N. Whitehead, *Adventures of Ideas*, New York, Cambridge University Press, p. 137.

28. E. Gutkind, *Choose Life*, New York, Schuman, 1952, p. 134.

29. C. M. Child, "The beginnings of unity and order in living things," in E. Dummer (editor), *The Unconscious*, New York, Knopf, 1927, p. 37.

30. This, it may be recalled, is the theme of Stephen Crane's famous story *The Red Badge of Courage*, which during 1951–52 was widely seen in its admirable movie version.

31. Albert J. Glass, "Combat exhaustion," *United States Armed Forces Medical Journal*, vol. 2, 1951, pp. 1471–1478.

32. See M. F. Ashley Montagu (editor), *The Meaning of Love*, New York, Julian Press, 1953.

33. Nelson N. Foote, "Love," *Psychiatry*, vol. 16, 1953, pp. 245–251.

34. Harry S. Sullivan, *Conceptions of Modern Psychiatry*, Washington, D.C., Wilham Alanson White Psychiatric Foundation, 1947, p. 20.

35. Erich Fromm, *Man For Himself*, New York, Rinehart, 1947, pp. 98–101.

36. Ian D. Suttie, *The Origins of Love and Hate*, New York, Julian Press, 1953, p. 36.

37. Leo Loeb, *The Biological Basis of Individuality*, Springfield, Illinois, Thomas, 1944, pp. 651–652.

38. Sir Charles Sherrington, *Man On His Nature*, 2d ed., New York, Cambridge University Press, 1951, pp. 382–383.

39. What could be achieved this way and by what means has been extremely though not impossibly set out in two novels, the earlier by Aldous Huxley, *Brave New World*, New York, Harper, 1932; the more recent by George Orwell, *Nineteen Eighty-Four*, New York, New American Library, 1948. See also Ray Bradbury, *Fahrenheit 451*, New York, Ballantine Books, 1953.

40. See pp. 105–131.

41. See G. Scott Williamson and I. H. Pearse, *Biologists in Search of Material*, London, Faber & Faber, 1947.

42. A neurosis has been defined as the process of making the best of your frustrations in an unsatisfactory sort of way.

43. Erich Fromm, *Escape From Freedom*, New York, Rinehart, 1941; Erich Fromm, *Man For Himself, loc. cit.;* Rollo May, *The Meaning of Anxiety, loc cit.;* Rollo May, *Man in Search of Himself*, New York, Norton, 1952; W. H. Auden, *The Age of Anxiety*, New York, Random House, 1947; M. W. Childs and D. Cater, *Ethics in a Business Society*, New York, Mentor Books, 1954.

44. James C. Moloney, "Psychiatric observations in Okinawa Shima," *Psychiatry*, vol. 8, 1945, pp. 391–401; James C. Moloney, *The Battle For Mental Health*, New York, Philosophical Library, 1952; James C. Moloney, *The Magic Cloak*, Wakefield, Massachusetts, Montrose Press, 1949, pp. 299–314.

45. During 1951 while on a visit to the Southwest I learned of a group of investigators who had arrived to study mental illness among American Indians. Not being able to discover a single mentally ill Indian they packed their bags and departed! It occurred to no one, apparently, to inquire why there were no mentally ill Indians. For an interesting discussion bearing on this subject see P. M. Yap, "Mental diseases peculiar to certain cultures," *Journal of Mental Science*, vol. 97, 1951, pp. 313–327; Erik H. Erikson, *Childhood and Society*, New York, Norton, 1950; John W. M. Whiting and Irving Child, *Child Training and Personality*, New Haven, Yale University Press, 1953; Douglas G. Haring (editor), *Personal Character and Cultural Milieu*, Syracuse, New York, Syracuse University Press, 1949; S.

Sargent and M. Smith (editors), *Culture and Personality*, New York, Viking Fund, 1949.

46. John E. Boodin, *The Social Mind*, New York, Macmillan, 1939, p. 155.

47. Otto Rank, *Modern Education*, New York, Knopf, 1932, p. 99.

48. Erich Fromm, *Ecsape From Freedom*, loc. cit., pp. 21–22.

49. See, for example, Geza Roheim's interesting work, *The Origin and Function of Culture*, Nervous and Mental Diseases Monographs, No. 69, New York, 1943.

50. For an illuminating discussion of this subject see Cathy Hayes, *The Ape in Our House*, New York, Harper, 1951.

51. For a discussion of this subject see Margaret M. Wood, *Paths of Loneliness*, New York, Columbia University Press, 1953. Paul Halmos, *Solitude and Privacy*, New York, Philosophical Library, 1953.

52. André Gide, *The Journals of André Gide*, vol. 1, New York, Knopf, 1947.

53. John Donne, *Complete Poetry and Selected Prose* (edited by John Hayward), New York, Random House, 1929, p. 538.

54. Sigmund Freud, "Psychoanalysis," *Encyclopaedia Britannica*, 14th ed. Chicago, 1929.

55. Harry S. Sullivan, "Psychiatry: Introduction to the study of interpersonal relations," *Psychiatry*, vol. 1, 1938, pp. 121–134.

56. For a criticism of the Freudian conception of "Narcissism" see Ian D. Suttie, op. cit., p. 32. For a beautiful proof of the statement in the text see P. F. D. Seitz, "Psychocutaneous conditioning during the first two weeks of life," *Psychosomatic Medicine*, vol. 12, 1950, pp. 187–188.

57. Alfred Adler, op. cit., pp. 282–283 and 284.

58. William Galt, "The principle of cooperation in behavior," *Quarterly Review of Biology*, vol. 15, 1940, pp. 401–410.

59. Kathleen Nott, "The topographical illusion," *Horizon* (London), vol. 19. 1949, pp. 367–371.

60. Beata Rank, "Aggression," *The Psychoanalytic Study of the Child*, loc. cit., pp. 43–48.

61. René A. Spitz, "The role of ecological factors in emotional development in infancy," *Child Development*, vol. 20, 1949, pp. 145–155; René A. Spitz, "Autoerotism," *The Psychoanalytic Study of the Child*, loc. cit., pp. 85–120.

62. David Beres and Samuel J. Obers, "The effects of extreme deprivation in infancy on psychic structure in adolescence: A study in ego development," *The Psychoanalytic Study of the Child*, vol. 5, New York, International Universities Press, pp. 212–235.

63. H. Hartmann, E. Kris, and R. M. Loewenstein, "Comments on the formation of psychic structure," *The Psychoanalytic Study of the Child*, vol. 3/4, loc. cit., pp. 11–38; H. Hartmann, "Comments on the psychoanalytic theory of the ego," *The Psychoanalytic Study of the Child*, vol. 5, loc. cit., pp. 74–96; Beata Rank and Dorothy Macnaughton, "A clinical contribution to early ego development," ibid., pp. 53–65.

64. René A. Spitz, "Relevancy of direct infant observation," *The Psychoanalytic Study of the Child*, vol. 5, loc. cit., pp. 66–73.

65. Edith Jacobson, "Contribution to the metapsychology of cyclothymic depression," in *Affective Disorders* (edited by Phyllis Greenacre), New York, International Universities Press, 1953, pp. 49–83.

66. Galt, op. cit., p. 405.

67. Ibid., p. 407.

68. Trigant Burrow, "The social neurosis: A Study in 'clinical anthropology,'"

Philosophy of Science, vol. 16, 1949, pp. 25–40. For a more extended treatment see Trigant Burrow, *The Neurosis of Man*, New York, Philosophical Library, 1953.

69. Alfred Adler, *op. cit.*, p. 110.

70. Trigant Burrow, "The social neurosis: A study in 'clinical anthropology,'" *loc. cit.*, p. 40.

71. Alfred Adler, *op. cit.*, p. 285.

72. The term "savage" was dropped when we learned that "savages" are, in fact, not "savage" or "wild." The term "primitive" is falling into disuse because we now know that the only things primitive about "primitive" peoples is their technological development—but then only by *unfair* comparison with our own. The term "nonliterate" refers more accurately and with less prejudice to such peoples.

73. Charlotte Buhler, "Die Ersten Sozialen Verhaltungsweisen des Kindes," in *Soziologische und Psychologische Studien über das Erste Lebensjahr*, Jena, Fischer, 1927; Charlotte Buhler, "Spontaneous reactions of children in the first two years," *Proceedings and Papers of the 9th International Congress of Psychology*, 1929, pp. 99–100.

74. M. J. Muste and D. F. Sharpe, "Some influential factors in the determination of aggressive behavior in preschool children," *Child Development*, vol. 18, 1947, pp. 11–28; K. Lewin, R. Lippitt, and R. K. White, "Patterns of aggressive behavior," *Journal of Social Psychology*, vol. 10, 1939, pp. 271–299; M. E. Bonney, "A sociometric study," *Sociometry*, vol. 9, 1946, pp. 21–47; M. D. Fite, "Aggressive behavior in young children," *Genetic Psychology Monographs*, vol. 22, 1940, pp. 151–319; L. Bender, S. Keiser, and P. Schilder, "Studies in aggressiveness," II, *Genetic Psychology Monographs*, vol. 18, 1938, pp. 546–564; R. R. Sears, J. W. M. Whiting, V. Nowlis, and P. S. Sears, "Some child-rearing antecedents of aggression and dependency in young children," *Genetic Psychology Monographs*, vol. 47, 1953, pp. 135–234.

75. Lauretta Bender, "The genesis of hostility in children," *American Journal of Psychiatry*, vol. 105, 1948, pp. 241–245; Lauretta Bender, *Aggression, Hostility and Anxiety in Children*, Springfield, Illinois, Thomas, 1953.

76. A. H. Maslow, "Our maligned animal nature," *Journal of Psychology*, vol. 28, 1949, pp. 273–278.

77. Katherine M. Banham, "The development of affectionate behavior in infancy," *Journal of Genetic Psychology*, vol. 76, 1950, pp. 283–289.

78. Beata Rank, *op. cit.*, pp. 43–48.

79. This notion, of course, draws its character from Freud's conception of the Id. See p. 260.

80. M. E. Harding, *Psychic Energy*, New York, Pantheon Books, 1947, p. 1.

81. For an extreme expression of this point of view, see Richard M. Brickner, "Normal vertebrate behavior as a cause of human trouble," *American Journal of Psychiatry*, vol. 108, 1952, pp. 801–812.

82. Charles R. Knight, *Prehistoric Man*, New York, Appleton-Century, 1949.

83. This fact is aptly enshrined in a contemporary quatrain:

> What a crazy world
> Its wonders never cease
> All the civilized at war
> All the savages at peace!

84. See Roy H. Pearce, *The Savages of America*, Baltimore, Johns Hopkins Press, 1953; C. Turnbull, *Black War*, Melbourne, Cheshire, 1948; J. G. Paton, *Missionary to the New Hebrides*, New York, Revell, 1907.

85. In a personal communication dated October 30, 1953, a scientific colleague, after visiting the people of the coral atoll Ifaluk in the southern Pacific, writes "It was the most completely non-aggressive society imaginable. They had heard about Christianity and were asking about it—we told them that they were closer to the Christian ethic than any people we had ever heard of, and that we couldn't see why they should change this!" And this is Admiral Peary on the Eskimos of West Coast Greenland: "They are savages, but they are not savage; they are without government, but they are not lawless; they are utterly uneducated according to our standard, yet they exhibit a remarkable degree of intelligence. In temperament like children, with all a child's delight in little things, they are nevertheless enduring as the most mature of civilized men and women, and the best of them are faithful unto death. Without religion and having no idea of God, they will share their last meal with anyone who is hungry, while the aged and the helpless among them are taken care of as a matter of course. They are healthy and pure-blooded; they have no vices, no intoxicants, and no bad habits—not even gambling. Altogether they are a people unique upon the face of the earth. A friend of mine well calls them the philosophic anarchists of the north. . . . To Christianize them would be quite impossible; but the cardinal graces of faith, hope, and charity they seem to have already, for without them they would never survive the six-months' night and the many rigors of their home." Robert E. Peary, *The North Pole*, New York, Macmillan, 1910, pp. 46–48.

86. Henry G. Maurice, *Ask Now the Beasts*, Occasional Paper No. 9, Society for the Preservation of the Fauna of the Empire (London), 1948. See also J. H. Moore, *The Universal Kinship*, Chicago, Kerr, 1905; Alfred E. Emerson, "Dynamic homeostasis: a unifying principle in organic social and ethical evolution," *Scientific Monthly*, vol. 78, 1954, pp. 67–85.

87. A. I. Good, "Gorilla-Land," *Natural History* (New York), vol. 56, 1947, pp. 36–46. The Rev. A. I. Good was born and brought up in the Cameroons, and has been a missionary there for over forty years. He writes (pp. 45–46), "In the sections in which gorillas are most common, the natives seem not to be afraid of them and pay little attention to them. Of course, they see them almost every day. They tell me, and I have heard this over and over, that occasionally a big male gorilla will make a pretense of attacking, but that it is a bluff. He will approach to perhaps 20 or 25 feet, act threateningly, roar fiercely, stamp on the ground, turn his rear on you in a disgusting manner while watching you over his shoulder, but will not push the attack home if you stand up to him. He does not like to have you around and evidently wants to scare you off his premises, but if you don't scare, he will finally go away." For a similar account see C. R. Joy (editor), *The Animal World of Albert Schweitzer*, Boston, Beacon Press, 1950, pp. 97–102.

88. A. H. Maslow, *op. cit.*, p. 274.

89. See Belle J. Benchley, *My Friends the Apes*, Boston, Little, Brown, 1944; Gertrude D. Lintz, *Animals Are My Hobby*, London, Museum Press, 1945. Every reader of the present volume should read this book for the moving and illuminating account of the life history of the gorilla which subsequently became known as "Gargantua," as well as for the commentary it provides upon western man.

90. See G. V. Childe, *Man Makes Himself*, New York, Mentor Books, 1951; G. V. Childe, *What Happened in History*, New York, Mentor Books, 1943; Grahame Clark, *From Savagery to Civilization*, New York, Schuman, 1946; G. V. Childe, *Social Evolution*, New York, Schuman, 1952; Ronald Latham, *In Quest of Civilization*, London, Jarrolds, 1946; Erich Kahler, *Man The Measure*, New York, Pantheon Books, 1950.

91. F. A. Hayek (editor), *John Stuart Mill and Harriet Taylor*, Chicago, University of Chicago Press, 1951, p. 279.

Chapter 9. LOVE AND THE PRIVATION OF LOVE

1. James Plant, *Personality and the Cultural Pattern*, New York, The Commonwealth Fund, 1937, p. 267.
2. As late as the second decade of this century the death rate for infants under 1 year of age in various foundling institutions throughout the United States was nearly 100 per cent! See H. D. Chapin, "A plea for accurate statistics in infants' institutions," *Transactions of the American Pediatric Society*, vol. 27, 1915, p. 180.
3. Ruth M. Bakwin and Harry Bakwin, *Psychologic Care During Infancy and Childhood*, New York, Appleton-Century, 1942, p. 295.
4. Margaret Ribble, *The Rights of Infants*, New York, Columbia University Press, 1943, pp. 4–7.
5. See John Bowlby, *Maternal Care and Mental Health*, New York, Columbia University Press, 1951.
6. Lawson G. Lowrey, "Personality distortion and early institutional care," *American Journal of Orthopsychiatry*, vol. 10, 1940, pp. 576–585.
7. For an important series of research findings on the personality of the institutionalized child see William Goldfarb, "The effects of early institutional care on adolescent personality," *Journal of Experimental Education*, vol. 12, 1943, pp. 106–129; also the following papers by the same author, "Infant rearing and problem behavior," *American Journal of Orthopsychiatry*, vol. 13, 1943, pp. 249–265; "The effects of early institutional care on adolescent personality (graphic Rorschach data)," *Child Development*, vol. 14, 1943, pp. 213–223; "Infant rearing as a factor in foster home replacement," *American Journal of Orthopsychiatry*, vol. 14, 1944, pp. 162–166; (with Bruno Klopfer) "Rorschach characteristics of 'Institution Children,' " *Rorschach Research Exchange*, vol. 8, 1944, pp. 92–100; "Psychological privation in infancy and subsequent adjustment," *American Journal of Orthopsychiatry*, vol. 15, 1945, pp. 247–255; "Effects of psychological deprivation in infancy and subsequent stimulation," *American Journal of Psychiatry*, vol. 102, 1945, pp. 18–33.
8. F. Bodman, *et al.*, "The social adaptation of institution children," *Lancet*, vol. 258, 1950, pp. 173–176; M. Castle, "Institution and non-institution children at school," *Human Relations*, vol. 7, 1954, pp. 349–366.
9. William Goldfarb, "The effects of early institutional care on adolescent personality," *loc. cit.*, p. 128.
10. David M. Levy, "Primary affect hunger," *American Journal of Psychiatry*, vol. 94, 1937, pp. 643–652.
11. William Goldfarb, "Psychological privation in infancy and subsequent adjustment," *loc. cit.*, p. 254.
12. René A. Spitz, "The role of ecological factors in emotional development," *Child Development*, vol. 20, 1949, pp. 145–155; René A. Spitz, "Hospitalism," *The Psychoanalytic Study of the Child*, vol. 1, New York, International Universities Press, 1945, pp. 53–74; René A. Spitz, "Hospitalism: A follow-up report," *The Psychoanalytic Study of the Child*, vol. 2, New York, International Universities Press, 1947, pp. 113–117; René A. Spitz, "Are parents necessary?" in *The March of Medicine, 1947*, New York, Columbia University Press, 1948, pp. 37–53; René A. Spitz, "Anaclitic depression," *The Psychoanalytic Study of the Child*, vol. 2, *loc.*

cit., pp. 313–342; René A. Spitz, "Autoerotism," *The Psychoanalytic Study of the Child*, vol. 3/4, New York, International Universities Press, 1949, pp. 85–120.

13. René A. Spitz, "Anaclitic depression," *loc. cit.*, p. 331.

14. See R. A. Spitz, "The psychogenic diseases of infancy," *The Psychoanalytic Study of the Child*, vol. 6, New York, International Universities Press, 1951, pp. 255–275. See also L. Bender and H. Yarnell, "An observation nursery: A study of 250 children in the Psychiatric Division of Bellevue Hospital," *American Journal of Psychiatry*, vol. 97, 1941, pp. 1158–1174; Harry Bakwin, "Loneliness in infants," *American Journal of Diseases of Children*, vol. 63, 1942, pp. 30–40; H. Edelston, "Separation anxiety in young children," *Genetic Psychology Monographs*, vol. 28, 1943, pp. 3–95; Harry Bakwin, "Emotional deprivation in infants," *Journal of Pediatrics*, vol. 35, 1949, pp. 512–521; Adrian H. Vander Veer, "The unwanted child," Publication of the Illinois League for Planned Parenthood, April 10, 1940, pp. 3–12; Eustace Chesser, *Unwanted Child*, London, Rich & Cowan, 1948; Percival M. Symonds, *The Dynamics of Parent-Child Relationships*, New York, Bureau of Publications, Columbia University, 1949.

15. August Aichorn, *Wayward Youth*, New York, Viking Press, 1935.

16. David Beres and Samuel J. Obers, "The effects of extreme deprivation in infancy on psychic structure in adolescence: A study in ego development," *The Psychoanalytic Study of the Child*, vol. 5, New York, International Universities Press, 1950, pp. 212–235.

17. Along these lines see Beata Rank and Dorothy Macnaughton, "A clinical contribution to early ego development," *The Psychoanalytic Study of the Child*, vol. 5, *loc. cit.*, pp. 53–73.

18. Portia Holman, "Some factors in the aetiology of maladjustment in children," *Journal of Mental Science*, vol. 99, 1953, pp. 654–688; see also Leo Bartmeier, "The contribution of the father to the mental health of the family," *American Journal of Psychiatry*, vol. 110, 1953, pp. 277–280; O. Spurgeon English and Florence Foster, *Fathers Are Parents Too*, New York, Putnam, 1951.

19. M. Bevan-Brown, *The Sources of Love and Fear*, New York, Vanguard Press, 1950, p. 40.

20. See George W. Corner, *Ourselves Unborn*, New Haven, Yale University Press, 1944, pp. 102–107.

21. See J. P. Scott and Mary-'Vesta Marston, "Critical periods affecting the development of normal and mal-adjustive social behavior in puppies," *Journal of Genetic Psychology*, vol. 77, 1950, pp. 25–60; J. P. Scott, "The relative importance of social and hereditary factors in producing disturbances in life adjustment during periods of stress in laboratory animals," in *Life Stress and Bodily Disease* (edited by H. G. Wolff, *et al.*), Baltimore, Williams & Wilkins, 1950, pp. 61–71; J. P. Scott, "The process of socialization in higher animals," in *Interrelations Between the Social Environment and Psychiatric Disorders*, New York, Milbank Memorial Fund, 1954, pp. 82–102.

22. John Bowlby, "Some pathological processes set in train by early mother-child separation," *Journal of Mental Science*, vol. 159, 1953, pp. 265–272.

23. For descriptive cases see Dorothy Burlingham and Anna Freud, *Infants Without Families*, London, Allen & Unwin, 1944; Anna Freud and Dorothy Burlingham, *War and Children*, New York, International Universities Press, 1943.

24. J. Robertson and J. Bowlby, "Observations of the sequences of responses of children aged 18 to 24 months during the course of separation," *Courier of the International Children's Centre*, vol. 2, 1952, pp. 132–142; J. Roudinesco, M.

David, and J. Nicolas, "Observation of children aged 12 to 17 months recently separated from their families and living in an institution," *ibid.*, pp. 66–78; J. Roudinesco, "Severe maternal deprivation and personality development in early childhood," *Understanding the Child*, vol. 21, 1952, pp. 104–108; Mary D. Ainsworth and John Bowlby, "Research strategy in the study of mother-child separation, *"Courier of the International Children's Centre*, vol. 4, 1954, pp. 1–47.

25. D. Rosenbluth, J. Bowlby, and J. Roudinesco, "Separation from the mother as a traumatic experience for the child: Some notes on obtaining a relevant history," *Courier of the International Children's Centre*, vol. 2, 1952, pp. 1–8.

26. H. D. Chapin, "A plan of dealing with atrophic infants and children," *Archives of Pediatrics*, vol. 25, 1908, p. 491.

27. H. D. Chapin, "Are institutions for children necessary?" *Journal of the American Medical Association*, vol. 64, January 2, 1915.

28. J. Brennemann, "The infant ward," *American Journal of Diseases of Children*, vol. 43 (March) 1932, p. 577.

29. Salimbene in J. B. Ross and M. M. McLaughlin (editors), *A Portable Medieval Reader*, New York, Viking Press, 1949, p. 366.

30. It is now believed that retrolental fibroplasia, first recognized in 1942 as a disease of premature infants (characterized by the appearance of a fibrous band behind the lens which draws upon and detaches the retina, thus causing permanent blindness), is related to the excess oxygen given premature babies during their first two weeks while in hospital. See J. T. Lanman *et al.*, "Retrolental fibroplasia and oxygen therapy," *Journal of the American Medical Association*, vol. 155, 1954, pp. 223–226; Leona Zacharias, "Progress in the study of retrolental fibroplasia," *The Sight Saving Review*, (Summer) 1953. Reprinted in *Child Family Digest*, vol. 9, 1953, pp. 47–52.

31. Philip J. Howard and Calier H. Worrell, "Premature infants in later life," *Pediatrics*, vol. 9, 1952, pp. 577–584.

32. Julius H. Hess, "Experiences gained in a thirty year study of prematurely born infants," *Pediatrics*, vol. 11, 1953, pp. 425–434.

33. A. R. Gilliland, "Socio-economic status and race as factors in infant intelligence test scores," *Child Development*, vol. 22, 1951, pp. 271–273. See also the same author's "Environmental influence on infant intelligence test scores," *Harvard Educational Review*, vol. 19, 1949, pp. 142–146.

34. See pp. 205–209.

35. Ralph Fried and M. F. Mayer, "Socio-emotional factors accounting for growth failure of children living in an institution," *Journal of Pediatrics*, vol. 33, 1948, pp. 444–456.

36. Griffith Binning, "Peace be on thy house," *Health*, March/April, 1948, pp. 6–7, 28, 30.

37. *Ibid.*, p. 30.

38. H. Durffee and K. M. Wolf, "Anstaltspflege und Entwicklung im ersten Lebensjahrs," *Zeitschrift für Kinderforschung*, vol. 42/3, 1933, pp. 273–320.

39. René A. Spitz, "Hospitalism: A follow-up report," *loc. cit.*, pp. 113–117. See also H. Hetzer and R. Ripin, "Fruehestes Lernen des Saeuglings in der Ernaehrungs-Situation," *Zeikschrift für Psychologie*, vol. 118, 1930, pp. 82–127.

40. N. B. Talbot, E. H. Sobel, B. S. Burke, E. Lindemann, and S. S. Kaufman, "Dwarfism in healthy children: Its possible relation to emotional disturbances," *New England Journal of Medicine*, vol. 236, 1947, pp. 783–793.

41. H. Lihn, K. Menninger, and M. Mayman, "Personality factors in osteo-

arthritis," in H. G. Wolff, *et al.* (editors), *Life Stress and Bodily Disease, loc. cit.*, pp. 744–749.

42.   Hans Selye, *The Physiology and Pathology of Exposure to Stress*, Montreal, Acta, 1950, p. 103; E. W. Bovard, Jr., "A theory to account for the effects of early handling on viability of the albino rat," *Science*, vol. 120, 1954, p. 187; W. R. Ruegamer, *et. al.*, "Growth, food utilization, and thyroid activity in the albino rat as a function of extra handling," *Science*, vol. 120, 1954, pp. 184–185; H. D. Kruse, "The interplay of noxious agents, stress, and deprivation in the etiology of disease," in I. Galdston (editor), *Beyond the Germ Theory*, New York, Health Education Council, 1954, pp. 17–38; H. D. Kruse, "The ratios of health and disease—how the presence, excess, deficit, or absence of conditions evokes disease," *ibid.*, pp. 39–52; H. R. Schaeffer, "Behavior under stress: a neurophysiological hypothesis," *Psychological Review*, vol. 61, 1954, pp. 323–332.

43.   Selye, *op. cit.*, p. 12.

44.   R. A. Spitz, "Infantile depression and the general adaptation syndrome," in *Depression: Proceedings of the 42nd Annual Meeting American Psychological Association*, 1953, pp. 93–108.

45.   Celia Burns Stendler, "Critical periods in socialization and overdependency," *Child Development*, vol. 23, 1952, pp. 2–12.

46.   O. H. Mowrer, *Learning Theory and Personality Dynamics*, New York, Ronald Press, 1950.

47.   M. F. Ashley Montagu, "Some factors in family cohesion," *Psychiatry*, vol. 7, 1944, pp. 349–352; Herbert Thoms, E. B. Jackson, L. M. Stowe, and F. W. Goodrich, Jr., "The rooming-in plan for mothers and infants," *American Journal of Obstetrics and Gynecology*, vol. 56, 1948, pp. 707–711; E. B. Jackson, *et al.* "A hospital rooming-in unit for four newborn infants and their mothers," *Pediatrics*, vol. 1, 1948, pp. 28–43.

48.   Ruth M. Bakwin and Harry Bakwin, *op. cit.*, p. 294.

49.   M. F. Ashley Montagu, "Some factors in family cohesion," *loc. cit.*, pp. 349–352.

50.   John Bowlby, *Maternal Care and Mental Health, loc. cit.*, p. 55.

51.   Lauretta Bender, "Psychopathic behavior disorders in children," in *Handbook of Correctional Psychology* (edited by R. M. Lindner and R. V. Seliger), New York, Philosophical Library, 1947.

52.   William Goldfarb, "Variations in adolescent adjustment of institutionally reared children," *American Journal of Orthopsychiatry*, vol. 17, 1947, pp. 449–457.

53.   Dorothy Burlingham and Anna Freud, *Monthly Report of Hampstead Nurseries*, May, 1944 (unpublished), quoted by Bowlby, *op. cit.*, p. 21.

54.   M. F. Ashley Montagu, "Social time: A functional and methodological analysis," *American Journal of Sociology*, vol. 44, 1938, pp. 282–284.

55.   John Bowlby, *Maternal Care and Mental Health, loc. cit.*, pp. 27–28.

56.   These observations have been fully confirmed by other investigators. See, for example, Fritz Redl and David Wineman, *Children Who Hate*, Glencoe, Illinois, Free Press, 1951, and the same authors' *Controls From Within*, Glencoe, Illinois, Free Press, 1952; Portia Holman, *op. cit.* See also Frank J. Cohen, *Children In Trouble*, New York, Norton, 1952.

57.   *Identification* is the process of molding by the person of his own ego after some aspect or the whole of one which has been taken for a model.

58.   *Introjection* is the process of finding or incorporating within the self motives or qualities which are those of another person or object.

59. John Bowlby, "Forty-four juvenile thieves: Their characters and home life," *International Journal of Psycho-Analysis*, vol. 25, 1944, pp. 19–53, 122, 154–178.

60. The *libido* consists of all those energies which comprise the dependency love drives, which may broadly be resumed under the term "love," love including not only sexual love, but self-love, love for parents and children, friendship, love for humanity in general, and even devotion to concrete objects and to abstract ideas.

61. The *pleasure-principle* may be defined as the tendency for mental life and the development of the personality to be shaped primarily according to the pleasure-pain aspects of inner and also of outer stimuli.

62. The *reality-principle* defines the tendency to shape mental life according to the requirements of external necessity, forced upon the person by the need for adaptation to his environment.

63. These ideas are beautifully developed by August Aichorn in *Wayward Youth*, *loc. cit.*, pp. 187–210. See also Kate Friedlander, "Formation of the antisocial character," in *The Psychoanalytic Study of the Child*, vol. 1, New York, International Universities Press, 1945, pp. 189–203; Erik H. Erikson, *Childhood and Society*, New York, Norton, 1951; Frank J. Cohen, *op. cit.*, Bruno Bettelheim, *Love Is Not Enough*, Glencoe, Illinois, Free Press, 1950.

64. John Bowlby, "Critical phases in the development of social responses in man and other animals," in *Prospects In Psychiatric Research* (edited by J. M. Tanner), Oxford, Blackwell Scientific Publications, 1953, pp. 80–85. Reprinted in *New Biology*, No. 14 (edited by M. L. Johnson and M. Abercrombie), New York, Penguin Books, 1953, pp. 25–32.

65. Konrad Z. Lorenz, *King Solomon's Ring*, New York, Crowell, 1952, pp. 40–42.

66. Konrad Z. Lorenz, "Die angeborenen Formen möglicher Erfahrung," *Zeitschrift für Tierpsychologie*, vol. 5, 1943, pp. 235–409.

67. René A. Spitz and K. M. Wolf, "The smiling response: a contribution to the ontogenesis of social relations," *Genetic Psychology Monographs*, vol. 34, 1946, pp. 57–125.

68. W. Grey Walter, *The Living Brain*, New York, Norton, 1953, p. 91.

69. Quoted in W. Healy, A. F. Bronner, and A. M. Bowers, *The Structure and Meaning of Psychoanalysis*, New York, Knopf 1930, p. 117. See also N. Tinbergen, *Social Behaviour in Animals*, New York, Wiley, 1953; N. Tinbergen, *The Study of Instinct*, New York, Oxford University Press, 1952.

70. For a critical examination of the Lorenz-Tinbergen studies see A. Ginsberg, "A reconstructive analysis of the concept of 'instinct,'" *Journal of Psychology*, vol. 33, 1952, pp. 235–277; D. S. Lehrman, "A critique of Konrad Lorenz's theory of instinctive behavior," *Quarterly Review of Biology*, vol. 28, 1953, pp. 337–363; Rex Knight, "Animal behaviour," *Nature*, vol. 174, 1954, pp. 857–859.

71. Dorothy Burlingham and Anna Freud, *op. cit.*

72. M. F. Ashley Montagu, "The premaxilla in man," *Journal of the American Dental Association*, vol. 23, pp. 2043–2057, 1936.

73. Joseph Needham, *Morphogenesis and Embryology*, New York, Cambridge University Press, 1942.

74. B. M. Spinley, *The Deprived and the Privileged: Personality Development in English Society*, London, Routledge, 1953; M. L. Farber, "English and Americans: values in the socialization process," *Journal of Psychology*, vol. 36, 1953, pp. 243–250; M. L. Farber, "English and Americans: a study in national character." *Journal of Psychology*, vol. 32, 1951, pp. 241–249; M. C. Erickson, "Social status and child-

rearing practices," in T. M. Newcomb and E. Hartley (editors), *Readings in Social Psychology*, New York, Holt, 1947, pp. 494–501; Allison Davis, "American status systems and the socialization of the child," *American Sociological Review*, vol. 6, 1941, pp. 345–356; Allison Davis, "Child training and social class," in R. G. Barker *et al* (editors), *Child Behavior and Development*, New York, McGraw-Hill, 1943; Allison Davis and R. J. Havighurst, *Father of the Man*, Boston, Houghton Mifflin, 1947; A. B. Hollinshead, *Elmtown's Youth*, New York, Wiley, 1949; C. B. Stendler, "The learning of certain secondary drives by Parisian and American middle class children," *Marriage and Family Living*, vol. 16, 1954, pp. 192–200.

75. These observations have been thoroughly confirmed by the first study on English personality types to be published, B. M. Spinley's *The Deprived and the Privileged*, London, Routledge, 1935; see also Geoffrey Gorer, *Exploring English Character*, Cresset Press, London, 1955.

76. E. M. Forster, *Abinger Harvest*, New York, Harcourt, Brace, 1947.

77. For an excellent and rare example of "sudden illumination," the discovery of the warmth and humanity and utter difference of the Italian personality from the American, by an American, see the late John Horne Burns' remarkable novel, *The Gallery*, New York, Harper, 1948.

78. An American Lady, *Change For the American Notes*, 1843, quoted in Yvonneffrench, *Transatlantic Exchanges*, New York, Library Publishers, 1952, p. 128.

79. T. W. Adorno, Else Frenkel-Brunswik, D. J. Levinson, and R. Nevitt Sanford, *The Authoritarian Personality*, New York, Harper, 1950.

80. *Ibid.*, p. 975.

81. David Levy, "Anti-Nazis: criteria of differentiation," in Alfred H. Stanton and Stewart E. Perry, *Personality and Political Crisis*, Glencoe, Illinois, Free Press, 1951, pp. 151–227.

82. David Levy, *Maternal Overprotection*, New York, Columbia University Press, 1943.

83. René A. Spitz, "Hospitalism," *loc. cit.*, pp. 53–14; René A. Spitz, "Hospitalism: a follow-up, II," *loc. cit.*, pp. 113–117. René A. Spitz, "Are parents necessary?" in *Medicine in the Postwar World*, New York, Columbia University Press, 1948, p. 46. René A. Spitz, "Anaclitic depression," *loc. cit.*, pp. 313–342.

84. Ian D. Suttie, *op. cit.*, p. 16.

85. Ralph S. Lillie, *General Biology and Philosophy of Organism*, Chicago, University of Chicago Press, 1945, pp. 208–209.

86. There have been no special studies on this subject for the Australian aborigines, the evidence is largely of a casual observational kind, and in a sense is therefore perhaps all the more valuable; the following works contain important material: Baldwin Spencer and Frank J. Gillen, *The Arunta*, 2 vols., New York, Macmillan, 1927; Baldwin Spencer, *Wanderings In Wild Australia*, 2 vols., New York, Macmillan, 1928; J. R. B. Love, *Stone Age Bushmen of Today*, London, Blackie, 1936; Jack McLaren, *My Crowded Solitude*, London, Newnes, 1926; Charles P. Mountford, *Brown Men and Red Sand*, New York, Philosophical Library, 1948.

87. V. Stefansson, *My Life With The Eskimo*, New York, Macmillan, 1913; V. Stefansson, *The Friendly Arctic*, New York, Macmillan, 1944; Robert Marshall, *Arctic Village*, New York, Literary Guild, 1933; Gontran De Poncins, *Kabloona*, New York, Reynal & Hitchcock, 1941.

88. Margaret Mead, *Sex and Temperament in Three Primitive Societies*, New York, Mentor Books, 1950; Margaret Mead, *From The South Seas*, New York, Morrow, 1939; Hortense Powdermaker, *Life in Lesu*, New York, Norton, 1933.

89. Alice Joseph and Veronica F. Murray, *Chamorros and Carolinians of Saipan*, Cambridge, Harvard University Press, 1951.

90. Cora Du Bois, *The People of Alor*, Minneapolis, University of Minnesota Press, 1944; Margaret Mead and Gregory Bateson, *Balinese Character*, New York, New York Academy of Sciences, 1942; Margaret Mead and F. C. Macgregor, *Growth and Culture*, New York, Putnam, 1951.

91. Ruth Benedict, *The Chrysanthemum and the Sword*, Boston, Massachusetts, Houghton Mifflin, 1946; Geoffrey Gorer, "Japanese character structure," New York, Institute for Intercultural Studies, 1942; John Embree, *The Japanese Nation*, New York, Farrar & Rinehart, 1945. John Embree, *A Japanese Village, Suye Mura*, London, Kegan Paul, 1946; James C. Moloney, *Understanding the Japanese Mind*, New York, Philosophical Library, 1954; Douglas Haring, "Japanese national character," *Yale Review*, vol. 42, 1953, pp. 375–392; Jean Stoetzl, *Without the Chrysanthemum and the Sword*, London, Heinemann, 1954.

92. M. C. Yang, *A Chinese Village*, New York, Columbia University Press, 1945; Olga Lang, *Chinese Family and Society*, New Haven, Yale University Press, 1946; F. L. K. Hsu, *Under the Ancestor's Shadow*, New York, Columbia University Press, 1948; F. L. K. Hsu, *Chinese and Americans*, New York, Schuman, 1953.

93. Geoffrey Gorer, "Burmese personaliy," New York, Institute for Intercultural Studies, 1945.

94. Wayne Dennis, *The Hopi Child*, New York, Appleton-Century, 1940; Laura Thompson and Alice Joseph, *The Hopi Way*, Chicago, University of Chicago Press, 1945; Gordon Macgregor, *Warriors Without Weapons*, Chicago, University of Chicago Press, 1946; Dorothea Leighton and Clyde Kluckhohn, *Children of the People* [the Navaho], Cambridge, Harvard University Press, 1947; Clyde Kluckhohn and Dorothea Leighton, *The Navaho*, Cambridge, Harvard University Press, 1946; Erik H. Erikson, *Childhood and Society*, New York, Norton, 1950; Laura Thompson, *Culture in Crisis*, New York, Harper, 1950; Victor Barnow, "Acculturation and personality among the Wisconsin Chippewa," Memoir No. 72, *American Anthropologist*, vol. 52, 1950, pp. 1–152; Alice Joseph, Rosamund B. Spicer, and Jane Chesky, *The Desert People: A Study of the Papago Indians*, Chicago, University of Chicago Press, 1950; John J. Honigmann, "Culture and ethos of Kaska society," *Yale University Publications in Anthropology*, New Haven, Yale University Press, 1949, pp. 1–365.

95. Margaret Mead, *And Keep Your Powder Dry*, New York, Morrow, 1942; Geoffrey Gorer, *The American People*, New York, Norton, 1948; James West, *Plainville, U.S.A.*, New York, Columbia University Press, 1945; W. Lloyd Warner, *American Life*, Chicago, University of Chicago Press, 1953; Conrad M. Arensberg, *The Irish Countryman*, New York, Macmillan, 1937; David Rodnick, *Postwar Germans*, New Haven, Yale University Press, 1948; Bertram Schaffner, *Father Land*, New York, Columbia University Press, 1948; A. W. Davis, and R. J. Havighurst, *Father of the Man*, Boston, Houghton Mifflin, 1947; R. J. Havighurst and H. Taba, *Adolescent Character and Personality*, New York, Wiley, 1949; A. B. Hollinshead, *Elmtown's Youth*, New York, Wiley, 1949; Claudia Lewis, *Children of the Cumberland*, New York, Columbia University Press, 1946; David Levy, "Anti-Nazis: criteria of differentiation," *Psychiatry*, vol. 11, 1948, pp. 125–167; Ruth Benedict, "Child rearing in certain European countries," *American Journal of Orthopsychiatry*, vol. 19, 1949, pp. 342–350; Geoffrey Gorer and John Rickman, *The People of Great Russia*, New York, Chanticleer Press, 1950; David Riesman, *The Lonely Crowd*, New Haven, Yale University Press, 1950; Ruth Métraux and Margaret Mead, *Themes in French Culture*, Stanford, Calif., Stanford University Press, 1954; Margaret

Mead and Ruth Métraux, *The Study of Culture at a Distance,* Chicago, University of Chicago Press, 1953; Geoffrey Gorer, *Exploring English Character,* London, Cresset Press, 1955.

For general and special readings in the field see Clyde Kluckhohn and Henry A. Murray (editors), *Personality: In Nature, Society and Culture,* 2d ed., New York, Knopf, 1953; Douglas G. Haring (editor), *Personal Character and Cultural Milieu,* Syracuse, New York, Syracuse University Press, 1949; S. S. Sargent and Marian W. Smith (editors), *Culture and Personality,* New York, Viking Fund, 1949; Patrick Mullahy (editor), *A Study of Interpersonal Relations,* New York, Heritage Press, 1949; Howard Brand (editor), *The Study of Personality,* New York, Wiley, 1954; J. S. Slotkin, *Personality Development,* New York, Harper, 1952; John J. Honigmann, *Culture and Personality,* New York, Harper, 1954; A. H. Stanton and S. E. Perry, *Personality and Political Crisis,* Glencoe, Illinois, Free Press, 1951; Harold Orlansky, "Infant care and personalty," *Psychological Bulletin,* vol. 46, 1949, pp. 1–48, abridged in W. E. Martin and C. B. Stendler, *Readings in Child Development,* New York, Harcourt, Brace, 1954, pp. 321–336.

96. James C. Maloney, *The Magic Cloak,* Wakefield, Massachusetts, The Montrose Press, 1949, pp. 299–323.

97. C. P. Mountford, *op. cit.,* p. 21.

98. Julian Huxley, *Evolution In Action,* New York, Harper, 1953.

99. Edmund B. Sinnott, *Cell and Psyche,* Chapel Hill, University of North Carolina Press, 1950.

Chapter 10. EXPERIENCE, CULTURE, AND PERSONALITY

1. See R. E. Money-Kyrle, *Psychoanalysis and Politics,* London, Duckworth, 1951.

2. J. McV. Hunt, "The effects of infant feeding frustration upon adult hoarding in the albino rat," *Journal of Abnormal and Social Psychology,* vol. 36, 1941, pp. 338–360.

3. Emil Fredericson, "Competition: The effects of infantile experience upon adult behavior," *Journal of Abnormal and Social Psychology,* vol. 46, 1951, pp. 406–409.

4. Emil Fredericson, "The effects of food deprivation upon competitive and spontaneous combat in C57 black mice," *Journal of Psychology,* vol. 29, 1950, pp. 89–100.

5. M. W. Kahn, "The effect of severe defeat at various age levels on the aggressive behavior of mice, *Journal of Genetic Psychology,* vol. 79, 1951, pp. 117–130

6. J. P. Scott and Mary-'Vesta Marston, "Nonadaptive behavior resulting from a series of defeats in fighting mice," *Journal of Abnormal and Social Psychology,* vol. 48, 1953, pp. 417–428.

7. M. W. Kahn, "Infantile experience and mature aggressive behavior of mice: some maternal influences," *Journal of Genetic Psychology,* vol. 84, 1944, pp. 65–75.

8. J. A. King and N. L. Gurney, "Effect of early social experience on adult aggressive behavior in C57BL/10 mice," *Journal of Comparative and Physiological Psychology,* vol. 47, 1954, pp. 326–330.

9. David M. Levy, "Experiments on the sucking reflex and social behavior in dogs," *American Journal of Orthopsychiatry,* vol. 4, 1934, pp. 203–224.

10. S. Ross, "Sucking behavior in neonate dogs," *Journal of Abnormal and Social Psychology,* vol. 46, 1951, pp. 142–149.

11. David M. Levy, "Instinct satiation, an experiment on the pecking behavior of chickens," *Journal of Genetic Psychology*, vol. 18, 1938, pp. 327–348.

12. B. Hymovitch, "The effects of experimental variations on problem-solving in the rat," *Journal of Comparative Physiological Psychology*, vol. 45, 1952, pp. 313–321

13. Frederick S. Hammett, "Studies of the thyroid apparatus: I," *American Journal of Physiology*, vol. 56, 1921, pp. 196–204.

14. Frederick S. Hammett, "Studies of the thyroid apparatus: V," *Endocrinology*, vol. 6, 1922, pp. 221–229.

15. Walter Freeman and James W. Watts, *Psychosurgery*, Springfield, Illinois, Thomas, 1951; John F. Fulton, *Frontal Lobotomy and Affective Behavior*, New York, Norton, 1951; Phyllis Greenacre (editor), *Affective Disorders*, New York, International Universities Press, 1953.

16. R. E. Money-Kyrle, *Superstition and Society*, London, Hogarth, 1939, p. 126.

17. Margaret A. Ribble, "Infantile experience in relation to personality development," in J. McV. Hunt (editor), *Personality and the Behavior Disorders*, vol. 2, New York, Ronald, 1944, pp. 621–651; Margaret Ribble, *The Rights of Infants*, New York, Columbia University Press, 1943; "The significance of infantile sucking for the psychic development of the individual," and "Disorganizing factors in infant personality," in Silvan Tomkins (editor), *Contemporary Psychopathology*, Cambridge, Harvard University Press, 1943, pp. 1–8, 9–15.

18. For an excellent brief survey see Margaret W. Gerard, "Emotional disorders of childhood," in Franz Alexander (editor), *Dynamic Psychiatry*, Chicago, University of Chicago Press, 1952, pp. 165–210.

19. Edward Bibring, "The mechanism of depression," in Phyllis Greenacre (editor), *op. cit.*, pp. 36–37.

20. Katherine M. Banham, "The development of affectionate behavior in infancy," *Journal of Genetic Psychology*, vol. 76, 1950, pp. 283–289.

21. O. H. Mowrer and Clyde Kluckhohn, "Dynamic theory of personality," in J. McV. Hunt (editor), *Personality and the Behavior Disorders, loc. cit.*, p. 89.

22. Margaret Mead, *And Keep Your Powder Dry*, New York, Morrow, 1942.

23. Gardner Murphy, Lois B. Murphy, and Theodore M. Newcomb, *Experimental Social Psychology*, New York, Harper, 1937, p. 555.

24. For provocative discussions of consciousness in these terms see Karl W. Deutsch, "Mechanism, teleology, and mind," *Philosophy and Phenomenological Research*, vol. 12, 1951, pp. 185–222; and Talcott Parsons, "Consciousness and symbolic processes," in Harold Abramson (editor), *Problems of Consciousness*, New York, Josiah Macy, Jr., Foundation, 1954, pp. 47–58. For an early proponent of these ideas see Robert Briffault, "Consciousness as a social product," in his *Psyche's Lamp*, London, Allen & Unwin, 1921, pp. 203–216.

25. Lawrence K. Frank, "Cultural coercion and individual distortion," *Psychiatry*, vol. 2, 1939, p. 14.

26. Alfred Baeumler, "Race: a basic concept in education," *World Educaion*, vol. 4, 1939, pp. 506–509 (translated from the German article in the *Internazionale Zeitschrift für Erziehung*, vol. 8, 1939). For a similar point of view see Cyril Darlington, *The Facts of Life*, London, Allen & Unwin, 1953.

27. George E. Simpson and J. M. Yinger *Racial and Cultural Minorities*, New York, Harper, 1953; M. F. Ashley Montagu, *Man's Most Dangerous Myth: The Fallacy of Race*, 3rd ed., New York, Harper, 1952.

28. Romanzo C. Adams, *Interracial Marriage in Hawaii,* New York, Macmillan, 1937; Edwin G. Barrows, *Hawaiian Americans,* New Haven, Yale University Press, 1947.

29. Erwin H. Ackerknecht, "White Indians," *Bulletin of the History of Medicine,* vol. 15, 1944, pp. 15–35. See also Howard H. Peckham, *Captured By Indians,* New Brunswick, N. J., Rutgers University Press, 1954.

Chapter 11.   ISOLATION VERSUS SOCIALIZATION

1. For Laura Bridgman see Maud Howe Elliott and Florence Howe Hall, *Laura Bridgman,* Boston, Little, Brown, 1903; Mary Swift Lamson, *Life and Education of Laura Dewey Bridgman,* Boston, Houghton Mifflin, 1881. For Helen Keller see Helen Keller, *The Story of My Life,* New York, Doubleday, 1903, 1954.

2. J. A. L. Singh and Robert M. Zingg, *Wolf-Children and Feral Man,* New York, Harper, 1942.

3. J. G. Speed, "Sweat glands of the dog," *Veterinary Journal,* vol. 97, 1941, pp. 252–256; T. Aoki and M. Wada, "Functional activity of the sweat glands in the hairy skin of the dog," *Science,* vol. 114, 1951, pp. 123–124.

4. For this information I am indebted to Dr. Edmund Spaeth, Professor of Ophthalmology at the University of Pennsylvania Medical School.

5. These have been entertainingly discussed in the chapter "Wolf! Wolf!" in Bergen Evans, *The Natural History of Nonsense,* New York, Knopf, 1946, pp. 86–99. Additional relevant material will be found in Wayne Dennis, "The significance of feral man," *American Journal of Psychology,* vol. 54, 1941, pp. 425–432; David G. Mandelbaum, "Wolf-child histories from India," *Journal of Social Psychology,* vol. 17, 1943, pp. 25–44; M. F. Ashley Montagu, "Wolf-children and feral man," *American Anthropologist,* vol. 45, 1943, pp. 468–472.

6. Kingsley Davis, "Extreme social isolation of a child," *American Journal of Sociology,* vol. 45, 1940, pp. 554–565; Kingsley Davis, "Final note on a case of extreme isolation," *American Journal of Sociology,* vol. 52, 1947, pp. 432–437.

7. Many of these accounts will be found in J. R. M. Singh and R. M. Zingg, *op. cit.*

8. A. F. Tredgold, *Mental Deficiency,* 7th ed. Baltimore, William Wood, 1947, pp. 153–154.

9. For further discussion of this subject see, W. Dennis, "The significance of feral man," *loc. cit.,* R. M. Zingg, "Reply to Professor Dennis," *American Journal of Psychology,* vol. 54, 1941, pp. 432–435; Anne Anastasi and John P. Foley, Jr., *Differential Psychology,* New York, Macmillan, 1949, pp. 182–192; W. Dennis, "A further analysis of reports of wild children," *Child Development,* vol. 22, 1951, pp. 153–158; L. J. Stone, "A critique of studies of infant isolation, *Child Development,* vol. 25, 1954, pp. 9–20.

10. G. E. Coghill, *Anatomy and the Problem of Behaviour,* New York, Cambridge University Press, 1929, p. 104.

11. *Ibid.,* p. 105.

12. *Ibid.,* p. 107.

13. *Ibid.,* p. 110.

14. Marie K. Mason, "Learning to speak after six and one half years," *Journal of Speech Disorders,* vol. 7, 1942, pp. 295–304; Kingsley Davis, "Final note on a case of extreme isolation," *loc. cit.,* pp. 432–437.

15. Arnold Gesell and Harry M. Zimmerman, "Correlations of behavior and neuropathology in a case of cerebral palsy from birth injury," *American Journal of Psychiatry*, vol. 94, 1937, pp. 505–536.

16. I am obliged to Nurse Russell and to Dr. R. Schopbach for making the history of this case available to me.

17. Alfred Adler, *Social Interest: A Challenge to Mankind*, New York, Putnam, 1938, pp. 220–221.

Chapter 12. THE DIRECTION OF HUMAN DEVELOPMENT

1. All these allegations, and more, are made about children by no less an authority than Miss Dorothy Thompson in an article entitled "I remember me," in *The Ladies' Home Journal*, February, 1954 and reprinted in *The Reader's Digest*, May, 1954.

2. H. S. Jennings, *Prometheus or Biology and the Advancement of Man*, New York, Dutton, 1925. Jennings' little book should be required reading, once a year at least, for every social scientist and for all biologists. See also, T. Dobzhansky, "What is heredity?" *Science*, vol. 100, 1944, p. 406; P. R. David and L. H. Snyder, "Genetic variability and human behavior," in J. H. Rohrer and M. Sherif (editors), *Psychology at the Crossroads*, New York, Harper, 1951, pp. 53–82.

3. See Robert S. Lynd, *Knowledge For What?* Princeton, Princeton University Press, 1939; George Norlin, *Things in the Saddle*, Cambridge, Harvard University Press, 1940; W. Macneile Dixon, *The Human Situation*, New York, Longmans, 1939; Earl C. Kelley, *Education For What is Real*, New York, Harper, 1947; Marie I. Rasey, *Toward Maturity*, New York, Hinds, Hayden & Eldridge, 1947.

4. Jealousy is a *disorder* of love.

5. For further discussions of love along these lines see Ashley Montagu (editor), *The Meaning of Love*, New York, Julian Press, 1953; Christopher Caudwell, "Love," in the same author's *Studies In A Dying Culture*, London, John Lane, 1938, pp. 129–157; Daniel A. Prescott, "Role of love in human development," *Journal of Home Economics*, vol. 44, 1952, pp. 173–176; Erich Fromm, *Man For Himself*, New York, Rinehart, 1947; Nelson N. Foote, "Love," *Psychiatry*, vol. 16, 1953, pp. 245–251; Ian D. Suttie, *The Origins of Love and Hate*, New York, Julian Press, 1943; Vladimir Solovyev, *The Meaning of Love*, New York, International Universities Press, 1945; Walter De La Mare, *Love*, New York, Knopf, 1943.

6. F. B. I. Report for 1953, *The New York Times*, April 25, 1954.

7. Marjorie Rittwagen, "Child criminals are my job," *Saturday Evening Post*, March 27, 1954, p. 19; M. L. Barron, *The Juvenile in Delinquent Society*, New York, Knopf, 1954.

8. J. Louise Despert, *Children of Divorce*, New York, Doubleday, 1953.

9. H. A. Bloch, *Disorganization*, New York, Knopf, 1952, p. 4.

10. J. C. Flugel, *The Psycho-Analytic Study of the Family*, London, Hogarth Press, 1921; Fritz Wittels, *Set the Children Free*, London, Allen & Unwin, 1932; Alfred Adler, *Social Interest: A Challenge to Mankind*, New York, Putnam, 1938; Anne L. Kuhn, *The Mother's Role in Childhood Education: New England Concepts*, New Haven, Yale University Press, 1947; Percival M. Symonds, *The Dynamics of Parent-Child Relationships*, New York, Bureau of Publications, Teachers College, 1949; James H. Bossard, *Parent and Child*, Philadelphia, University of Pennsylvania Press, 1953.

11. Quoted to me by Dr. John Rosen of New York City and Doylestown, Pa.

12. See, for example, John LaFarge, *The Manner Is Ordinary*, New York, Harcourt Brace, 1954, p. 166, who writes, "a priest's celibacy is a true fatherhood, as that of a woman dedicated to life in a religious community is a genuine motherhood." See also P. A. Sorokin, *Altruistic Love*, Boston, Beacon Press, 1950.

13. Weston La Barre, *The Human Animal*, Chicago, University of Chicago Press, 1954, p. 210.

14. It is of interest to note that the first word which a human being is most likely to utter is "mother"—it is also the last word which men are likely to utter. The last word, however, that a woman utters is likely to be some unselfish thought for another.

15. Plato, *The Republic*, Bk. V, 461—and numerous others.

16. Heinrich Pestalozzi, *Aphorisms*, New York, Philosophical Library, 1947, pp. 4–5.

17. E. M. Forster, *A Room with a View*, New York, Knopf, 1954, p. 306.

18. J. H. Burns, *The Gallery*, New York, Harper, 1948.

19. R. Métraux and M. Mead, *Themes in French Culture*, Stanford, California, Standford University Press, 1954.

20. On this subject see W. A. R. Leys, "Human values in the atomic age," *Annals of the American Academy of Political and Social Science*, vol. 1, 1953, pp. 127–133; M. F. Ashley Montagu, "Living in an atom-bomb world," *Technology Review*, vol. 52, 1950, pp. 205–228; see also the film, made by the author of this book, "One World or None," obtainable from the National Committee on Atomic Information, Washington, D.C.

21. For an illuminating discussion of value from this point of view see Hadley Cantril, *The "Why" of Human Experience*, New York, Macmillan, 1950. For useful works on value theory see Ray Lepley (editor), *Value: A Cooperative Inquiry*, New York, Columbia University Press, 1939; Clyde Kluckhohn, "Values and value orientations in the theory of action: Explorations in definition and classification," in T. Parsons and E. A. Shils (editors), *Toward A General Theory of Action*, Cambridge, Harvard University Press, 1951, pp. 388–433; W. C. Trow, "The value concept in educational psychology," *Journal of Educational Psychology*, vol. 44, 1953, pp. 449–462; Abraham Edel, "Concept of values in contemporary philosophical value theory," *Philosophy of Science*, vol. 20, 1953, pp. 198–207.

22. Arnold Brecht, "The myth of 'is' and 'ought.' " *The Political Philosophy of Arnold Brecht*, New York, The New School for Social Research, 1954, pp. 115–116.

23. Hugh Miller, *The Community of Man*, New York, Macmillan, 1949, a book which I regard as one of the most brilliant and important published in our time, but which has received far too little attention.

24. For a close approach to the ethical point of view arrived at in these pages see the works of three philosophers: Hugh Miller mentioned above; A. Campbell Garnett (*The Moral Nature of Man*, New York, Ronald Press, 1952); and W. T. Stace (*What Are Our Values?* Lincoln, University of Nebraska, 1950). See also Walter A. Weisskopf, "The ethical role of psychodynamics," *Ethics*, vol. 62, 1952, pp. 184–190.

25. See M. F. Ashley Montagu, *Helping Children Develop Moral Values*, Chicago, Science Research Associates, 1953.

26. See further on this subject, Anders Nygren, *Agape and Eros*, London, S.P.C.K., 1953; J. Burnaby, *Amor Dei*, London, 1938; M. C. D'Arcy, *The Mind and Heart of Love: A Study of Eros and Agape*, London, Faber, 1945; Paul Tillich, *Love, Power, and Justice*, New York, Oxford University Press, 1954.

27. On this subject see Josué de Castro, *The Geography of Hunger*, Boston, Little Brown, 1952; Harcourt Brown, *The Challenge of Man's Future*, New York, Viking, 1954; F. Le Gros Clark and N. W. Pirie, *Four Thousand Million Mouths*, New York, Oxford University Press, 1951; but above all read Murray D. Lincoln, *Plenty—Pattern for Peace*, Columbus, Ohio, Farm Bureau Insurance Companies, 1952.

28. O. Spurgeon English and Stuart M. Finch, *Introduction to Psychiatry*, New York, Norton, 1954, p. 11.

29. Julian Huxley, *Evolution In Action*, New York, Harper, 1953, pp. 162–163.

30. In this connection see the little-known book by Leo Tolstoy, *The Law of Love and the Law of Violence*, New York, Rudolph Field, 1948.

Appendix A LEARNING THEORY

1. For a survey of learning theories see E. R. Hilgard, *Theories of Learning*, New York, Appleton-Century-Crofts, 1948. See also W. K. Estes *et al.*, *Modern Learning Theory*, New York, Appleton-Century-Crofts, 1954; Kentucky Symposium, *Learning Theory, Personality Theory and Clinical Research*, New York, Wiley, 1954.

2. A rat psychologist has been defined as one who is always pulling habits out of rats.

3. See especially Dorrian Apple, "Learning theory and socialization," *American Sociological Review*, vol. 16, 1951, pp. 23–27. See also B. F. Skinner, "Are theories of learning necessary?" *Psychological Review*, vol. 57, 1950, pp. 193–216.

4. J. L. Moreno and F. B. Moreno, *Spontaneity Theory of Child Development*, New York, Beacon House, 1944, p. 9. For an extensive treatment of "spontaneity," see J. L. Moreno, *Who Shall Survive?* 2d ed., New York, Beacon House, 1953.

5. Jean Piaget, *Play, Dreams and Imitation in Childhood*, New York, Norton, 1953, p. 148.

6. J. L. Moreno and F. B. Moreno, *op. cit.*, p. 41.

7. For a discussion along these lines see Clark L. Hull, *A Behavior System*, New Haven, Yale University Press, 1952, p. 327, *et seq.*

8. E. R. Guthrie, "Conditioning; a theory of learning in terms of stimulus, response, and association," *Forty-First Yearbook of the National Society for the Study of Education*, Part 2, Bloomington, Illinois, Public School Publishing Co., 1942, p. 17.

9. Clark L. Hull, *Principles of Behavior*, New York, Appleton-Century-Crofts, 1943.

10. *Ibid.*, p. 386.

11. Edward L. Thorndike, *Animal Intelligence*, New York, Macmillan, 1911, p. 244.

12. Lawrence E. Cole, *Human Behavior*, New York, World, 1953, p. 264.

13. This discussion owes most to the following workers: Neal E. Miller and John Dollard, *Social Learning and Imitation*, New Haven, Yale University Press, 1941; John Dollard and Neal E. Miller, *Personality and Psychotherapy*, New York, McGraw-Hill, 1950; Clellan S. Ford, "Culture and human behavior," *Scientific Monthly*, vol. 55, 1942, pp. 546–557; O. H. Mowrer, *Learning Theory and Personality Dynamics*, New York, Ronald Press, 1950; Gardner Murphy, *Personality*, New York, Harper, 1947; J. W. Tilton, *An Educational Psychology of Learning*, New York, Macmillan, 1951.

386 Appendix C

14. G. W. Allport, *Personality*, New York, Holt, 1937, pp. 191–207, especially p. 194.

15. Clark L. Hull, *Principles of Behavior, loc. cit.*, p. 197; E. R. Hilgard and D. G. Marquis, *Conditioning and Learning*, New York, Appleton-Century-Crofts, 1940, p. 176.

16. N. E. Miller and John Dollard, *op. cit.*, pp. 49–50.

17. O. H. Mowrer and Clyde Kluckhohn, "Dynamic theory of personality," in *Personality And The Behavior Disorders* (edited by J. McV. Hunt), New York, Ronald Press, 1944, p. 82.

18. D. K. Spelt, "The conditioning of the human fetus *in utero*," *Journal of Experimental Psychology*, vol. 38, 1948, pp. 338–346.

19. M. A. Wenger, "Conditioned responses in human infants," in *Child Behavior and Development* (edited by R. G. Barker, J. S. Kounin, and H. F. Wright), New York, McGraw-Hill, 1943, pp. 67–86.

20. G. Murphy, L. B. Murphy, and T. Newcomb, *Experimental Social Psychology*, New York, Harper, 1937, pp. 162–163.

21. For an excellent demonstration of this see Milton H. Erikson, "Experimental demonstrations of the psychopathology of everyday life," in Silvan S. Tomkins (editor), *Contemporary Psychopathology*, Cambridge, Harvard University Press, 1943, pp. 517–528.

22. M. F. Ashley Montagu, "Conditioning and reconditioning in the psychotherapeutic situation," *American Journal of Psychology*, vol. 58, 1945, pp. 391–392.

23. G. Murphy, L. B. Murphy, and T. Newcomb, *op. cit.*, p. 163.

24. *Ibid.*, p. 164.

25. Helene Deutsch, *Psychology of Women*, New York, Grune and Stratton, 1944, vol. 1, 1936.

26. Gardner Murphy, *op. cit.*, pp. 193–194.

27. Jean Piaget, *op. cit.*

28. N. E. Miller and John Dollard, *op. cit.*, pp. 94–95.

29. M. F. Ashley Montagu, *Coming Into Being Among the Australian Aborigines*, London, Routledge, 1937.

30. N. E. Miller and J. Dollard, *op. cit.*, pp. 184–185.

31. S. Freud, *Group Psychology and the Analysis of the Ego*, London, Hogarth Press, 1922, pp. 60–80.

32. S. Freud, *New Introductory Lectures on Psychoanalysis*, New York, Garden City, 1933

33. J. P. Seward, "Learning theory and identification, II. The role of punishment," *Journal of Genetic Psychology*, vol. 84, 1954, pp. 201–210.

34. F. Alexander, *Fundamentals of Psychoanalysis*, New York, Norton, 1948, p. 92.

35. O. H. Mowrer, "Learning theory and identification. I. Introduction," *Journal of Genetic Psychology*, vol. 84, 1954, pp. 197–199.

36. A. Balint, "Identification," in S. Lorand (editor), *The Yearbook of Psychoanalysis*, New York, International Universities Press, p. 321, p. 326. See also Ives Hendrick, "Early development of the ego: identification in infancy," *Psychoanalytic Quarterly*, vol. 20, 1954, pp. 44–61.; Edmund Burgler, "The 'leading' and 'misleading' basic identifications," *Psychoanalytic Review*, vol. 32, 1954, pp. 263–295.

37. Neal E. Miller and John Dollard, *op. cit.*, p. 61.

38. G. Murphy, L. B. Murphy, and T. M. Newcomb, *op. cit.*, p. 192.

39. *Ibid.*

40. *Ibid.*, p. 199.

INDEX

387